DEADMAN WRITING

by

JONATHAN WILSON

**DEADMAN
PUBLISHERS**

3 Woodfield Road, Ayr KA8 8LZ, Scotland
Tel 01292 269238

Copyright Jonathan Wilson 2002

Cover design and photograph by kind permission of The Sunday Herald

Printed and bound by Thomson Litho Ltd, East Kilbride, Scotland

Edited by Henry Wilson

Thanks to the Editors and Staff of The Sunday Herald.

ISBN 0-9543338-0-2

This book is dedicated to the readers of Jonathan's columns in The Sunday Herald, whose support and encouragement gave him the impetus to achieve his goals with a great sense of achievement and pride.

Jonathan Wilson – Foreword

In writing this foreword I have just re-read Jonathan's articles. I'd read them before, of course. Like many others I was compelled each Sunday, drawn irresistibly to the back page of the supplement, before turning to the rest of the week's news, having had my "fix". Because Jonathan's writing was addictive, as I discovered again on re-reading. I suspect that many of you reading his words, either again or for the first time in this new book, will find them, as I do, compulsive reading.

Why? No doubt there is a little of the morbid curiosity in all of us- what Jonathan himself called "coffin watching". A bit of "I wonder if he's still there today", drawing us to the back page. But this alone cannot explain Jonathan's literary success and his lasting popularity with his readers. He made us laugh as well as cry. Through Jonathan's writing the readers came to feel that they really knew him, and they came to care about what happened to him. Patients and friends of mine would worriedly call me, fearing the worst, if his article failed to appear. In tackling his illness-and mortality-head on, week by week, he touched a nerve in all of us, and made us care. No subject was taboo. Not life, nor death; family experiences or his funeral arrangements. Let alone the state of the NHS or his most recent medical experiences. Unflinchingly honest, as only a dying man can be.

It certainly made being his doctor a challenge!

Jonathan never thought of himself as courageous. He even wrote about not being brave. Just " living with uncertainty" was how he put it. But to me he was very brave. At every stage of his illness, from the earliest days after I first met him, and he realised that he was incurable, through each successive set-back, and through 5 years of physical pain and suffering, at no time did he complain to me or express self-pity. Indeed, his main concern was always for how you were. Right up until the last night, he was apologising for calling me out.

It was a real privilege to have known Jonathan and to have helped care for him. He taught me a great deal about what it is like to live with cancer. But his greatest gift, his legacy to us all, is his writing. Through his words; his experiences, thoughts and feelings, will all live on forever. As will his memory.

Dr. John Bass.
Medical Director, Ayrshire Hospice.

Deadman Writing:

On the 26th January 1997, Jonathan Wilson was admitted to the Victoria Infirmary, Glasgow with acute, lower abdominal pain and constant vomiting. A blockage of the lower intestine was suspected and Jonathan was taken to the operating theatre to investigate the problem, he was in theatre for six hours.

Our first intimation of Jonathan's condition was by means of a phone-call from the Hospital, details were sparse, merely informing us that he had surgery for a suspected blockage of the bowel. When we arrived at Jonathan's bedside, my wife Susan, a nursing sister of 30 years experience was concerned to see no signs of a colostomy, which would have been the norm for his condition. Since it was the weekend no senior doctors were available, and although the nursing staff were kind and attentive, it was what they did not say that concerned us. We arranged an appointment with the Consultant Surgeon for the following Monday.

Upon the meeting, the consultant was visibly upset. We were told that he had Cancer of the descending colon, and that it had spread to his stomach, spleen and liver. He stated that there would be no treatment: no hope of a cure, He gave Jonathan 3 months to live! Since Jonathan was single, the diagnosis and subsequent prognosis was given to us, and we asked the Consultant to allow us to break the news to Jonathan. This we did without giving him the bleak prognosis. He was shocked and frightened and for the first and last time since, cried in fear. We were upbeat to him, and Jonathan immediately asked about treatment. At that moment, we all agreed to pursue this path. From that point, Jonathan was acutely positive, without being aware of the Consultant's short Prognosis. He embarked on intensive chemotherapy – Jonathan was 26 yrs. old

Prior to his diagnosis, Jonathan had been a successful athlete, representing Scotland at schoolboy level, and latterly, while studying Law at Glasgow University, had represented British Universities. He was an avowed non-smoker, drank little and was extremely fit. His life, by day, consisted of Retail Management of Designer Fashion outlets: at night, he promoted new dance clubs, and worked as a DJ, he had even DJ-ed at the Ministry Of Sound in London. He had also worked for a year as a manager of an up-market boutique on a cruise ship plying the Caribbean.

When he was discharged from hospital, Jonathan came back to live at home in Ayr with us. His aunt Therese employed him as a Marketing Executive with her Fabric Company, supplying him with a company car and a laptop computer. She decided to give him a brief, which would exert Jonathan mentally, and constantly, bullied him for reports with exacting deadlines to meet. This raised the competitive and bloody-minded side of Jonathan's nature and he constantly strived to prove his worth- and succeeded.

During this period, Jonathan was undergoing a series of Chemotherapy treatments and was constantly ill with the side effects; notwithstanding, his new employment distracted him from his illness and drove him to achieve his set goals. Six months after his initial diagnosis, and twice the length of his prognosis, Jonathan decided to do a sponsored Parachute jump for Cancer charity. He set off for Perthshire early on the Saturday morning; he had previously arranged the use of his aunt Therese's flat at nearby Gleneagles for the weekend. He had packed his designer gear, in order, to celebrate his successfully completed jump with his fellow parachutists

Unfortunately, his main parachute failed to open, and he was forced to descend from 6000 ft. with only his emergency chute; causing him to break both legs and ankles. Once again, we received a distressing telephone call detailing his injuries, from Perth Royal Infirmary. Because he was undergoing chemotherapy, Jonathan was unable to have a general anaesthetic, and so had his fractured bones set by only a local anaesthetic.

Since he resided so far from Perth, we were allowed to take him home: on the same day, his niece Abbie was born. The drive home was extremely fraught, due to his injuries, and he was sick from his constant pain- he was already displaying his high pain thresh-hold. Two days later was Jonathan's 27th birthday, and he insisted on going to a restaurant to celebrate; complete with plasters, astride a wheelchair. Three weeks later, he set off to Amsterdam for a pre-booked holiday, for which he had paid, as a birthday present for a friend. He made his plasters a fashion statement by painting them green, in commemoration of his beloved football team, Celtic.

During the next 18 months, despite his constant treatment and various side effects, Jonathan fulfilled many of his dreams: Holidaying in Paris, Barbados and Rome, where he had an audience with the Pope.
In early 1999, Jonathan discovered that the Glasgow Herald was launching a new Sunday edition, complete with a Magazine supplement. He wrote to the Editor, detailing his condition, and insisted that his was an on-going story that needed to be told, and would be a successful addition to their magazine. He submitted a couple of dummy articles for their perusal, and was subsequently given a four weeks trial. From that beginning, Jonathan progressed to be the magazine's most popular columnist by its 177,000 readers. He referred to his readers, good naturedly as "Coffin Watchers: His column title was "Dead Man Writing." – His own idea.

Despite no formal training as a journalist, his columns became a "must read", every Sunday. His intention was to take the taboos out of discussing Cancer, and detail his experiences and trials – "warts and all". His hope and aim was to provide an insight into cancer suffering to enable relatives and carers of such victims to understand what may be going through their loved one's minds – more than likely, unstated by them.

In May 2001, Jonathan was voted the Runner Up award for Columnist Of The Year at the Scottish Press Awards, and finally received the ultimate accolade in May 2002, when he was named: Columnist Of The Year by the Jury of Judges of the Scottish Press.

A Palliative Care CD-ROM has been produced to assist in the training of Oncologists and Palliative Care Nurses, based around Jonathan's articles. Christopher Ecclestone, one of Britain's most respected actors, who incidentally donated his fee to the Ayrshire Hospice, speaks his written words.

Henry Wilson

2 May 1999

AN INTRODUCTION

TODAY Jonathan Wilson joins the Sunday Herald magazine as a columnist. Jonathan, from Ayr, is 28 and has terminal cancer; his bowel, liver, kidney, colon and stomach are all affected. He has a hospital check-up every three months, and every three months they give him another three to live. His condition was first diagnosed three years ago.

Even if Jonathan was not dying, he would be a great columnist. Before he retired due to ill-health, he had a life that Tara Parker-Tompkinson might recognise – if she was male, Scottish and very athletic, that is. When he writes about his spangly life, it will be from the perspective that every party could be his last. Of course he will not just be writing about parties.

Jonathan is not a journalist. What his writing has is a scary clarity, an insight that comes from his circumstances, not from any kind of authorial fireworks or flashy technique. The column's title, Dead man writing, was his idea. Like the progress of his illness, none of us have any idea how this will all turn out.

But this is something that he really wants to do before he dies and we think it makes compelling and illuminating reading.

Andrew Jaspan.

2 May 1999

Brave Is For Heroes:

OVER the years I have been called many things and deserved most of them.

Since I have been diagnosed with terminal cancer, people insist on calling me brave. These are people I know and trust. Some of them I respect and love. So why?

According to my largest dictionary, bravery means having or displaying courage, resolution or daring: not cowardly or timid. Which leaves me asking what it is about cancer that, as well as killing you, bestows you with heroic resolution. Was I cowardly before I had cancer? I don't think so. Before my diagnosis I faced death before; once when I was the passenger in a relationship, sorry car crash, where the driver decided mummy's car really could do cartwheels in a field. Another time, whilst diving in the Cayman Islands, I got caught in an under-sea current, which threatened to pull me down to a depth that my body could not handle. Looking down on what is a six-mile express elevator to hell left me feeling strangely detached. It was not a case of, I am going to die, I am starting to lose consciousness but I feel brave. The current simply let go of me and I lived to fight (and contract cancer) another day.

Brave to me is someone like Simon Weston, the soldier who received 80 per cent burns to his body in the Falklands. He will always bear the physical scars on his face, as well as the psychological scars of seeing his friends and comrades die a horrible death while he survived. He said recently that the hardest thing he has to bear is the helplessness he feels when thinking about the comrades he could not save. Feeling guilty after all he has gone through seems strange, yet sometimes I experience something similar. My present partner, Pauli, knew I had cancer when we started dating, so you could not say I hid it from her. Yet when I think that our relationship will not run the course that normal relationships do, I feel I am cheating her, that I am robbing her of valuable time that she could be spending with someone who is a longer-term prospect. I can't get engaged or married or have kids, since I don't know if I will be here in three months.

13

It strikes me that it is Pauli who is brave. I have the unenviable comfort of knowing my fate. For those we leave behind, there can only be questions and self-doubt. There have been times when I simply could not have carried on without the support of others, and in this light, I don't seem so brave after all. Am I being unfair to myself, and the thousands of people who suffer from cancer? Being able to joke about it does not mean that I am immune to pain and suffering. You want facts?

I need medication to sleep at night. Most nights I can't sleep because I am so scared. I need medication to assist the machinations of going to the toilet, numbers one and two. I vomit almost every day. Solid food is a once-a-week treat. I have to take an abnormally high dose of painkillers to take the edge off of the indescribable pain that accompanies having tumours on the spleen, bowel, liver, small intestine and stomach.
Unfortunately, if I were to take the dose that would alleviate my pain, you would not be reading this article. In fact, I would not be able to spell article and my parents would have to wipe the dribble from my lips, and carry me to my wheelchair for daily walks.

In the interest of having some semblance of a life, I forego my full dose of medication, although I do not kid myself. This is where I am eventually headed: bedridden, unaware of my surroundings and pumped so full of opiates that day will turn to night, will turn to day, will turn to night. Editor and my Creator willing, I will return to the subject of euthanasia later. It's not just for old people.

Am I brave? It's not for me to judge. Sure, I'm going to die soon, but we all die sometime. In my black moments, I think of life as a cancer.
From the moment we are born, aren't we all dying? The only difference is that I am forced to confront my mortality, while my friends consider their choice of floor coverings and low-fat yogurts. Yet, my thoughts are no darker than the middle-aged or elderly person, when they think of death.
Perhaps the ones who find my stance brave, are the very people who have thought of their own mortality and have realized the true value of life that is empty without friendship and companionship, that you must fill it with as many experiences and as much knowledge as you possibly can.

My definition of bravery is, knowing your limits, reaching them, but still having the temerity to carry on. Only then can you face death without fear.

9 May 1999

Chic With Cheek:

LIZ Tilberis, fashion editor of Harpers Bazaar and formerly of Vogue UK, died of cancer last month.

She was the woman who persuaded Princess Diana to pose twice for Vogue at a time when Di was very selective about her appearances in the press, never mind the most influential fashion magazine in Britain.

Tilberis was 51 when she died. In this country that is obsessed with diets and looks, she was a size 14, with the cropped hairdo that comes after the ravages of chemotherapy. I met her once, at a Donna Karan fashion party, where she shook my hand and air-kissed me before moving on to the next prole. I looked at her and found myself asking: "Is this rather plain woman the reason why Brit is hip?" I was waiting to see her divining light. Instead, I got a polite smile and a musical request: You've Got a Friend In Me, played by that annoying self-depreciating piano-playing singer from the Bayou that every American-made film seems to feature these days.

I had judged her on her looks, appearance and taste in music, even though by reputation I knew her to be talented, artistic and successful. Her recent death reminded me of this episode, especially when I have to contend with people's perceptions of what a cancer sufferer should look like. The irony is certainly not lost on me. I have been battling cancer for over three years now, with every day presenting its own challenges. There are days when I physically cannot get out of bed, and there are other days when, pain notwithstanding, the rustling of the morphine patches is the only hint that I am ill.

Before I found out I had cancer, I led the sort of life that any young male in Glasgow leads. Of course my education gave me a head start - at St Aloysius you get an excellent education plus an introduction to networking. I was also seriously sporty and know how to say "On your marks, get set, go" in five different languages. As I got older, I stopped wearing short trousers and discovered the real reason for girls. With the youthful stamina to go clubbing five nights a week, plus a love of music, I worked as a DJ long before it was fashionable to be one (have you noticed how everyone in Glasgow is now a DJ?).

So I met a lot of people over the years and shouldn't be surprised that news of my illness spread. Most people associate cancer with old people, not someone young and fit. Acquaintances I hadn't seen for ages contacted me with best wishes, old girlfriends who had sworn never to speak to me again sent flowers and prayers. The whole experience was quite humbling, which was a surprise, as I don't do humble. When I first ventured out after my operation, I suppose I did look "unwell". I had lost two stones, my hair and a lot of self-confidence. Since then, however, I have restored myself to my former glory. So much so that, when I was at Babaza recently, the response was similar to the one I had on meeting Liz Tilberis. Except the reaction was the opposite. At least ten people could not believe I was out and looking so well.

"I heard you were at death's door, but you look better than ever," exclaimed Billy Peterkin, the former owner of the Nile bar. This sentiment echoed around the club all night. One sad girl refused to believe I had cancer. "Prove it," she demanded. Unfortunately I had left my cancer-victim Visa card at home.

The morphine patches, she reckoned, were just a new type of nicotine replacement therapy.
I told her to read this column as proof (while at the same time cunningly boosting the circulation figures) but something tells me that anyone who thinks I am bogus will not be reading any sort of paper, much less a big one like this.

Lots of cancer-sufferers hide the effects of their illness. When I go to the Beatson Centre, for treatments or an appointment, the waiting room is always full to capacity. I go on my own, primarily to shield family and friends from contact with anything that will remind them that I have cancer. But others take friends, parents, partners and children with them. I always people-watch – as the clinic is always running at least an hour behind, there is ample opportunity. When the nurse comes out and reads the name of the next patient, I always try and guess whom it will be. I am never right. From babies through to teenagers and adults through to the elderly, cancer respects no age group, gender or race.

Of course I know people mean well when they tell me how good I look, and I am conceited enough to believe them. At the same time, I sometimes feel frustrated and angry because I don't feel good. Far from it. I feel terrible most of the time but who's interested in that? What it comes down to is that people are uncomfortable with cancer and, by telling me that I look great, they can avoid any awkward moments or stilted silences.

As for me, I will continue to look gorgeous and suffer in silence.

16 May 1999

Turning Into Dad:

THERE comes a time in every man's life when he takes stock of his achievements.

With the millennium – or Y2K as I will have to start calling it now I am a media-type person – ominously approaching, it's hard to avoid the universal questions. Why am I here? How long do I have? And, more cynically, how can I make some money out of this?

Slowly, yet unmistakably, even the most self-assured of today's movers and groovers are feeling anxious as their own carefully constructed, magazine-friendly template of modern living is starting to crack. The age group who benefited most from the post-Thatcher boom is now approaching the new millennium just as self-doubt and fear start kicking in. It can come from committing to a relationship, fathering a child or, the ultimate nightmare, turning into our Dads. This process is similar to the old horror flicks in which the young man struggles against his transformation into a werewolf. Substitute the fangs and hairy hands for a mortgage and two kids and you get the idea.

Of course to me, all this indecision and worry is non-applicable. If I see 2000 then I will be delighted but, in the grand scheme of things, it will still not lead to marriage or kids, the two things I covet most. So it's hard for me to watch the 99% of guys my age who are still hanging on to their youth. In fact I would include females too. Be honest, how many of you out there in the 25-35 age group are still chasing that summer-of-1988 feeling, out every weekend looking for the perfect clubbing moment that existed once and is now threatening your hearing and self-esteem as you squeeze yourself into uncomfortable, unflattering clothing that look great on the person that you used to baby-sit 10 years ago, and who is now at the bar buying you a drink.

One thing that is guaranteed to make you look old is trying hard to look young. I was lucky. When you work as a DJ you tend to get fed up with clubbing, and only go to clubs when you are working, or on special occasions.

I used to work with a woman who was married, had a management job, used to go clubbing every weekend, take drugs and be moody and unpredictable for the rest of the week. I hope that when the light bulb above her head is lit she will see what an embarrassing period of her life it was.

At least women are mature enough to talk to each other about problems in their life. Men grunt and dismiss it as girl talk while secretly we long to divulge our problems. Male pride prevents us from talking about all the things guys should talk about, but never do. Instead we bond by remembering obscure Seventies confectionery (Spangles anyone?) and reminiscing about childhood books. Their underlying themes offer worldly advice. Worried about promotion? Read "Charlie and the Chocolate Factory". Problems with girls? "Adrian Mole'", is your man. By far the most influential book of my youth was Catcher in the Rye. It speaks to people on so many levels that JD Salinger has had to live as a recluse. Despite buying a secluded ranch in New England he frequently encounters uninvited guests on his property, all because people think he has the answer to these scary pre- millennial questions.

Although I have read Catcher in the Rye countless times, I still have absolutely no idea what Y2K holds for me.

I do take some hope from the following. Nike USA has commissioned a French shipyard to build a super cruise ship. This won't follow the eat-all-you-can, dance-until-you-burst model.

It will have an indoor running track, tennis and squash courts, a simulated indoor rock face for climbers, a multitude of gyms including free and computer weights and a very large number of instructors. I would imagine Nike merchandise will feature prominently too. It sounds like you would need a holiday to get over this one.

So although I might not be around to see it, I don't think the calendar will change the hustling, networking how-the-hell-are-you to the consumer-led sheep. They will still buy magazines selling the impossible dream: apartment, car, woman, and wardrobe, watch. Any millennium anxiety will be exorcised by an article pointing out which shirt to buy and which bar/nightclub/restaurant to wear it to.

Remember, be cool – if you act like a joke, people will see you as one. Did I tell you about the guy who had cancer?

22 May 1999

Free-Falling:

THE most difficult thing about writing this column is deciding what to leave out.

Should it be a tastefully written log that will cleverly and wittily document my demise, or should I keep it real. I'm worried that I won't have any private thoughts to fall back on, to act as a buffer when the going gets tough. Which is a laugh, as the going is always tough.

For the last three weeks I've been experiencing a new type of pain. When you live with pain every hour of every day you immediately notice when something else goes wrong. I gave it a week to see if it went away and when it didn't, went to see my consultant. After the cursory examination, in which he presses the source of the pain and I howl with varying degrees of volume, I am told to get dressed. There was something wrong. "I cannot be 100 per cent sure without a scan, which I am scheduling for this week, but I think this new pain is being caused by bone cancer." He went on to say how, in my condition, bone cancer was quite common and fairly treatable, but I was still reeling. What have I done in a previous life to deserve this? You build up your spirit each time you receive bad news, you re-evaluate your goals and, most importantly, you take the hit head-on because there is no other way to deal with it. You can't push it aside to deal with it later because that just eats you up, makes you bitter and angry.

I was asked this week if I felt cheated in life and I could honestly answer no. In a lot of respects I am quite a fortunate person. I have a loving family, both my own and my partner's, and I have more friends than anyone I know. I have had the best education possible and I have managed to cram more experiences and achievements in my 28 years than most people manage in twice that time. Of course there are things I have yet to achieve: I want to own a Ducati motorbike because my mother's previous argument, that I would kill myself is now redundant. I also quite fancy a Porsche, although this will have to wait until my book is a bestseller. That also means waiting until I have written a book.

When I saw the advert for a parachute jump for Cancer Research, it was like killing two birds with one stone. Only later did I realise how apt this saying is. Although the thought of doing a parachute jump after just one day's training was fairly daunting, my devil-may-care attitude, along with the excellent instruction, meant I soon found myself sitting in a small plane with three other would-be skydivers. I was the last one to exit the plane, and the feeling you experience on letting go is ... well indescribable really. I wasn't aware that anything was wrong until I glanced up and, instead of seeing a large billowing expanse of silk, I saw the aeroplane I had just departed with my parachute attached to it like a large umbilical cord, all twisted and tangled. Now in our training we had prepared for this remote eventuality and, as the co-pilot held out his knife, I knew he was going to cut the now useless parachute free to allow me to freefall and then deploy my reserve chute.

From 6000ft the view was stunning, the fields and hedgerows looking like a large jigsaw puzzle. As I got closer, I realised I was falling at some speed. I'll never forget those last couple of hundred feet, I was furiously reciting my landing procedure, knowing that if I landed on anything other than my feet I would be up Bear Creek without a paddle. The impact was tremendous, it felt like I was a cartoon character, my body turning into a concertina, I swear I felt my body disappear as I was reduced to a head on a pair of feet.

At first I thought I had just sprained my ankles, and actually tried to stand up, but for the second time that day I returned to earth with a bump. It wasn't until I was X-rayed that I discovered I had broken my legs and ankles. Even better news was to follow. Because I was in the middle of chemotherapy, I could not have a local anaesthetic while the surgeons reset my bones. My illness has given me a high threshold for pain but I passed out after just five seconds. Fortunately.

I fall back on experiences like these when I get news like the bone cancer. I am not so stupid that I think I can rationalise all my ills with a cute story or fond memory. An anecdote is not a local anaesthetic.

Whatever happens, well, it happens. It's just that now I can use it for a column.

30 May 1999

Smoke Gets Up Your Grass:

I APOLOGISE , in advance for this week's article.

You may find my prose a little languid, the writing a little louche. It's because I have just smoked a joint. Much as I hate to disappoint my family and friends, I am not talking about the salting and curing of a ham bone but the illegal act of consuming marijuana. Before you run off to the phone to claim your Crimestoppers reward, I am going to explain what lead a committed anti-smoker to start doing this regularly.

As the illness progressed through my body, I found the pain getting to the unbearable stage. I could not sleep, my judgment was questionable and I was generally no fun to be around on account of being in a pain-induced bad mood. By this time I was on first-name terms with all the consultants in the palliative care department. I was extremely fortunate to encounter Dr Marie Fallon, an honorary consultant, who made sure that if a new drug came onto the market, or a new surgical procedure was perfected, I was first to get it. Despite the best chemical and surgical options available, nothing quite managed to control the pain. I even turned to a renowned homeopathic doctor to see if nature had any remedy to help me. I tried various supplements and tablets but, apart from assisting my bowels, the only tangible effect was a thinning in my wallet.

Doctors and nurses had officially recommended taking marijuana, but I had dismissed this, as the thought of smoking, itself a cause of cancer, was repugnant. However, as the pain reached dizzying heights, I desperately sought out a friend who smokes dope and tried it myself. I can honestly say that, although it didn't take all the pain away, it took off the edge. Sleep is now possible and I am no longer a foul-tempered wretch. Using a combination of morphine and marijuana I am able to control the worst of the pain. A joint effort, if you like. It's not without its dilemmas. Eric Mann, who has chronic arthritis, is in prison for a year because he was growing cannabis in his attic. Surely even the most disciplinarian section of our

21

society can see the injustice of jailing an old sick man for cultivating his own crop of painkiller. At least in jail he will have access to all the illegal drugs that he can afford.

There is no doubt that alcohol and tobacco are far more harmful than cannabis. I am in favour of the Dutch model, where the supply is legalised and regulated. In Holland, you buy cannabis through regulated outlets, you must be over 16, and it is not served in premises that sell alcohol. Holland has the lowest incidence of drug-related deaths, or crimes associated with drugs, in Europe, yet hoping for an enlightened approach in Scotland is like asking Tommy Sheridan to sing God Save the Queen.

The medical profession's official approach to cannabis and its family of drugs is one of caution. They acknowledge some beneficial effects, but are unwilling to put their name to something that hasn't been totally researched. But surely the testimony of countless cancer, MS and arthritis sufferers must count for something. I smoke in the relative privacy of my home. I am pretty confident that if I were caught in possession, I would only receive a caution. I have found the police to be understanding, and sometimes compassionate, when apprised of the big picture.

Several chief inspectors have publicly called for the legalisation of cannabis so resources can be freed up to catch the people who deal in harder drugs.

So are my pain-killing spliffs a bad thing? Compared to the problems caused by alcohol and cigarettes. I would say no. I have never heard of an altercation caused by people under the influence of cannabis, the way alcohol brings out the worst in people. I am collecting people's thoughts on this issue and plan to present them to my M.P. In the meantime; I am hoping to enjoy a marked improvement in my descriptive writing, due to my imagination being artificially stimulated. I have had none of the reported side-effects of smoking dope, such as lack of ambition and a compulsion to eat snacks at strange hours.

Look at President Clinton; it certainly didn't stop his meteoric rise to the top, although his choice of smoke has changed dramatically.

I would like to take this opportunity to say that I do inhale.

And, while I'm up, does anyone want anything from the garage?

6 June 1999

Winners and losers:

THE chances are that I have never met you, but I can make three assumptions.

First, you are a special person, to me at least, because you are reading my article. As I have recently discovered, time is the most precious of all commodities, and barring advances in quantum physics, we have a finite amount. My second assumption is that you are a caring person. Who else wants to read about a guy dying of cancer? If you didn't care you would be off doing something else. Perhaps you have a relative with cancer and you're looking for an answer or even just a small insight. My final assumption is that maybe you are a little scared. What is it that makes me the writer and you the reader? How easily could the roles be reversed? There is a one in four chance that you, or someone in your family, could be in my situation by 2001.

So what insurance can you take to prevent you or your loved ones from contracting this disease? None. And for those of you in the cheap seats, the answer is still none. Cancer can strike the young. Although I no longer have a spring in my step, and have been known to use a walking stick when crossing the road, my 28 years on this planet hardly qualify me as an old timer. A healthy diet and exercise regime does not preclude you from cancer, either. From the age of 13 I was on a no-fat high-carbohydrate diet to supplement the twice-a-day, seven-day-a-week training schedule that enabled me to run four-minute miles and swim ten miles non-stop. At the top of my athletics career, I actually beat Steve Ovett. (OK, he was 38 and I was 21, but world class is world class). Salad and a weekly game of five-a-side or aerobics class cuts no ice with "Mr.C."

If this sounds bleak, I apologise. There are thousands of sufferers out there who win their daily battles, take the pain and endure this disease with dignity, trying to lead as normal a life as possible. They accept that some tasks, which were previously, no problem will now seem insurmountable, accept their new limitations and settle for the next-best alternative. I find this constant life of compromise hard and keep up a constant whine of "I used to be able to do that" or, my current favourite, "I wish I had your problems".

One strategy is to constantly set myself new targets. I had always wanted to run the New York marathon and, because I had run marathons before, I had always put it off, until next year, or the year after, because I knew I could do it and it wasn't a big deal. Then I got cancer. Once I'd got over the initial trauma, I managed to settle into a routine, which, whilst not exactly being a normal life, was as close as I was going to get. My hopes start to creep up again. When I managed a week without being sick, or the chemotherapy was coming to an end, I decided to try training for the New York Marathon. My consultants thought I was crazy. But they were used to me. Mindful that I was still very sick, I took things easy. At first I walked around the block, and then the next day around the golf course, and, after a couple of weeks, into Prestwick and back. That was a grand total of four miles, still 22 miles 385 yards shy of a marathon.

I then decided that I should try out some slow jogging, nothing fancy, just a slow plod to get me going. This was not like any running I had done before. When I found out I had cancer, the surgeons removed most of my stomach. As I started running, my stomach felt like an industrial-size washing machine with a baby's bib inside. My formerly complete stomach was bumping about inside my ribs.

I felt like the poor girl at gym class who was the first to get boobs. I tried a tight T-shirt, hoping it would hold everything in, but that only made it difficult to breathe. Lets face it; I wasn't going to be able to compete in the marathon. The pain was too much. I dejectedly wrote to the Star Foundation, a charity that organises trips away for terminally ill children. I had planned to give them any sponsor money I made from the marathon. They wrote back with words of consolation, but I couldn't get images of sick, bald kids in wheelchairs out of my head.

Not only had I let them down, but also I'd let myself down.

By putting off something that I could have done, I had lost the chance to make a difference.

13 June 1999

Que Sera Sera:

WHEN I was just a little girl, I asked my mother what would I be? Would I be pretty? Would I be rich? Here's what she said to me. Que sera sera, whatever will be will be, the future's not ours to see, Que sera sera

Simplistic as it is, I bought into this "feelgoodism" as soon as I was old enough to question the meaning of life. Here in Scotland we have our own version of this philosophy: what's for you won't go by you, usually dispensed by a well-meaning parent or relative after a relationship/job disaster. So when people ask how I cope with cancer, or if I feel angry, I shrug my shoulders and say "Que sera sera". It has taken me a long time to arrive at this easy flippancy. There were sleepless nights, tossing and turning, arguing life versus death, euthanasia versus opiate dependency. I have also done my grieving, made my peace with God and tried to right as many wrongs as I can. Now I'm trying my best to live whilst dying. Most feedback has been positive but there are some people who think my approach is wrong, that you should accept cancer gracefully, retire from life and fade out in quiet dignity.

I can understand this viewpoint: why fight an inevitable conclusion and endure pain when you can lie back, transcend consciousness and enter a world of beautiful dreams courtesy of morphine, the drug most commonly used to deal with pain caused by cancer? There have been times when I have stayed in bed for two or three days, high on morphine, not wanting to get up and face reality. But I always do, eventually. My critics are from a different era, when illness was commonplace yet never mentioned and newspapers were hardly printed on Sundays, never mind having five pull-out sections and magazines with diaries of dying people.

I find the reactions of some younger people harder to understand. Out last week, at the second birthday party of a club called Trash, it was great to catch up with old friends, let them see I was still alive and so on. What wasn't so great was the small minority who felt I should not be out enjoying myself. One asked

when I was going to die, her twisted reasoning being that my ill-person's presence was tainting other people's night out. She even organised a bunch of friends to come and laugh at "the guy with cancer".
I left soon afterwards.

Oscar Wilde thought that the only thing worse than being talked about is not being talked about, and lots of people in the street or in shops have said how much they like this column. Health professionals have also said how helpful it is to get feedback about treatment issues. I also find that girls in nightclubs are not the only ones to be surprisingly ignorant about the disease and its progress. Surgery is usually the first option. If a tumour can be cut out of the body, so much the better. I lost half my stomach this way, as the surgeon skillfully removed the diseased part then joined the two healthy bits together again so it still works. It just takes less food to fill it up.

Chemotherapy is the word that fills me with dread. Its reputation precedes it: images of bald, pale people attached to a drip filled with chemicals that, as well as destroying the cancerous cells, kills healthy ones. During one course of chemo (as we veterans call it) there was a mistake in my dose and I got ten times more than I needed. Within 30 seconds, sweat began to pour from my body. Within minutes I was vomiting constantly and Chris, my younger brother, had to lift me to the toilet, as I was unable to stand.

Some quick thinking from the nurses and a knockout jag from a doctor and I was back to normal. I have had many types of chemo, and all of them have been tough, but the alternative is much worse. My hair did fall out and I lost weight, but I won the big prize: remission.

The third type of treatment, radiotherapy, is considered the least invasive in terms of side effects. Having had it last week, however, I can tell you it is not all downhill. I am so lethargic that a walk from bed to bathroom leaves me so exhausted that I have to lie down to recover. Unlike chemo, which is injected into all your body, radiotherapy is an invisible beam precisely directed on to the affected part of the body. You are told that it isn't going to cause any lasting damage, but you should see how fast the nurses run from the room just before the treatment starts. You are left lying on a steel operating table with this big laser-type machine, like the in Goldfinger that cuts James Bond in half.

If all this sounds horrific, then consider this. When I was diagnosed with cancer, they said I had six months. Three years on, and after many different types of treatments and setbacks, I am still here.

Que sera sera – much to the chagrin of others, I intend to stay a little bit longer.

20 June 1999

Living Obituary:

AS someone who constantly listens to music, any music, I am not a natural Radio Five Live listener.

By some stroke of good fortune I discovered a programme called Living Obituary. Every week they have some celebrity on and ask them who they wouldn't invite to their funeral, and what songs they would want played. I think this is a great piece of broadcasting because it avoids the usual vacuous questions put to famous people, plus I am fascinated by other people's views on death.

And if that marks me out as morbid and funereal, I have to admit something else. I have planned my own funeral. Having been to so many sad, gloomy funerals, for people who were so full of life that they would cringe at their own departure, I decided to take matters into my own hands. At first I was at a loss as to how to do this without being crass and insincere. Then help arrived, inside the gilded envelope, which contained a wedding invitation. Theirs, I realised, was a ceremony celebrating the union of two people for the rest of their life. Mine was to be a celebration of the life of one person. My twisted logic enabled me to draw parallels between the two events and also to discover that organising a funeral is a lot easier than planning a wedding.

My girlfriend's sister is getting married this summer, to one of my old school friends, so I am getting to see the tortuous process first hand. No wedding is complete without hours of list making and brochure-scouring. Then there are endless sessions of protracted negotiation, which would leave Kofi Annan tongue-tied and confused. I've seen the tears, I've seen the tantrums, and I have watched friends and relatives at each other's throats. I have watched as a young woman, an empowered company director loses the power of speech and cognitive thought while trying to choose a dress. "Are you sure you like it?" followed by "does my bum look big in this?" must be repeated in every wedding dress shop in the country.

Of course parents traditionally revel in devising of their children's milestone ceremonies. Today's parents may not always bother with christening but even the most resolutely free-thinking middle-youth mummy wants to make a fuss over birthdays, Christmas, Bar Mitzvahs and so on. Parents plan things. It's what they do. I have a gay friend who hasn't come out to his parents. He is starting to get worried as his mother mentions the m-word more and more frequently. How can he tell them that their only son is gay, when they are already getting excited about whether to have prawn cocktail or melon for starters, with a chicken supreme main course. The fact that their boy has not brought a girl home in the last 10 years is conveniently overlooked.

My parents won't get to plan my wedding. At the moment, the cancer leaves me unable to promise if I will be here at Christmas. Vowing to have and to hold someone till death do us part would, for me, be a pretty short-term commitment. We all know what happens to people with terminal cancer and, for my parents' sake, I have done some forward planning, which should make things that little bit easier for my family. So the wake is booked, there's money behind the bar and I have made up a couple of tapes to be played. They are both quite up-tempo. I have also left instructions to evict anyone who doesn't enter into the celebration of my life. I want my wake to be as much fun as the wedding I'll never have.

When I see couples getting into a state about whether to have lilies or roses, I want to tell them to chill out, leave the fussing to someone else, and enjoy their day.

As for my own big day, I can assure Mum, Dad, my family and friends that there is no need to worry.

It's going to be one helluva party.

27 June 1999

Diamond Geezer:

DURING my extremely short journalistic career, John Diamond has been a ghostly presence.

His is a name that floats around whenever it comes up in conversation that I am writing this column about dying of cancer. He is a broadcaster, writer and general media-type person who is at present battling with throat cancer. He is currently in remission, in other words, dying.

When I started, a number of people told me about Diamond. I immediately told myself not to read his columns because (a) he was a writer before he had cancer, therefore the quality of his writing would far exceed mine and I would get depressed, and (b) even though we had different types of cancer, we would have many similarities. If I read something in one of his columns it would mean I could not write about it for fear of being accused of plagiarism. I acknowledged his existence while trying to insulate my writing and myself.

If I think the person making the comparison is really interested, or wants to have a go at what is currently called "media coffin watching" – jumping on Old Nick's bandwagon, wrapping up death in a neat little package ideal for the supplement – I have no hesitation in justifying myself. After all, if you were to exclude every article that was based on personal experiences, most magazines printed with a Sunday paper would disappear. Everything from fashion, cooking, "home thoughts from abroad", even gardening, are based on the writer's life.

So having ranted about what Diamond and, in my own way, I am doing, it was interesting to meet the man who did it first, albeit on the small screen. "Tongue Tied", the second documentary about Diamond's encounter with Mr. C, was on BBC1 last year. It was like being transported straight into his life. He has a beautiful wife (the writer Nigella Lawson), two adorable children and my first response was to think: you lucky bastard. How can he be lucky? I could not help but compare our circumstances. JD: wife, kids, successful career, aged 45. As a former heavy smoker he was, by his own admission, the cause of his own cancer. JW: single, unattainable dreams of getting married, no kids, unable to do a proper job, 28 and the unlucky victim of a genetic form of cancer.

Throughout the programme I was torn between thinking how sad it must be to leave your wife and kids behind, not knowing how things will pan out, and getting angry that I am not able to have a wife and kids, although my partner puts up with me and my quirks better than any wife could. Perhaps I am the lucky one with no loose ends when I die. I wouldn't say his attitude was flippant at the start of the programme, but as it progressed and the prognosis got more serious, his character changed, from "Cheeky Charlie the Carcinoma King" – when his greatest concern was if he would be able to make radio programmes with an incomplete tongue – to world-weary John Diamond, sucking tea through a syringe and playing the odds and hoping chemotherapy might give him an extra six months to live. It must be hard being a former broadcaster and having to have your wife translate everything you say because you have a prosthetic tongue.

I found myself agreeing with a lot of his observations. When you have cancer, every day is different; therefore every column that you write will be different. It's called mood swings and everyone gets them. Self-hate is a common feeling, you don't want people to see you like you are: weak, sick, and pitiful.

He also wondered if it was appropriate to write about cancer in a jaunty weekend column. I was also worried about this; cancer is still taboo and I thought my conversational style may be too irreverent for such a subject. Yet I look at John Diamond, TV star, famous author and star columnist all because of cancer, and it gives me renewed hope.

At one point near the end of the programme he says: "I don't care if I have oversold my cancer, it was good for me." I feel the same way: one in three of us will be touched by cancer at some time in our life so we can't close our eyes to it. No matter how mercenary our individual motives, it's good to get it out there in the public domain.

As for media coffin watching, John Diamond made two statements that assured me that what I have to say is different. He wondered if people would still love him if they met him as John Diamond, cancer sufferer, not John Diamond, charming successful media person. Secondly, he doesn't believe in Nietzsche's theory that whatever doesn't kill us makes us stronger.

I have never doubted anyone's love since my diagnosis, and I believe that I am a stronger person for it.

4 July 1999

Looking For Some Answers:

FOR the first time since I was first diagnosed as having cancer, I really feel like I am dying.

I noticed it first about four weeks ago. The pain just refused to go away. Increasing the painkillers only made me tired, and you can only smoke so much marijuana before you come sick. Anyway the pain was still there.

Normally this does not bother me too much, as I have a high pain threshold, and these things normally resolve themselves. Not this time: I am writing with a resolute grimace, a mask of pain. To make things worse, even the slightest physical exertion is causing fatigue and I am sleeping for 15 hours a day.

After I had dealt with the initial blow of having cancer, I wanted to know how the disease would progress. How would I know things were getting worse? What were the tell-tale symptoms that would herald my demise? But trying to get a straight answer from a doctor or consultant was impossible.Even though I know no two cases are the same, surely there would be some signs to indicate that things were getting worse? Eventually one doctor painted, in broad strokes what to expect: increasing tiredness due to tumours on my liver and spleen and the upping of my pain-killing medication. Increasing pain as the tumours grew and spread around my body, and finally a general decrease in my quality of life.

Up until last month I was coping not too badly, I could eat out in restaurants by having a starter and skipping the main course. As I pointed out to my girlfriend Pauline, there is always room for dessert. I was also able to go out with the rabble of alcoholics that I call "the boys" for a monthly drinking binge. You do not often expect compassion and understanding from a bunch of lads, who can fine-tune their consumption to one vodka and red-bull short of a spew, and pursue women-any woman-as long as they will relinquish a snog and a phone-number at the end of the night. No matter if the phone-number is never dialled :it's the acquisition that's important.

My friends, god love them, shouldn't have to know about cancer at their age. Yet they do. Many a night has seen me out in a club with these guys, one eye on the girl with the ridiculously short black dress, and the other eye on me. I ask more of my mates than any normal friendship requires, yet they never fail to deliver.

I don't know if my world-view is distorted, but I think you can measure a person's wealth by the number of good friends they have. In this respect, I will always be a rich man. I don't have anything against those who devote their lives to the pursuit of monetary gain. It's just that money isn't going to buy me happiness- or time. I have always hidden my pain and lethargy-it's hard enough for people who love me to know that I am suffering, without them having to see it. I now realise that this was not the best course of action. I am not saying that people take me or my illness for granted, but every day that I hide my suffering, it makes it easier for those around me to put the thought of my illness behind them, as they concentrate on their own lives.

Pauline and I had always talked about starting our own company. With her design skills and my commercial background, we were confident of making our mark in the world of Interior Design. We encountered the usual hurdles that most small businesses do, but my recent decline in health has caused a whole new set of problems.

I was going to do the mundane bits and leave Pauline free to be creative, but now she has to cope with some of my duties, leaving me time to be sick, and I feel guilty at letting her down.

But I know that she is determined to succeed, whatever hurdles life throws in her way, and that gives me some comfort.

From all the E-Mails that I receive, a lot of you look for a moral in my writing, a message about the meaning of life.

Because I walk the line between life and death you think that I am privy to insider tips on how to live your life. Alas I'm not. But what I would say is that if you want something badly enough, you will get it, and success is all the sweeter, if you have worked for it.

Even if, like me, you have to take a lot of morphine, and smile through the pain.

11 July 1999

The Jury's Out On Dr. Death:

I HAVE been waiting to write this for weeks.

But somehow, every time I put a finger to keyboard, some "do-gooder", with his own agenda hijacks the headlines. I'm talking about euthanasia, and I had wanted to write an unbiased article without sensationalism or soap box-ising.

Too much to ask. Euthanasia is a highly emotive subject and I can see why both sides make such a strong case.

Before I found out that I had cancer, I was firmly against it. I believed that nothing was as precious as life. Now that I have cancer, I still believe in the sanctity of life, but I can now relate to those who argue that there are special circumstances in which life should be terminated because it is in the best interests of the patient. My argument has not been helped by Dr. Jack Kevorkian, more commonly known as "Dr.Death", the doctor, in America, who was recently convicted for murder after video-taping himself giving a lethal injection to Thomas Youk, a 52 year old accountant, who was suffering a degenerative brain disorder. Youk would have lived for, perhaps another five years, but those five years would have seen him turn into a vegetable. He wanted his family and friends to remember him as a warm, clever man who provided for his family: not as a dribbling, incontinent shell.

Kevorkian was well known for his views on Euthanasia, and was contactable through a network of doctors, by those who wanted his assistance. By his own calculations, he had assisted in the "mercy-killings" of over 150 patients.I find this a little ghoulish. He took whatever dignity, Mr.Youk had thought possible by Euthanasia, when he sent that video to be broadcast on National television. Kevorkian had been to trial five times previously, but was found not guilty, due to lack of evidence. After the video, he was charged with murder, rather than assisted suicide. I suspect that his own vanity was his down-fall-he chose to represent himself, and did so from a viewpoint that consent is a defence to murder. This is plainly not the case, as Euthanasia is not legal, and his strategy of placing Euthanasia in the public domain did not work. He was convicted and given a life sentence.

Here in Britain, we have been through a similar trial, involving Dr.David Moor. He boasted of assisting in over 300 cases of Euthanasia with a level of showmanship reminiscent of Kevorkian. What is it about assisting in Euthanasia that brings out the flamboyant and self-righteous in people? Watching both men on television, they reminded me of one person-Donald Findlay Q.C. Maybe you can't choose your martyrs, but surely there must be a more caring and discreet doctor out there, one who wouldn't bound down the stairs of the High Court, beaming like a victorious prize fighter.

Euthanasia does not sit comfortably in our neat, little ordered lives. I suspect that it has been going on for generations, kept quiet because doctors wanted to keep their jobs while helping patients as best as they could. Just like Dr.Moor, but without the PR strategy.At the moment, the law allows doctors to lessen pain, even if this hastens death, as long as the primary aim is not to cause death. But how can a doctor know how much painkiller is needed? In my own case, I have reached the maximum dosage and yet am still in great pain. I cannot sleep, sit down, concentrate on television, anything.

If I were an animal, a beloved family pet, I would have been put out of my misery ages ago.

By being human, I am denied a peaceful and dignified demise by those who measure their compassion in piety and politically defined morality.

Much as I dislike the way in which Euthanasia has been brought to the public eye, I think we should re-examine the law as it stands. As I write, the radio is telling me that every hospital will have a designated doctor who can halt treatment (that's drugs or even food) to critically- ill patients, when it is in the patient's interest. Of course there will be the usual clamour from religious and pro-life groups. But the British Medical Association has issued exacting guidelines: and to quote from their code of conduct:" It is not an appropriate goal of medicine to prolong life at all costs, with no regard to it's quality or the burdens of treatment."

There is no denying, Euthanasia is an emotive subject, but we have to remember that death cannot be postponed to a later date. It comes to us all, and for some of us it is accompanied with pain, horrendous pain.
To make my attentions official, I have put the following clause in my will. I would be grateful, if you, the readers, would witness it:

"I Jonathan Wilson, of my own free will, and without any reservation or extrinsic persuasion or dress, ask that my wholly intolerable pain and suffering be ended in the most rapid, humane and painless method, with the help of a medical professional."

18 July 1999

You've been Framed!

THIS week, for a couple of hours, I changed my persona from "Deadman, Writing" to "Deadman doing TV show".

Do not panic, dear reader. After that experience, there is very little chance of me defecting permanently.

Scottish Television asked me to take part in a programme about the legalisation of cannabis for medicinal users, in a series called "Living Issues". As I have previously admitted, I sometimes smoke dope to assist my multitude of other painkillers. Whilst I am not proud of it, I have reached the stage where I am giving anything a go. The ends justifying the means, kind of idea. So I agreed to go on 'telly' to talk about my illness and how cannabis is helping my fight with cancer, on the understanding that I was not going to be presented as a hash-smokin', pot-headed beatnik, indiscriminately and inarticulately advocating the legalisation of cannabis. The producer assured me that I had been invited on the programme to show how someone who is terminally ill has to break the law in order to help manage the pain associated with his or her illness.

The recording date approached. I would never say I was the sort of person who gets nervous about speaking in public, in fact I thrive on an audience, but I have to admit to a feeling of anxiety as my TV debut approached. I turned for advice to the one person I trust in all matters concerning the media, "Auntie" Anna Burnside. (The auntie bit is in deference to her experience with all mediums of mass communication rather than her age. It is her weekly joy and privilege to knock my rough and creatively spelled ramblings into a column.) Her advice was short and to the point. "Don't worry, it's easy. If you make a mistake, or say something you didn't mean to say, then just cough or say shit. That means they have to edit it out. Oh, and wear something by Helmut Lang." I felt a lot more confident. Even if I don't feel it I can always be relied on to look the part, due to my expansive (and that is expansive, not expensive) wardrobe. My anxiety disappeared, I felt relaxed and confident. This was going to be a doddle.

I glanced at the list of the names of my fellow guests. There was a woman called Liz Ivol who suffers from MS, Free Rob Cannabis, who was loosely described as a campaigner, then a chap called Matthew Atha, an expert witness in all matters to do with drugs. He testified at the recent trial of Eric Mann, the wheelchair-bound arthritis sufferer who was jailed for a year recently for intent to supply cannabis. Also appearing were Peter Stoker of the National Drug Prevention Alliance and Dr Ian Oliver, former chief inspector of Grampian Police and no stranger to controversy himself. Six guests on a debate about drugs ... so there would be three against three, then. Another clue as to the nature of the discussion came two days before shooting. The researcher phoned and asked me not to wear a suit or a tie or anything "formal", as the studios get very hot and I would feel uncomfortable. Out went the Helmut Lang suit. I decided on linen, smart yet casual.

At the studios, I was shepherded into a room with Liz Ivol, who turned out to be a real character. Despite having multiple sclerosis, she manages to grow her own marijuana and has been charged for possession of a controlled substance. Also sharing our room was Mr. Cannabis. (He changed his name by deed poll.) Mr. Cannabis also had convictions for drugs offences. This shouldn't have surprised me, as he boasted about his many scrapes with the law. Even his clothes were made from hemp, the flax obtained from the marijuana plant.

I felt a twinge in my stomach. How, I asked him, had marijuana helped his health? He replied he was 100 per cent healthy: no cancer, no MS or arthritis. The light bulb finally lit up over my head when an assistant told me the other three guests were in a separate room because it was usually better to keep the two sides apart until the cameras were rolling. I went to the toilet but the damned window was nailed shut. Before I had a chance to formulate an escape strategy, it was time to start filming.

Everything after that was a bit of a blur. Liz Ivol and myself talked about our illnesses, how marijuana helped, and how we felt about breaking the law. With his constant exclamations of indignation, and extensive knowledge about cannabis and the law relating to it, Mr. Cannabis, obviously a regular on these types of programmes, was guaranteed a good deal of camera time.

Dr Oliver, whose reputation precedes him, turned out to be sympathetic and well informed about cannabis and its healing effects. In a suit and tie, just like his two allies, he came across very well, his measured words and confident stature no doubt helped by being appropriately dressed for the freezing studio. Half an hour is not a long time on television and I remember school debates being more civilised. In retrospect, I would have to consider my big TV debut a flop. It has reminded me that integrity is not a universal trait within the media.

All things considered, I am lucky to have this column where it is.

25 July 1999

Pain v Gain:

HELLO reader, giving me a fleeting thought while wolfing down the whole meal toast, marmalade and fresh-ground coffee, planning how to spend the rest of your Sunday.

While empathising with the fact that I have cancer, perhaps you think that my life isn't too bad. "He's young, good-looking, got a bit of cash, and he gets to write about his life in a magazine," you might say to yourself, before wondering whether or not to have another slice. It is easy to think about someone who lives and writes in the media as an entity, and forget that there is a real person behind the words you read. Allow me to let you into a secret, a little known fact of life – writing about it does not make living it any more enjoyable. The last two weeks have been really tough. I was kidding myself on before, when I thought I was hard done by, that cancer and all the trimmings were beating me. Just when I thought the pain couldn't possibly get worse, I would develop a new plateau of suffering, a private, secret place where pain and I were re-acquainted at the next level.

Simple tasks, like going to the toilet, become a nightly event that I need to steel myself for. The other night, there I was on the pan, the dog's rubber bone between my teeth. I chew on it when the pain gets too tough to handle. I was screaming with pain, not just whimpering, but crying out, taking anyone's name in vain who would listen. As it happened, I must have been wailing louder than I realised, because later on that night my mother asked what CD I was listening to earlier on, and that she really liked it. I didn't have the heart to tell her that the CD was called, "Doin' The Toilet Feels Like Giving Birth", and the artist was yours truly.

And if that just sounds like typical guy talk from someone who will never have to do the contraction-push-swear-like-Liam-Gallacher thing, you may be interested to learn that I recently spent three days in hospital being evaluated for an epidural-type procedure which may take away the soul-destroying pain that I am currently experiencing in my lower lumbar region. And for those of you who are too thick to understand what an epidural is (that's men who don't have stomach cancer) this is the injection given to women in labour to help with the pain of childbirth. It basically freezes the middle part of your body. Dr Johnstone, the "pain" consultant who looks after me, has put her head together with one of the top anaesthetists at the Beatson Oncology Centre, to come up with a plan that involves me receiving a number of injections into my spine. This will hopefully numb the pain in my back, leaving me to concentrate on my cancer-ridden stomach area.

Now, with all the tests, operations and procedures that I have undergone since I found out that I had cancer, nothing really frightens me. I've had tubes inserted in places where you just don't want tubes inserted. Let's face it; some orifices were made for disposal, not reception. But I would be lying if I were to tell you I wasn't scared or concerned at the thought of needles going into my spine. And there is, of course, a margin for error. Translation: I could be paralysed from the waist down and lose control of my bowels and bladder. So on one hand I have pain. Lots and lots of pain that stops me sleeping, resting and basically doing all the other things that you see in the Kellogg's Special K adverts. On the other hand I have a surgical procedure that might make my final couple of months a bit more bearable. Or it could turn them into a living hell.

I know there are people out there who are paralysed, and there are the people who look after them, and this apology is to you: I don't think I could handle being in that situation. And I don't think I could bear having to wear a nappy and a catheter because I did not have control over my lower body functions. This week, in a rare show of weakness, I admitted to my mother that I knew what hell was, because that was where I was living just now. But if I went ahead with this procedure and it failed ... let's just say this column will be ending a lot quicker than anticipated.

My previously upbeat attitude is slowly being worn down by the numbers game. There is a ten per cent chance of the procedure failing to work. Forty per cent of people who survive the first year of stomach cancer live for up to five years and 88.2 per cent of all statistics are lies. I frequently tell myself how lucky I am, knowing roughly how long I have. How many of you have that luxury?

Which reminds me, I must get round to buying Barney a new rubber bone. I'm sure it's all my drugs making me paranoid, but he has started to howl whenever he is put outside to do the toilet.

1 August 1999

Choose Drugs:

WE are trying something new this week. I am wired to a contraption called a syringe driver.

The purpose of this device is to inject a dose of morphine on the hour, every hour, to alleviate my pain. This means that every 60 minutes I get a kind of a hazy feeling as the morphine kicks in with the languorous onslaught of unremitting exhaustion.

But in between, and as the hour is almost up, the pain gets stronger and sharper. I said to a friend the other day that I wished he could experience the pain that I'm trying to describe, just for one or two seconds. Then I realised what I was saying, and I had to make it clear that I really wouldn't want this kind of pain to be passed on to anyone, even the imbecilic people who ask why I am still alive. What I would like is to feel normal again, even if it were for just a minute, to see what that is like. Your part in this experiment, patient reader, is that you get to guess where I am in the cycle by assessing the tone of my writing. If the use of language and punctuation is truncated, staccato and to the point, then you know I am at the end of the dose and shortly about to receive another, whereas if my prose becomes mellifluent and free-flowing you will know that I am on a one-way trip to Planet Janet via Morphine Central.

Although I have only been a writer for a few months, I am delighted to find I am in good company when it comes to morphine use. Out of step with the times, maybe, but far from unique. When Britain was expanding in the Victorian era, at the height of the Empire, tea, coffee and tobacco were not the only exotic imports to arrive on these shores.

Opium dens opened up (which makes me feel better about the opiate patches I wear as an additional painkiller). These dens of iniquity allowed all vices to be experienced at once, which is the kind of thing I used to enjoy in the old days. Queen Victoria herself was said to have advocated morphine for period pain and it was generally considered to have wide-ranging, almost magical powers as a fix-it-all for any ailment.

With the exception of the fictitious character, Sherlock Holmes, created by Sir Arthur Conan Doyle, I have yet to come across any character, real or fictitious, which used morphine as a drug of recreation. This is not to say, of course, that people don't abuse it. The pharmacy where I get my patches refuses to hand over the prescription in person, preferring instead to deliver it in a little van. I suppose it must have a considerable street value. I must confess to a perverse pleasure every two days as I replace the patches and wait for a couple of hours as the slow-release mechanism does its magic and takes the slightest edge off of the pain. My parents think I should take the full dose of painkillers, but that would leave me incapable of driving or operating machinery. I can take or leave the forklift truck but I need my car to see my girlfriend, the one person who keeps me sane. And I am unwilling to take a drug which would stop me taking another – if I can't operate machinery I would be unable to make my caffe latte, one of my daily salvations.

I actually had a car crash last week. It was on the day from hell: the shop fitters who were supposed to be at the shop I am setting up with my girlfriend ... well, in the time-honoured tradition of shop fitters, hadn't turned up, again. The glass bricks that B&Q promise to have in stock all the time ... well surprise, surprise, surprise, they didn't have them in stock. I had to drive across town on a wet Friday afternoon to collect them from another store.

With a hundred other things on my mind, I just wasn't able to anticipate the indecision of another driver.

Fortunately nobody was hurt and the cars were the only casualties. But, although nobody except my father would say it was my fault, I am sure that people were probably thinking someone as sick as me shouldn't be driving. Yet I get my reflexes tested whenever I am up at the hospital, and the last time they were quicker than average. How many other drivers can say that?

Living with cancer is tough. The constant concessions and changes to my lifestyle make my head spin. But when I analise it, I would have to say that the drugs have changed things more.

As far as my writing is concerned, I'm with Samuel Taylor Coleridge on this one.

It can only be a good thing.

8 August 1999

Tablets of Stone:

A RECORD slipped through my anti-chart music protection systems recently.

It was by an Australian guy, not a soap star, and it was basically an old dance record with a monologue over the top. His lyrics were snippets of information and advice such as "Wear sunscreen" or "Be nice to your family, they are all you have". This got me thinking, because I have started passing on information and advice to my friends, family and peers. So what is this gem of knowledge, this treasure trove of wisdom that will change your life, unlock the door to riches untold and unbridled good fortune?
Become a Pharmacist!!!.

That's it. The road to good fortune begins in the pharmacy. Now, before you form a lynch mob and set off down the M77 for Prestwick to sort me out, let me explain. It all started at the Beatson oncology ward at Glasgow's Western Infirmary, where I am a regular visitor. The last time I was there my insomnia, coupled with the nurses having to take my blood pressure every half hour, meant that I was able to witness at first hand just how hard the doctors and nurses – especially the nurses – have to work. One night an old man died. They tried to save him for 20 minutes before calling time. You could really feel the disappointment and distress they felt at losing a patient. A couple of the nurses were in tears; the rest of them bravely got on with their jobs, one of which was to wake me up, just as I was getting to sleep, to take my blood pressure.

Where, you may be wondering, is the pharmacist? Good question. After the consultant had done her rounds and confirmed that I was free to leave (this was at 9.03am), all I had to do was wait for a day's supplies of tablets from the pharmacy. Then I could be on my merry way.

I phoned my friends and family, told them the good news, and started planning my day. I reckoned on the tablets taking at the most an hour and a half to climb the two floors from the pharmacy to my ward, and even this was on the generous side. I set my alarm and settled down for an hour's sleep to make up for the previous night's insomnia. As my head hit the pillow, the alarm went off. Or that's what it felt like. As I rubbed my eyes, I glanced at my sideboard, expecting to see a little white bag from the pharmacy. Not a sign. One of the nurses phoned to see where my medication had got. They promised it soon. But not soon enough for my schedule.

I had to sneak into the smokers' lounge (I kid you not, there is a smokers' lounge in a cancer ward) to use my mobile phone to rearrange the plans, which were beginning to crash all around me. Out of the window went my idea of meeting my editor so that we could discuss my tardiness in meeting deadlines. I had also wanted to spend some time with my girlfriend, Pauline. Quality time would have been good, but I would have settled for any sort of time. Most of our recent time together has been spent on our business. One of our shop fitters has been having language problems. When we initially hired him, he spoke excellent English, and was especially fluent when we handed over a large wad of cash for materials.

However, as the work has progressed (and I use that verb in the loosest possible fashion) he has resorted to his native language – bullshit. His girlfriend's teeth went on fire and his workshop was leaking black blood.

Perhaps I have these two the wrong way round – but whatever the reason, Pauline and I were totally stressed-out. I had prescribed that well-known chill-out remedy, a couple of hours of retail therapy.

Midday came and went. The nurses were sympathetic but helpless. They phoned again ... only to be told that they were not to phone again. The pharmacy would phone when the drugs were ready. It is not as if I was waiting for anything exotic or unusual – we are talking about bog-standard sleeping tablets. I could go to the gates of many primary schools in the west of Scotland and buy these tablets from the local friendly dealer.

They finally arrived at 4:48pm, seven hours and 51 minutes after I was supposed to be leaving. I was actually going to go down to the pharmacy and ask if they were using straws to pick the tablets up and then negotiating a difficult obstacle course before depositing them in the bottle. I could see the whole picture: Kool and the Gang's greatest hits booming in the background as all the pharmacists did a great big conga around the room, wearing party hats and blowing streamers, with piles of unfilled prescriptions in the corner.

I realise that the fact I am dying makes me particularly resentful and might have affected my ability to see things from the pharmacists' point of view, so I decided not to confront the situation. Instead I am telling everyone I know, that pharmacy is the career to aim for.

As far as my cynical eyes can see, the requirements are: inability to show any sympathy or understanding, especially for those people who can measure their longevity in days – and ability to put tablets into a bottle at the rate of one every 48 minutes

In response to this article:

The Secretary of the Scottish Pharmaceutical Society wrote a withering letter to the Sunday Herald's letter page condemning Jonathan's "tongue in cheek " remarks.

A regular reader of Jonathan's column, was moved to pen a rebuttal of his "starched-collar" stance:

"A Spoonful of sugar."
Colin Rodden's letter of August 15 seemed to re-affirm my, and many other people's, perception of the Pharmacist's Fraternity, as he attempted to defend his profession as its Secretary for Scotland.

Jonathan Wilson's article on the subject was very honest-and representative of the feelings of a vast number of the populous, who have spent hours awaiting tablets being counted into bottles and stamped with a label.

Having followed the progress of Wilson since his column started, I have been struck by his determination, inspiration and sense of humour-and his column is a read, I await every Sunday.

Surely a man of Mr. Rodden's intellect could appreciate, that seven hours in the life of a frustrated, dying man, is the equivalent of years in the lifetime of the more fortunate of us.

Perhaps I could prescribe the following for Mr.Rodden: "lighten- up tablets: – one to be taken every day. If symptoms persist, contact your doctor for a humour by-pass.

Ian Cartwright.
Glasgow.

15 August 1999

Tumour Humour:

WHAT do you give someone who is dying of cancer and is in pain 24hrs a day?

You give them something that causes more pain in the hope that their brain and nerve endings can't cope with the overload of sensory information. So, in the interests of pain control, I find myself hooked up to a 'TENS' machine. It's basically a small box that passes an electric shock (more like jolt) through my body to confuse it into thinking things aren't as bad as they seem, which, if you read last week's article, should please the pharmacists among you.

The pain has decided to increase itself this week, and I have found myself bedridden, which was unfortunate, as a London Production Company, which has been commissioned to do a celebratory piece on the Millennium, contacted me. The programme will take the form of a poem, written by some famous poet, who was short listed to be Poet Laureate, and whose name escapes me because I am not in the least educated in such matters. The poem will be read by famous actors, amongst them, Christopher Ecclestone (Cracker, Our Friends in the North), and it will be screened on New Year's Eve 1999, and will then feature daily in the Millennium Dome.

And where do I feature in all this? Apparently I am deemed to be of sufficient media stature to warrant a role in this programme, and to utter a verse or two of this fine poem, ironic when my own ignorance means I am unable to tell you its author. What blew me away is just how quickly I have become an 'it' person. Regular readers to the column will no doubt remember my pathetic attempts at stardom on previous television programmes, perhaps at most uttering one coherent sentence. Granted my column is slightly more reflective, but even then the team always guides me on this magazine. Yet here I am meeting with the editor of the programme to see where I fit in. Unfortunately on the appointed day of the meeting I was forced to take a large dose of painkillers, which rendered me incapable of driving. I managed to contact this lady who had come all the way from London to see me to tell her the bad news.

"Not to worry, I'll just come to your house," she said. Now I ask you to close your eyes and imagine the Wilson household. We have a 15-month toddler called Abbie, who is a whirling dervish of mess and mass-destruction, two dogs, one of which is a puppy called Homer and bites everything in sight, and then add to this mix a drug-addled twenty-something desperately trying to straighten up and stop drooling. Morphine does not lend itself well to acting with sophisticated charm and by the time she had arrived chez Wilson, I was still struggling to say "Hello, pleased to meet you," without dampening my shirt.

To be fair, I put up a fair display of a young guy with cancer struggling with life, which was what she was after. She painted a picture of how she envisaged the programme to look; she even had picture and storybooks. Hell I was impressed! We had tea and cake, and spoke about her programme and my cancer. One of the more pleasing aspects was that she never once said 'You look too healthy to be sick,' which is a comment I face daily. I suppose it's a sort of defence mechanism for people who don't know what to say to a young guy with cancer. I've also found that humour often takes a lot of the pressure out of a difficult situation.

When people now ask me how I got cancer, I tell them that I went to Russia on a school holiday, and I ate in the canteen when we were visiting the Chernobyl power station.

Some people get it, some don't, but it's a lot more interesting than saying that I have a defective gene, which causes cancer. And being an 'it' person, more and more people are recognising me – in the post office, at the petrol station, in the massage parlour. Joke.

I noted with interest that Tara Palmer-Tompkinson, my fellow 'it' person, had a breakdown, and had to go to a specialist dry-out clinic in Los Angeles. Now that I'm a 'media person', I suppose I should start looking out for a suitable location to 'retire' to. Perhaps Juan-les-Pins in France, or Barcelona; I'm sure the heat would do me good.

However when I suggested these locations to the bean counters at the Sunday Herald, they laughed and suggested an afternoon in Millport. I guess my media status isn't all it's cracked up to be.

Before I sign off this week, I wonder if you would join me for a moment of reflection for Helen Rollason, the BBC sports presenter who died last week of stomach cancer. She was diagnosed at roughly the same time that I was, so I followed her ups and downs on TV with a vested interest. I sympathised with her as her hair fell out, and privately cheered whenever I saw her on TV, or heard her on the radio, presenting a sports programme. Like me she was given six months to live, and yet managed to stretch this to two and a half years.

This last week has been the toughest so far, and has given me an insight as to what to expect as my life draws to a close.

I'm not being defeatist, and I'm sure not giving up, but sometimes you have to face reality and see how high the hurdles are so that you know how high to jump.

22 August 1999

Family affair:

THERE I was, lying on my bed, face down, wondering what I could write about when it struck me.

Well, actually, it pricked me. At this point, I should tell you that I was receiving an injection from my mum. She has been a nursing sister for over 20 years, so she is allowed to perform certain tasks that would normally require a doctor. This is good, because it means I am freeing up resources that could be used for others, while having someone on hand 24 hours a day to deal with my pain.

I've never thought about how my illness affects my parents. I was always the golden boy, eldest of three children, apple of their eyes. Despite some deviations from their preferred straight and narrow path, I am more or less the person they wanted me to be. Except for having cancer, or course. If it's possible to be proud of someone who has cancer, then my parents are proud. Sometimes I feel like breaking down in tears, just for the hell of it, just to show them that I am not perfect. But I can't, of course, because fake tears aren't my style. I've sat and thought and struggled to come up with something more traumatic and horrible as outliving your children. When I am really ill, my father lifts me in and out of the bath. An impressive task, as I weigh at least a stone more than him. But the mechanics of the action get me all morbid and thinking about my funeral. Then, at least he will have five helpers to carry me.

When I was well, he would come and watch me running all over the country. I'm sure he could have thought of better ways to spend his days off, but he came all the same. The only races we have now are the 30m dashes to the toilet to be sick. Even then I would be disqualified. My dad more or less carries me to the bathroom. I wouldn't call it funny, but it is certainly strange the way I feel a lot closer to my parents since we found out about my cancer. The consultant told my parents first, so that I would at least have friendly faces giving me the bad news. As my mum told me, my reaction changed from incredulity to despair. The nurse pulled the curtain around my hospital bed as the three of us cried. I was crying because, as soon as you hear the word cancer, you automatically think of death. I think my parents were crying because I was the eldest son, the young man chosen to carry on the Wilson clan and traditions.

With all the treatments, doctors and sickness, you sometimes lose sight of the big picture, namely those who love you, how they are handling it. Cancer affects the whole family, not just one person. Our previously organised household is now geared up to look after a cancer sufferer. Every morning at 5am I drag myself up to my parents' bedroom to wake up my poor mother so that she can stick a big needle into my butt, so that I can have a few hours of pain-free sleep. I always laugh and joke with her about how sore it is to get a jag from her, but the truth is that there is something comforting about being looked after by your own flesh and blood. And anyway, I'm so goddamned skinny, my backside is the only place with anything remotely resembling fat. It's less painful there.

This is not meant to be a sad picture of family life chez Wilson. In fact we can talk and laugh about things that most other families would find taboo. You need thick skin to survive in this house, and yet as soon as something happens, or is said about my illness, the hilarity is replaced with sincerity. I wonder how many other households throughout Scotland are familiar with the language of cancer?

I have decided not to go ahead with an operation, which could lessen some of my pain. The downside is that it involves an injection to my spine, therefore a risk of infection or paralysis. Life is tough enough just now; if I was paralysed then I think I'd call it a day. Plus, I don't think my dad's back is up to it.

Life with cancer is a constant juggling act, quality of life versus treatment versus longevity. And not just for me. It involves the whole family.

29 August 1999

Agony Uncle:

I CAUGHT myself doing a terrible thing yesterday. Terrible in my book, anyway.

There I was, talking away to a friend who is going to work in Milan for the summer, when I found myself saying, "Don't drink too much, and watch you don't get burnt in the sun". Sound enough advice in itself. What was terrible was that it revealed that, while I have been lying in bed with Sister Morphine, I have failed to notice my turning into a horrible grown-up. I can't remember how many times I have been embarrassed by the clucking of a concerned adult just as I was about to set off on some foreign adventure. Now, suddenly, I am doing it myself.

I think I might have inherited this tendency from my mother, a great giver of good advice. Her personal favourite is to buy factor 50 sun block whenever any of us go on holiday. This guarantees that we have that just-back-from-Auchtermuchty look, even if we have spent a baking fortnight in Marbella. On the back of our family's sun tan bottles it says: PROPERTY OF NASA: TOP SECRET, To Be Used In Conditions Of Extreme Sun Exposure.
Thanks, Mum.

Now I have noticed that I'm at it too. There is a pattern to my new advisory position, a reason why I suddenly spout words of wisdom to friends. I have found out that having a terminal illness gives a person an amazing clarity of thought. I see things now that I never noticed before. (And in case you think that it's just the Class A's talking, I have not taken any stimulants to help me get through this article.) Without going down the religious road, I feel each person has only one life. That means it's imperative to use this time to its fullest. And if that means pulling a friend aside and telling him to stop wasting time with a dead-end job, or telling another that he is not suited to his present girlfriend, then so be it. Does having cancer give me carte blanche to draw judgment on other people's lives? Is my advice any more relevant than the words of any Joe Boggs off the street? I like to think that it is, for the important reason that, whereas before I may have bitten my tongue, I now say and write what I think.

49

I have heard of people who have brain tumours and, by some freak of nature, this unlocks parts of the brain that were previously thought to be redundant. They become super-intelligent, or supremely gifted in aspects of their life: music or maths or the arts. Unfortunately this has not happened to me. I'm still plain old Jonathan, no wiser than before, and certainly not as sharp, due to the pain-killing shots. But I am prepared to speak my mind. Despite the newly found clarity, I can still be as pedantic as I was before.

I'm finding that, on average, I am spending four days out of every seven in bed. This is either due to the pain or to the drugs taken to control it. To some people, four days spent in bed must sound pretty appealing and, to be honest, if I didn't have to spend the hours curled in a foetal position to alleviate the agony, then I would probably think so too. It has got so grim that I am actually reconsidering my decision not to have the spine injection operation. Having to spend more than half of the week in bed is not really living.

This has also caused havoc with my journalistic schedule, as I am often rolled in a ball of pain when I should be writing an article. As I live in Ayr, I was instructed to get on email so that I could transmit my columns straight into the editor's computer rather than having to drive to Glasgow clutching a piece of paper or a computer disc.

In theory, this should have been easy. Every shop, magazine and newspaper seems to contain a free CD-rom, so that you too can join the information highway. Instead, panic set in. Too many choices, too little time. I had 20 free CD-roms in front of me, and was quite unable to decide on one. This went on for some time, causing editorial consternation at my inability to choose between AOL and CompuServe when I did not know whether I would be around for Christmas. One offered ten email addresses, but only 30 hours of free time on the net. I rejected this as it was obviously for rich schizophrenics. Another offered 25 free hours every month for the rest of your life. Not really much good to me.

Then I saw it: guaranteed unlimited use for the next three years. I signed up on the spot.

I wish I had the same guarantee on my body.

5 September 1999

Brave Smarts:

NO matter how often I deny it, some of you persist with the impression that I am brave.

Writing about cancer for a magazine does not take any sort of superhuman effort. It does not require nerves of steel. Just plenty of drugs and a patient editor.

Your persistence in praising my bravery, flattering though it is, is symptomatic of the way the word has lost some of its currency. In tabloid speak, brave has come to describe the angst of a footballer who plays on despite a head wound as well as the woman who loses her husband in an accident at sea. It is even used on the child, far too young to understand the concepts of bravery or cowardice, which undergoes a serious operation or has a critical illness.

Before I found out I had cancer, I showed absolutely no signs of bravery and committed no acts of valour. I never even gave blood, although my younger brother did so on many occasions. Whenever possible, I liked my mother to be there, holding my hand, when I was throwing up. If that is not positively cowardly then I don't know what is. Of course nowadays I regularly undergo painful and humiliating medical procedures that would have previously had me running and shouting for mummy. I can't speak for women, but for a guy to have a catheter inserted is quite an ordeal. But you get on with it, you learn to relax and trust the medical staff that looks after you. In fact my sympathies are with them as administering must be worse than receiving. Anyone for an enema?

When I was younger I never stopped to think about my body, the wonder of how it all fitted together to keep me in good health. It's only now, as I find out about how each new tumour affects my health that I realise just how vulnerable we all are. All it takes is for one organ to stop working and you are suddenly faced with your own mortality. Living with cancer means that every day you wonder if it's going to be the last. When I heard that I had cancer, the rest of the doctor's words and my parents' reassurances fell on

51

deaf ears. There is a poster in the Beatson centre that says, "Cancer is a word, not a sentence", but to me that was it, I was going to die. Three years later, I am mellow enough to sleep at night and accept that I am Jonathan Wilson, cancer sufferer.

Now, although I am far from fit, my visits to the clinic are becoming further and further apart. There was no conventional treatment open to me: the growth of my tumours rendered chemotherapy, radiotherapy and surgery useless. I was offered a place on an experimental drug-testing course. They explained that there was about a one per cent chance of the drug having any noticeable effect, but what the hell, when your options are limited, you do desperate things. Plus I felt faintly heroic at the thought of helping someone five years down the line.

Twice a week, for ten weeks, I received the experimental therapy, which was actually a derivative of the ink that squid use to protect themselves from predators. Despite all our technologies and medical advancements, it's ironic to note how we revert to nature for cures and remedies. As expected, the treatment had no real effect, but I did have some fun over the phone with the doctor in charge. I almost managed to convince him that I was developing webbed feet and hands. "Is this a normal side-effect?" I asked him. It was only once he asked me to describe "webbed" that I burst out laughing.

After that, I was given a three-month rest, then another check-up. At first I thought this was a good thing; you get to see a consultant and even if it is only for five minutes, you feel part of the system that things are happening. There is a downside: you are surrounded by reminders that you are a member of an exclusive gang with bald heads, white faces, walking sticks and colostomy bags. Everyone looks at the floor or the ceiling, or just anywhere apart from making eye contact with a fellow sufferer because, although most fellow sufferers are friendly enough, there is an unspoken tradition that respects people's private thoughts. An interruption would perhaps upset an important train of thought.

Sometimes you have to work up the courage to attend an appointment, especially if it is to receive the results of a scan. When it came to my turn, all I was told was that my disease was stable and to return in two months for my next check-up. As the nurse administered a cursory blood check, I wondered what exactly "stable" meant. I wasn't in remission, I wasn't cured, so stable had to mean that I was dying, but at a satisfactory rate.

There is a saying that good health is the slowest way to die. I hate these cute sayings, almost always coined by an American with too much time on his hands. So it is with no great certainty that I can tell you how I am for another two months.

That's what cancer does to you, teaches you a new skill – how to live with uncertainty.

And as long as I don't start confusing that with bravery, I will manage just fine.

12 September 1999

Age of Reason:

I PASSED another milestone last week. Or should that be millstone?

I had my birthday and, to be honest, I never thought I'd reach this far. Since my initial diagnosis, all the statistics and predictions were that I would never get to blow out 29 candy pink candles.

I was planning to have a big birthday party at some salubrious Glasgow restaurant, perhaps running a competition for my readers. The one who supplied the funniest and most appropriate epitaph would win a free night of eating and drinking, courtesy of me. But as usual, illness reared its ever-present head. So I hastily organised a party at home, for family and 50 of my closest friends. The day before, I was taken on a magical mystery tour by my girlfriend Pauline. I was told to pack for a couple of days, with one formal outfit, and the plenty of warm clothes. Obviously Spain was out of the question. My daily need for morphine injections meant I was puzzled as to what possible destination we could be headed for. Little did I know that, behind the scenes, my mother and Pauline had frantically organised a stay at the only Michelin-rated lighthouse in Scotland and arranged for the local district nurse to come to the hotel and give me a quick fix while the other diners were polishing off their sorbet.

If trying to live with cancer is tough, trying to organise a birthday surprise for someone living with cancer is just about impossible. So by the time we returned home for the party proper, I was a little weary and in two minds as to whether it was a good idea. But by the time the guests started to arrive, I perked up. Drugs and bonhomie are a good combination, but to be surrounded by the people whom you love and who love you is the best feelgood cure I know. As well as being the party I never thought I'd have, it was the first time four generations of Wilsons had been in the same room together. My grandmother, Agnes, is typical of most Glasgow grannies. She was brought up during the war, when families of eight shared one room and survived on rations that would have today's social security claimants on the phone to their MEP. Some of her stories beggar belief. The funniest thing about her is that she doesn't know how hilarious she is.

Recently, for instance, a French tribunal found Henri Paul guilty of causing the crash that lead to Princess Di's death, and exonerated the photographers. My gran, however, was not as forgiving. "I blame those Pavarottis on their motorbikes," she stormed. She probably thinks the three tenors are what she has in her purse. While my mother and father were establishing themselves in their respective careers, she cared for me and my brother Chris. I lost count of the number of punishment exercises she signed in lieu of my father. This meant that parents' evenings came as a bit of a surprise. Despite having sanctioned all those detentions and lines, his eldest son was still disrupting all his classes. I used to detest those long waits on parents' evenings, probably akin to the long walk taken by the condemned man on the way to the electric chair. I don't have children, and I never will, but I firmly believe in parents' right to discipline their children without it turning to abuse.

I can remember having inch-deep welts on my behind from my father's belt for misbehaving at school. Did it stop me misbehaving? No. But it did have a deterrent effect on Chris, who soon developed a more mature approach to his studies. Whereas I favoured cramming the night before, Chris worked all year round. No one was prouder when he got his first class honours degree than his elder brother.

Unfortunately the path to higher education was not one chosen by my little sister Madeleine, who had a baby girl, Abbie, at the age of 15. Just as most teenagers are planning their futures, she was learning the intricacies of motherhood. Two years on, I have a beautiful niece who is looked after by her grandparents.

So while it was good to see Abbie and my gran and my 29th birthday all on the same day, I do have some reservations about my family extending itself so soon. Somewhere between the Seventies and Eighties, there has been a development of a subculture where educational achievement and attainment of employment is not considered enviable. Why bother working or studying for a job with money when you can have an easy life courtesy of the government? Of course, it's not really the government who pays, but you, tax-paying reader. There are towns and villages – Scotland's unemployment black spots – where wealth is measured by how many kids the household has.

While it was applied incorrectly and mismanaged terribly, the Child Support Agency was a step in the right direction. We must be stupid to allow a system, which rewards mindless and thoughtless virility. Fortunately I'm just a magazine columnist on drugs who writes the odd controversial article because I can. But the next time you look at your wage slip and see how much is deducted, make sure you know where the cash is going.

What a thing to write. I must be getting old.

19 September 1999

Booked In:

AS befits my reputation as the Fred Astaire of media "coffin dancers", I have invested in some new reading material.

I am hoping to find that will help me to complete what will be my literary epitaph. Both the editor and I agreed a while ago that I should have a final piece written for the inevitable end. I just can't bow out without a final dig at those who have crossed my path.

I am disappointed to discover that, despite the fact that I'm dying, the great philosophers still do not speak to me. My first attempts to steal some of their deep thoughts, was back in the eighties. I went to university, listened to "Hue and Cry" and bought books that, at the time, looked so cool. The second attempt was not much more successful. As I struggled with the big words and bigger concepts, it occurred to me that I was spending too much time thinking about dying in general, and cancer in particular, when I should be living.

So what you will not get is 19th-century philosophy, re-jigged for the Prozac 50 mg (25 mg. Is so yesterday) generation. As it all goes murky around the edges, I ask for your forgiveness, in advance. I am trying to hold onto to some sort of meaning, to continue caring and writing this column. My theatre of discussion is getting smaller every day. One of my on-going dilemmas has been whether or not to have an epidural-type operation, which may, or may not, relieve the back pain that has reduced me to a bed-dwelling hermit, who is slowly becoming addicted to morphine injections. I decided that enough was enough: the life I had was not a life at all; it was an existence, and a feeble one at that. I was going for it. Arrangements were made, and as it turned out, it would be most convenient to have the procedure done at the Ayrshire Hospice.

Over the last few months, I have visited this place a number of times. Each time there was a steady stream of workmen, all busy making the attractive building more amenable to the patients. The wards themselves are huge, with large windows looking out onto the well-kept gardens. An army of volunteers, friends and relatives, of patients, past and present, help the full-time staff with housekeeping and distributing meals-tasks which are carried out by the nursing staff in state-run hospitals. This has always struck me as a crazy arrangement. Why spend thousands training nurses, then use them as glorified cleaners and waitresses? No wonder they go abroad to modern, well-equipped hospitals and actually do the jobs they were trained to do.

So, there I was, booked into my single room in the Hospice, fuming silently about the inadequacies of the NHS.

I had an en-suite bathroom, TV, with satellite and video. Nurses who took a real pride in their work, came by every ten minutes or so, just to check up on me. As my mother remarked, "The last London hotel room she stayed in, was not as nice".

The Chief Administrator of the Hospice, Dr.John Bass, had been to my house to talk me through the procedure. He knew I was apprehensive, but he was also aware of the pain I was going through. He was keen to have me on my feet again, and had even arranged for me to meet the consultant who would be performing the procedure, so that I could ask questions and voice any fears that I had.

Eventually, my decision came down to Macho pride; if pregnant women could handle it, so could I.

Naturally, I insisted on my mother being present, to hold my hand. I squeezed tight as the consultant probed with his needle until he found the correct spot. He then injected a large dose of steroids, which would, hopefully, kill the pain for three to four weeks.

To avoid any discomfort, I had been first injected with a local anaesthetic, which "relaxes" the muscles from the stomach downwards. This explained why an adult nappy had been placed beneath me. It was a strange sensation. To slowly lose all control of your bladder and bowels. Thankfully for all concerned, both were empty at the time.
I fell asleep and awoke later feeling pain-free, and a bit sheepish for even worrying about something so straightforward and easy. One of the side effects of any sort of lumbar puncture is a drop in blood pressure, so I stayed in the Hospice for a further two days. The standard of healthcare was consistently superb and I would have no qualms about coming back.

In fact I was so comfortable, watching telly and by being cosseted by the nurses, that I did not make any progress, at all, in reading my inspirational books or writing my final column.

26 September 1999

Love Hurts:

THAT'S that. The season is officially over.

I can polish my patent leather Patrick Cox shoes and put them into their cotton bag which can, in turn, go to the back of the cupboard. I can banish my lurid Moschino waistcoat until next spring. If I last that long.

I am of course talking of weddings; I attended the last one of the year last weekend. It was rather special as it was my girlfriend's sister's wedding and she was getting hitched to an old school friend of mine, so I had two good reasons to be there. My illness, however, thought otherwise and did its best to keep me at home. My mother injected enough painkillers and anti-sickness drugs to floor a medium-sized elephant. In this state, I reckoned I would be OK as long as I had a parent at either side of me to hold me up, nod my head and offer a hand to shake should I encounter someone I knew.

The three of us made it down the aisle to our seats, where we collapsed in a gracious heap. Fortune was indeed smiling on me, for the service was to include the full Catholic mass as well as the traditional wedding service. By my reckoning at least one third of the congregation was non-Catholic, so I could afford to make some mistakes and not look like a complete fool. At school, one of the priests had a 'clicker' to help us around this problem. One click: stand up. Two clicks: sit down. Three clicks meant the priest had been sampling the communion wine beforehand. It gives me no pleasure to say it, but as I am dying and have to take my entertainment where I can find it: I enjoyed watching the non-Tims' reactions to the various parts of the service, which required participation from the congregation. Some tried to copy what the person next to them were doing, which was fine if they were sitting beside a Catholic. Others stoically and heroically chose to make their stand and not participate, which I understood completely, you couldn't accuse someone of being a bigot if you aren't one yourself

Although I had an absolutely blindingly good day, happy occasions like weddings only serve to illustrate all the things that I can never have. But although I have come to terms with the idea that this can't be for me, I still have to live in a society where marriage is considered the ultimate goal. At this wedding, both parties had served their time. They had dated for about ten years, and if you do not know someone by then, it's time to give up. Despite the fact that any smart person should have caught on early to the fact that love is messy, mad, chaotic and random, at the genesis of a new romance we naively claim it is precisely this love, which gives order and meaning to our life.

And still love has reduced better men than me to weak, sniffling wrecks. Love in its nature is amorphous yet two-faced. We can never truly know ourselves until we have exposed our frailties to it, and we can't see ourselves fully until the fever has ended and we either make up or break up. That's why I enjoyed myself all the more at the wedding. As William Shakespeare wrote: "We are all actors on a stage" and I can foresee a happy ending to this particular drama.

I also believe that, in love, we do things that we wouldn't normally contemplate. Every insurance policy has exclusions for war and acts of God, but I would definitely add love. It is a hurricane force, a far greater danger than Floyd, Bill or Ben.

Of course my looming mortality makes me examine life and death more intimately than the average Joe and I have started thinking of the poles of our existence as love and death as opposed to life and death. Speaking as someone who is equidistant to all three, I have come to the conclusion that there can be no life without love. Where would I be without the love of my partner? As I can certainly testify, what some of us think is a life is merely an existence. Being alive is not life. It is love that makes us feel most alive. It controls joy, hope, peace and contentment. Like death, it offers both suffering and redemption.

I am not afraid of loneliness – it's not the worst fate a man can encounter – the woman I adore empowers me to be more of a person than I could otherwise be. Would I have the confidence to write if I was single? I don't think so. I need the incendiary burst of energy that results from the love of a good woman.

There is one thing I do dread, a feeling much worse than being lonely. The bitterness of having had love and lost it forever.

3 October 1999

Wee Problem:

PEEING in public is an important ritual. If you are male, that is.

Get your little friend out at any other time and your same-sex friends will not be amused. But a man who can urinate in front of his mates has passed the first initiatory test of manhood.

Before I was ill, I had never experienced any problems. The only times I remember having difficulty were at a motorway cafe, when I was flanked by two 7ft bikers wearing knuckle dusters, and at a wedding when an elderly guest stepped up on the urinal next to me and started to berate me on my choice of waistcoat. But now, with the medication and the simple anatomical fact that my insides are not what they used to be, I have become more aware of my performance as I step up to the raised ceramic plinth. For the man too self-conscious to pass water in the company of other men, a visit to the gents can be a veritable nightmare. He may even leave the lavatory without spilling a drop, considering the alternative, a full bladder, to be less painful than the shame of standing at the urinal for half an hour to no result.

It was all so different when I was younger. As a child, I considered communal peeing great entertainment. Our family holidays were always in Brittany, and the long drive meant stops at motorway cafes. I always felt a great surge of pride as I stood next to my father and released that day's intake of Orangina. I felt like a member of a secret society, especially as my mum and sister had to sit down. My brother and I often used to recreate the famous scene in Star Wars where Obi-Wan Kenobi and Darth Vader battle to the death with their light sabres. Of course we swapped the energy beams with our own version of liquid death. With my friends, slashing afforded ample opportunities for competition. Who could pee the highest? The furthest? Whose pee was the greenest? The stinkiest and steamiest?

I'm not Jewish but, when I was younger, my parents decided that I should get the snip. Purely for hygienic reasons. I was so proud with the new improved version that I whipped it out whenever I could. Of course

I was only four at the time. (That's my story and I'm sticking to it).It was only in my mid-teens, when I had lost the self-consciousness of childhood, that I noticed how I sometimes dried up when urinating in proximity to others. I mentioned this problem to my friends.

"Have you noticed how it is hard to piss when you are standing next to someone in the toilets?" I asked. "No," came the answer, as one by one they backed away from me.Fortunately I was never short of a girlfriend at school, so the gay rumour didn't last too long

The owner of a sensitive bladder is in a difficult position. You can't just practise at home, unless you have a particularly strange or understanding family. "Hey Dad, fancy some mutual urination later on?" Just as agoraphobics need to confront the very crowds that terrify them, so the self-conscious urinator must enter the public lavatory and unzip the cursed fly. Although courageous, this course of action is fraught with danger.

To perform, our shy boy – we'll call him Jon, for no particular reason of course – needs to stand and compose himself. This takes time, and as he stands at the urinal, many men may enter the Gents, pee and leave.

Some are bound to notice poor Jon, who is neither peeing nor shaking off the drips that accompany the end of a successful visit. They will therefore suspect that Jon is there to examine their wares. Poor Jon, already under pressure, will suspect he is under suspicion. Any composure he had attained will now vanish, because of either the menacing muttering on one side, or the gentle encouragement on the other. And all he wanted was to spend a penny.

Some people might advise Jon to use the cubicle. But the "sitting down" or "mummy" leads only to suspicion. "What's up with Jon? Hasn't he got a wee man? What's wrong with it? Is it too small, too spotty, wrong colour?"

I do feel sorry for the bloke who has to stand next to the reluctant urinator. With neither man able to squeeze out a drop, each suspects the other of dark motives. It could be worse though.

You could be in Los Angeles, doing your business, when George Michael stands next to you.

Before you know it, your shy bladder syndrome is famous all over the world.

10 October 1999

You Drive Me Crazy:

SOME cars, like their owners, are a shambles!

My brother, for instance, has petrol vouchers, empty crisp packets, Coke cans, fag ash, unopened mail, and in the boot, he carries a week's supply of clothes, in case he needs a" fresh?" new outfit for some unforeseen event.

Contrast this with my own two cars:(both old" bangers", worth about 50p.each!) And my Virgoan tendencies become apparent. I vacuum my car after a haircut, so that the little loose hairs that fall off my newly scalped head don't annoy me, and thus affect my driving. Mock all you like, but I find petrol stations particularly offensive. They are decorated with huge posters, which promote a cleaner, safer world-if you use their petrol. Ironically, while you are inside paying for that very petrol, you tend to stock up on the very commodities, that will clutter up the back seat of your car for the next six months. One of my friends, Jack, had this horrible, old Vauxhall Astra. Inside it was so damp, that watercress grew in the boot. The ashtrays were so full of cigarette butts that he had to use the glove compartment instead. The numerous empty Coke cans, rattled and clattered to a sound not unlike the clinking noise made by the Hare Krishna followers, who stop and ask you to say "Gouranga"and wear orange robes.

My girlfriend shares my unfeasibly high standards of in-car hygiene-She is just no good at living up to them!

At least she has a sort of excuse: her dad is a car dealer so she seldom has the same car for a week. Each time she changes cars, she is given a nice clean, fresh one out of the packet, and returns the old, dirty one to the long-suffering guys with the jet-hose and ashtray deoderising equipment.Every time she gives me a lift, I complain about the lack of legroom. It's not that her father stocks particularly small, cramped cars with sticky seat-shifting mechanisms. It is the stack of bric-a-brac stashed under my feet: cassette covers for scraping the windscreen, muddy and torn magazines, old lipsticks, and sticky sweet papers. I always find this funny as, for no good reason, I expect women's cars to be prim and tidy; complete with a box of refillable tissues attached to the dashboard.

I don't agree with the theory, that a man's car is an extension of his penis. In my experience, it is an extension of his attic!

Where else can you store the stuff that you want to hide from everybody! Just hide it in the back, in the cubbyhole underneath that rubber mat, that once carried your spare wheel, but is now empty because you can't be bothered to take the flat tyre to the garage to be repaired. Advertisers, always keen to poke around in corners to find revealing information about our consumption habits, closely examine what we keep in our cars. They scour our sweetie wrappers for revealing details. The bits and pieces in our glove compartment can explain arrogance, shame, and timidity. They claim to be able to identify an audience just by one piece of rubbish.

I remember one particularly annoying, smug middle-class example. She gets in to the car, only to find that He has moved the seat, left his tape in the cassette player, eaten all the sweets and left the wrappers strewn over the passenger seats. What did she expect? If she wanted the car hoovered, she should have done the sensible thing- married a Virgoan!

Perhaps cars are supposed to be messy. I mean, who designed those little ashtrays anyway? YOU push one end in, and out pops the other, ready to receive the ash, except it's full of Opal Fruit wrappers.

And what about the space underneath the two front seats? If car designers really cared about in-car cleanliness, these spaces would be made into drawers, instead of being left as black holes where Coke cans can go to die.

Not that I am a total hygiene freak. A certain amount of car junk is characterful, and there is nothing sexy about a totally clean car. Even if I do not approve of lace doilies on back seats, or tins of those travel sweets that look as if they are covered in talcum powder.It is the quality, not the quantity, of trash that counts. I have been known to use my car to transport the odd chemical cocktail-I am dying of terminal cancer, after all.

I will leave it to one of my favourite authors: Hunter S. Thompson, to describe the ideal dashboard clutter: – "Two bags of Grass: 75 pellets of Mescaline: Five sheets of high-powered acid paper: A salt shaker full of cocaine, and a whole galaxy of multi-coloured uppers and downers: A quart of tequila: A case of Budweiser and two dozen Amyls"

Broom Broom!!

17 October 1999

Bar Necessities:

IT'S probably the oldest profession in the world, and at sometime in their lives, about 90 per cent of our population has tried a hand at it.

(That rules out prostitution, then.) I am of course talking about bar tending, the noble provision of alcohol and associated ancillary services.

Every time I come into Glasgow, which is about twice a week, another new pub or bar has sprung up. When I was in my prime it was all so much easier. Each nightclub had its own feeder bar, somewhere to meet acquaintances old and new before heading out to the Tunnel, Rhapsody or Reds. I can remember great nights in October Cafe, D'Arcy's and the Lounge, safe in the comfort that familiarity breeds. If you wanted a quiet night with your girlfriend there were cosy romantic places with soft seats, dimmed lights and the soundtrack to match. And there was the local, two minutes' stagger from your front door, full of familiar faces, some friendly some not, where the barperson (to be PC about it) knew your drink and served it quickly.

I got my first job in a bar when I was 15. I lied about my age on the application form and, a week later, I was a glass collector at Bar Luxembourg. (This site is now occupied by Trash – the nightclub, that is.) Having started on this bottom rung of the ladder, I was soon promoted to barman and let loose on the public. The pubs came and went, but once a barman always a barman; while at university I worked at the bar whilst studying for it. When I returned to Britain from my world trip, I needed a job fast so of course I turned to the old trusty mainstay of slackers, degenerates and pseudo-intellectuals, and started pulling pints in The Granary in Shawlands.

The Granary makes for a great study in sociology, politics and economics. There were the regulars during the day, nursing their pints of bitter like a firstborn. The restaurant was busy 24-seven and at night the place was packed with the mix of people that a neighbourhood as diverse as Shawlands throws up. The weekends were crazy and, on some occasions, the police would ask us to close the doors because we were so busy. By this time I had climbed the career ladder to bar manager. The hours were rubbish and there were always problems but I loved every second of it. When you work in such a frenetic environment, people are thrown together in a kind of instant intimacy. People you wouldn't normally talk to or get to know would suddenly become trusty friends, allies in the battle to hold off the advancing thirsty punters. I probably made some of my best friends there, before I moved on to the real world.

I consider myself a good barman, despite never having set foot behind a gantry for three or four years now. Over in the Continent, however, I would probably be rated no better than average. In France, Italy and Spain working in a bar accords you more status than here in Britain. We tolerate remarkably low standards. In a pub here if you ask for a gin and tonic, you will probably be asked if you want ice and lemon. Who wants to drink it without?

In Ireland barmen have to serve a five-year apprenticeship. They have an active union, which caused a nationwide panic by threatening a strike was called in 1988, when opening hours were extended but wages weren't. Watching an Irish barman pulling a pint of Guinness is akin to watching the artists painting on the left bank of the Seine. There is no wastage, and if they are a true master they can paint a shamrock in the froth with the flow of liquid. I don't like to boast but that's how I served mine and taught bar staff to do the same.

So where would I recommend people to go for a properly served drink? Well, I naturally gravitate to the top end of the market and reckon that, at the Arthouse Hotel, Groucho St Judes and that old favourite, One Devonshire Gardens, you are assured of service, the finest ingredients and the perfect ambience. I always look at how a bar is set up. If it has fresh-cut celery, Tabasco and Worcester sauce, salt and pepper, cherries and lemon and a supply of toothpicks, the chances are I will be served a well-presented drink. It will also cost at least three quid, which I consider a small price to pay for the perfect accompaniment to a good evening. But then, I never know when a gin and tonic is going to be my last.

And now that I have retired: how to spot the ideal barman? I recommend watching The Shining. It has a lovely bar, and the bartender has a welcoming smile and the line every punter wants to hear. "Your money is no good here," he says to the disintegrating Jack Nicholson. "Sir."

24 October 1999

Raring to Go:

HELLO, dear readers. I am in a good mood.

The last two weeks have proved to me the importance of a strong mental attitude when dealing with cancer. In fact I have come to the conclusion that a powerful will and plenty of determination can see you through almost any situation.

For those of you who have not been paying attention, a chance to catch up. I have a primary cancer of the bowel and secondary tumours in my stomach, liver and spleen. Basically, my whole torso has become a carrier for the disease, which will cause my demise. The pain, which I thought I was coping with admirably, has returned. Worse than that is the sickness that accompanies it. The slow but surely mounting feeling of nausea is very high on my list of things I hate. As if that was not bad enough, I have been put on a course of steroids to try and build me up, as it's hard to get a properly balanced diet when you feel queasy all the time. But the steroids get my appetite going just as my nausea reaches its peak. I end up feeling ravenous, wanting to eat, yet knowing that whatever goes down will come back up without touching the sides.

These anti-social afflictions have come at a bad time because I have just started to make small forays back into the land of the normal. When I was first diagnosed as having cancer, I was staying in a flat in Shawlands with an Australian guy called Phil. We became great friends, and my illness hit him pretty hard as we trained and worked out together. (I think his pride was hurt by the fact that, all the time we were competing, I was slowly dying.) When his visa ran out, he had to return to Australia. I never thought I would see him again. But he had always planned to come back, and last week he did. Ten of us went out for dinner, with Phil as guest of honour.

Eating out is difficult when you have lost half of your stomach. I tend to order a starter instead of a main course, to avoid that bagged-up, bloated feeling. However, I do have a weakness for fillet steak in peppercorn sauce, and Arigo, the venue for the reunion, has turned the rare steak into an art form.

One of the benefits of my shortened lifespan is that I don't have to worry about ill health in my old age. I can stuff myself with pesticide-enhanced genetically modified whatever the hell I like, knowing it will make no difference whatsoever. I do care about the quality of food and produce my friends and family eat, but I also know that the healthiest diet in the land won't save you if, like me you have a faulty gene which turns your stomach into Cancer Grand Central.

So I managed to put away a 16oz fillet and a couple of glasses of Trentino. And, even better, I was up for more, which was a definite bonus. It's at this point of most nights out that I say my goodbyes and head home feeling sick while my friends head for a nightclub and further shame and bad behaviour.

The only club within staggering distance was The Shed, on Shawlands Cross. As my medication seemed to multiply the effects of the alcohol I was taking it easy, honest, but sometimes the pain means that my walking style becomes more of a hobble. I wasn't drunk, just in pain.

Now I have found that door stewards in the more professional nightclubs are happy to let me in once they realise my pallor and illness and not too much cheap tequila cause wobbly steps. So we were allowed in to The Shed. Eventually.

As I stood watching the writhing and squirming all around me, I wondered if it would be a good idea to carry some sort of official medical card which would convince people like bouncers that I had cancer and so sometimes walked with a bit of a stoop. It would have helped me out of a recent embarrassing situation, when I was on the bus and was so knackered I had to sit down on the seat at the front reserved for the elderly and infirm. The looks and the not-so-quiet remarks from those behind me were quite upsetting, yet what was I going to do? Stand up on the seat and shout, "I am the infirm?"

Nausea is gross but the psychological barbs hurt more. But with the help of my friends, my strong mental attitude and plenty of red meat, I am managing to live that little bit extra.

31 October 1999

Starry Starry Day:

ONE of the many discoveries I have made in my new career as a columnist is that some articles write themselves while others need to be teased and flattered before they emerge from the sub-conscious to make an appearance on the page.

I have also worked out that it is much easier to write about your life if you actually have a life worth writing about. Great wordsmiths can rely on their literary skills to even make the most mundane of existences sound exciting. As this is not an option open to me it occurs that the editor has made the following trade-off: big talent who stays in the house all day for social butterfly with IQ of 50. Last week, however, I thought it was all going to change. First of all I got the chance to combine my life-long social sophistication with my newfound power in the media. (Mum, sorry Ms Wilson, could you hold all calls? Sweetie thanks.)
You may have seen me in the Big Issue, joining in the debate about Labour MSPs' stance on cannabis as a medical treatment. While it is flattering to be asked my opinion, this has freaked me out ever so slightly and I would like you to know that there is more to me than "Jonathan Wilson, 29, Prestwick, cancer sufferer".

Then came something even more exciting. I can't give too much away, because I have been sworn to secrecy, but Channel 4 has been commissioned to make a programme based around the most amazing poem written by Simon Armitage. I know that this does not sound promising. In the course of my private education I sat through poetry classes so dry and boring that the very words onomatopoeia and alliteration give me a hot flush. I thought that poetry, for all its implied beauty and craft, just goes over the heads of 99 per cent of the population. So when I was approached to do this TV programme based around a poem, I had my doubts. But there were quite a few buts. The director was to be Brian Hill, a Bafta award winner and Christopher Ecclestone was the narrator. I have always admired his work, whether he was playing the police inspector stabbed to death by a bald psycho Bobby Carlyle in "Cracker", or as the disintegrating

accountant in "Shallow Grave". My favourite is the part he played in the reconstruction of the Hillsborough disaster – he was utterly convincing and totally heartbreaking.
I ended up saying yes.

A day with Chris Ecclestone certainly showed me that fame affects people differently. His first words were: "What do you take in your tea?" He is just this great guy. Obviously integrity and personal happiness are more important to him than the quick cheap buck that some actors seem to chase. We had some scenes together which I found difficult and emotional but he never resorted to fake sincerity. Without wishing to sound like Oprah Winfrey, I could tell he shared the pain and anguish I was feeling as I talked about how cancer has scarred my life.

This programme, which is called" Killing Time", will be broadcast on January 1 2000 on Channel 4. They also have a pavilion in the Millennium Dome itself, and for the year that the dome stands (and here I will resist the temptation to launch into a rant about the fact that all this money is being invested in a structure that will be pulled down after one year) they will be showing the programme, continuously. I would urge anyone who goes to the dome to try and catch the programme – I don't think you will be disappointed. And if you are, I don't think I will be around for you to slag off, the way my pain increases every day.

That was another thing that touched me about the way the programme was put together. Here was this film crew, working on a major project, probably with enough awards and plaudits between them to keep the kids off the mantelpiece, yet all I had to do was wince slightly and filming would stop to see if I was OK to continue. I truly felt like a star for the day and I can see that it could be addictive.

It's a heady and dizzying business. Chris (as I now call him) was telling me that he was just back from the States were he was shooting a film with Nicholas Cage – salary $15 million. As we started to talk it turned out that we even have a friend in common, a Scottish guy who is becoming a real player. Funny how Scots so often rise to the top.

Of course my day of glamour could only last so long and, sitting on the shuttle home, I wondered if acting would have worked for me. It was cancer that has pushed me into writing.

What misfortune might have given me the urge for camera-lights-action?

7 November 1999

Choose Life:

LIFE is for living. A simplistic statement perhaps, but an important one.

This basic truth has been brought home to me over the last couple of months, as I've tried to superficially gloss over my ever-decreasing health. Small things like being breathless after walking to the all-night garage 200 metres from my house.

I fell down the stairs the other night because my leg muscles are just not strong enough to support my bodyweight. (And I use the term bodyweight in its most technical sense. The last time I was this light I had just started shaving.) These are the leg muscles, formerly known as the sculpted pieces of art that carried me faster than anyone else I knew. I felt so vulnerable, so pathetic as my mother helped me to my feet. I know that to most people I do not look particularly ill, but the last couple of months have been a struggle. But jelly limbs apart, I have been doing my best to behave like a normal member of the human race. This has included trying to look beyond morphine injections and doctors' appointments when I sit in front of my computer to write, and here at least I have had some success. My article on bar tending was so well received that Colin Barr, the man responsible for Glasgow's reputation as a great night out, invited me to the opening of his latest business venture, Republic Bier Halles in Gordon Street.

Well it was quite a good night and I was just thinking that I could easily get the hang of literary carousing, seeing out my days as a social commentator and drinking a good deal of free vodka when a thought-provoking email arrived. Without much regard for my tender feelings, this guy left me in no doubt that he wanted to read more about cancer, its effects on my health, on my mental fortitude and on my family, and less of my thoughts on the perfect gin and tonic. It's not that I can't take a slagging, and I knew when I started this job that I would have to be prepared to get deep, meaningful and personal. It's just that it's wearing enough feeling ill and exhausted every minute without writing about it too. And I do really appreciate all the responses to my column, even the negative ones. I receive a lot of email every week, and my usual policy is to gather it up and then blitz it all at once. Similarly, I treasure the old-fashioned type of post that you send me. Remember paper and pens? Whatever happened to them?

As readers you have been so positive and supportive that it helps me keep going. As my time gets shorter, I do feel my physical abilities diminishing. Being pig-headed and obstinate helps, but there comes a point where even I have to admit, I'm just not going to get through this. This may sound defeatist, but the daily grind of tablets, lack of sleep, bodily functions once taken for granted that are now cause for celebration ... these things give a clear message that the end is nigh. And a lot of the people who contact me seem to find this part of my experience the most enthralling. Not because you are all vultures and ghouls who can't wait to see me go, but because so many of you have been touched by cancer.

It can't be easy to watch someone you have loved all your life fade away. Not that everyone fades away, indeed I hope to go kicking and shouting, but a lot of your emails have hinted at a quiet, almost resigned end with very little communication or feedback. You tell me that you had no way of knowing what your friend, or relation was going through. And it's emails like these that do so much to help keep me going. It is not an easy thing to talk about or write about, but I have started, so I might as well keep going till I finish.

I have said before that I do not want to become a poster boy for cancer sufferers. I do want to do my utmost to tell people just how prevalent this horrible disease is. As I will be telling you soon, I have a grand plan to promote cancer awareness. My family and friends think I am totally off my head, but what is the alternative? Sit about in my "jammies" and think back to when life was sweet and easy and I didn't have to concentrate for half an hour before having a pee?

Some decisions are made for you, while others you take for yourself and damn the consequences. And that is going to be the motto while I live out the last part of my life.

14 November 1999

Ring of Fire:

SO this is writing? It certainly feels like it.

It's 4am and I haven't slept for three days and, at last, I feel like a true writer. I feel like Hemingway, like F Scott Fitzgerald and JD Salinger, the names from my adolescent past that formed the literary backbone of my formative years.

There is, I have discovered, a seductive relationship between writer and that part of night, which is darkest. Unfortunately, it is my illness that binds me to this bewitching time, not the banana daiquiris that helped Hunter S Thompson to write his best sellers. (The specifics of sleep deprivation – what I have started to call my burning ring – are not the nicest of things to discuss. But I am dying of cancer, not suffocation by orchid petals.) One thing I do have in common with the bold Doctor Gonzo is my consumption of chemicals. For me it's steroids: I class them the way some people group alcohol or tobacco or other drugs, as a stimulus to their prose. In the course of one week I've put on half a stone, can't sleep for more than three hours at a time, and to be quite honest, I don't feel too bad about it. This is because I've made a life decision. A real one. An honest-to-goodness decision that makes me feel proud to be alive again. And that hasn't happened for a while, I can tell you.

This is the after-effect of a fit of depression so dark and deep that I scare myself when I think back on it. If I didn't have a particularly strong character, you wouldn't be reading a column this week. Or any week. I would have clicked my little red shoes together and said: "There's no place like home." Kansas would have taken the form of a tub of Valium and a bottle of special reserve Jack Daniels that I have kept for this very occasion.

In retrospect, I don't think it was all self-pity. One of my closest friends is a relief worker in the Far East. She teaches English in a refugee camp while war rages all around her. She could be arrested, interned,

71

tortured ... she makes me feel proud to be human and be her friend. Last week she had to come home, back to Edinburgh. Her little sister has cancer. Twenty-two years old, living in the civilised comfort of the western world, where we pride ourselves on our healthcare and hold forth on why some things cause us illness. It is relatively easy for me because it was in my genes. I'm a dud. But how do you explain to a 22-year-old that she has cancer?

Anyway, this has only strengthened my resolution to do something. It started off as vague a notion, inspired by the charity ads that pop up in magazines. "Walk the Himalayas for Cancer Research". It does sound tempting. I happened to mention this when I was in London filming a TV programme recently, that I had this crazy plan to do a walk, or some kind of event, for a cancer charity. As a kind of swan song. (I know. Yuck. I'd had a real tough week.)

Now my family and friends know how crazy I am and the thought of me marching through the Sahara or up the Himalayas to raise cash for cancer research didn't faze them much. My new media chums, however, immediately started talking book and documentary options. I guess I hadn't realised the marketing potential of a guy who is almost ready to say his final farewells pitting what is left of his body against nature. Will my previous high fitness level be enough to sustain me through a challenge that normally fit people struggle to complete, or will it make really compelling television as viewers watch me fail?

As I see it, cancer research will be the winner either way. Even if I were unable to finish the challenge, I would still be putting out the message that life does go on, even when you have cancer. And I wouldn't undertake a venture like this if I weren't sure I could complete it. But I will need all the financial, physical and moral support I can get. And that, reader, means from you.

So that's part one of my big plan. I am going to undertake an arduous trek in aid of Cancer Research, and hopefully, with your help, raise money and awareness. With a bit of luck this should lead to a TV programme where everyone can watch yours truly really suffering. (I can see an audience for this already.)

If a guy with cancer can achieve this, then just imagine what you could do.

21 November 1999

Consuming Passion:

HERE'S a pop quiz.

Your young neighbour has terminal cancer. He parks his car on the public highway, as close to his gate as possible, because walking has become a bit of a problem. The tumours in his stomach mean one foot in front of the other is a major effort.

You decide to visit Kingdom of Leather and purchase a suite large enough to house the eight buffalo it probably took to cover the outsize brute in hide. It is now sitting in the back of the delivery truck, just ten feet from its intended delivery address. You send the delivery boy over to demand that I move my car, even though he has confessed that he had seen my disabled badge and didn't mind carrying his load the extra five feet.

Of course this was enough to send me into a fit of steroid-induced sofa rage. Normal, stable, well-slept Jonathan would have gladly got up, dressed and moved the offending vehicle to facilitate the relocation of the wide-load sofa, recliners or whatever you damn well call them. As is clear from this irrational over-reaction to a leather couch, the new steroids and I aren't getting on too well. At first, three hours of sleep followed by 21 jittery nervous hours awake seemed OK. Other cancer suffers can do it, why shouldn't I? But it is making me so intolerant. I am incensed by rampant consumerism, which is pretty ironic given that I used to be a right little yuppie. New gadget? I had to have it, never mind the cost.

Now I have had the idea of doing a walk or trek to raise cancer funds, I have had to do some serious sums and a little maths put the venture at about £3000. While I was at it, I looked at my past life and didn't like what I saw. Piles of designer clothes that I didn't need. Boxes of consumer durables, gadgets costing hundreds of pounds. I have two watches that are worth more than a family saloon. I have two cars. What the hell am I going to do – drive them both at the same time? Am I really better than my annoying neighbours? If I didn't have cancer, would I still be out shopping every weekend while the queue up at the

Beatson Oncology Centre a the Western Infirmary stays at manic proportions? It takes something like cancer to put your life into perspective, to take stock of what really matters in your life: family, friends and the peace of mind to know that, whatever happens, you have given it your best shot.

So where is this leading? After much thought, I have decided to get rid of the lot in a giant car boot sale, all in aid of cancer research. I've no doubt that, with your help, generous Sunday Herald readers, I should make £10,000 easily. Especially when I start typing begging letters to the big firms who can write cheques to offset their tax liabilities at the end of the year.

The individuals who offer to help and the pensioner who puts 50p in the collection box means more to me personally than the faceless corporation which juggles its budget, but the end will justify the means. Charity has become a business itself and, being a beggar of sorts, my column will end every week with details of how to contribute and how well we are doing every week. And, as I am all in favour of fair exchange, I will be letting my generous readers choose what challenge I should undertake. It seems only fair, as you lot are going to be paying for it. I am also very conscious of how the new, downsized me will affect my nearest and dearest.

For the last two months I have been pretty hard to live with. All I can think about is charity money, how to raise it, am I fit enough, is this trip a just big ego-boosting battle: Jonathan Wilson versus cancer?

Am I being vain? I feel that I am lucky to have a platform to talk about cancer and that I should use it, not just to raise cash, but public awareness also. I constantly bang on about the fact that, by 2000, one in three of us will be affected by cancer in some form or shape. But am I doing this to the detriment of the friends and family that I claim to hold so close and dear? Is cancer eating me up in a different way, consuming my mind in the same way that the tumours are devouring my insides?

At least my neighbours should be happy because I'm going to sell both my cars. Charity begins at home and I could not, in all conscience, ask people for money while owning two vehicles. This does not mean I am going to turn into a social pariah just as all those festive invites start dropping in.

Just expect me to turn up by bus.

28 November 1999

Family Planning:

NO matter how crap you feel, or unattractive you look, good news just seems to put a bounce in your stride and a smile on your face. So, despite being back in the excellent Ayrshire Hospice for another battery of tests, I am lying back in my bed feeling pretty mellow, without the depression, which has gripped me over the last month.

The reason for my good mood is the happy thought of the pitter-patter of little baby feet. It just fills me with joy. And before anyone marks me down as a card-carrying Labour toady, it is my sister Madeleine's announcement that she is pregnant that has put me on a high. (Not that I begrudge Tony and Cherie the joys of another shot at parenthood), as long as I don't have to look at him in a sweater, brandishing a cup of coffee, smarming to the press pack. My illness means that parenthood is not an option for me. I do it vicariously, as Uncle Jonathan, and then hand my sister's first child, Abbie, back to her mother or grandmother without even having to change a nappy. Yet Abby still thinks I'm a star, mostly because I have an endless supply of confectionery. This is due to having the constant munchies through taking these damn steroids. They have another side effect, which is to make me look like the beaver in The Lady and the Tramp. You see, I do take the part of generous uncle very seriously. I'm just hoping that young Abby, who is just commencing her potty training, doesn't copy the sounds her uncle makes while going through what Jeff Goldblum seemed to experience when making The Fly.

I've been thinking hard about how to leave Abbie and her siblings so that they will always remember me well. Of course there will be these columns and I have connived with my more softhearted relatives to ensure that there will be enough schmaltz pictures of me to jog their memories. I even considered the video option; recording all the things I would have done differently for the benefit of my as yet unborn nieces and nephews. Knowing my family, however, Dad would probably record over the tape.

When I got over the initial shock of realising that I was dying of cancer, I knew I had to have a plan. I was always a man with a plan, but to survive that little bit longer, I have had to set myself goals. The last one was my friend Mark's wedding. It was a big deal to me; I was surprised I made it. So, I later heard, were quite a few of the other guests. My next goal is the walk that I have been going on about for the last couple of weeks. I am hopeful that it will happen in February or March. This seems a bit ambitious, but I really believe that if you reach for the sky, you get the stars. Aim low and all you achieve is mediocrity. And if that was not enough, I plan to write a book about the walk. It will also include some of the emails that you send me: beautiful prose and tragic stories of love not spoken, and fights and arguments unresolved. And all of them tinged with cancer. Some weeks I receive over 100. A lot of my columns are influenced by what you send me, and I think your messages have shaped the person that I am just now.

As far as the plans for the big walk go, I am pre-selecting at least four treks. I am then going to ask you, dear readers, to help me pick one. The charity will be chosen at random, as the big point is that by 2000, one in three of us will be touched by this disease. While the money is of course crucial, the message is equally important. Cancer is not just an old person's disease.

The bank account is set up, so that I can't run off to Spain with your hard-earned pennies and, by next week, I hope to have a short list of the walks available.

Watch this space.

5 December 1999

Survival International:

I THINK I'm getting paranoid.

Every time I open a paper or turn on the TV, I seem to hear the word "cancer". The £300,000 awarded to the family of Ruth Picardie, the Observer journalist who died of breast cancer, after her misdiagnosis was big news, but it's making me edgy. I feel it is becoming a cause celebre, a bandwagon worthy of a well-placed sound bite, when it is actually much bigger than that. We deserve a lot more than an admission that "one of my best friends has cancer".

Go on, say it. Cancer. It's not so hard, is it? It's just a disease. Yet it manages to kill so many of us. What upsets me is that cancer care in our country is such a lottery. It's the medical equivalent of Who Wants to be a Millionaire? I know I am getting a bit jittery about this, but I even find it uncanny that Chris Tarrant's stylist dresses him all in black. Perhaps I am being too morbid, too close to the subject, but I have been doing a bit of research on the internet, comparing survival rates in different parts of Britain with Europe and the USA, and it makes grim reading. It's not as if our doctors are any different. In fact, our oncologists are probably rated as highly as anywhere in the world. We have a National Health Service, which is the envy of most countries – just compare it with the insurance-driven Medicare system of the USA. We could be excused for feeling a bit superior, that bit more civilised, but, as with most things in life, money focuses the mind. Or, in this case, money focuses the resources.

For British citizens with cancer, surviving for anything more than five years is considered a cure. This is certainly not my definition of a cure, although I'd happily grab those years and refuse to let go. Yet in America, five years is the norm, despite their imperfect, socially discriminatory form of healthcare. Even Hank and Velma, with their minimal health insurance, have access to a hospital geared up for the most sophisticated treatment of cancers, tumours and their hideous relations.

When I was first diagnosed with cancer three years ago, I wasn't even given six months to live, yet if I lived in a trailer park in the American Midwest, I would have a better prognosis. Something is wrong somewhere. Let me change that – something is wrong here. It's not that there are no centres of excellence for cancer here. At my home-from-home, the Beatson oncology clinic, I would wager that in ten years' time half of the types of cancer that are killing us at present will be eradicated. (That's 125 of the 250 varieties, which are scything through the population at present, although I will not be here to see it.)

I know I was lucky. I was fast-tracked straight into the cancer system and seen by one of the top oncologists in Britain, and therefore by extension, in the world. But that was only because my parents decided to buy a home and settle in Ayr. If they had settled in Falkirk I would still be getting the same high standard of general care, but I would not have had the crucial specialist advice and treatment that was such a help at the start of my illness. In the waiting room at the Beatson, I've struck up conversations with people from Stornoway, Dumfries, all over Scotland. This is the attitude you must take if you want to improve your chances with cancer. You have to take control of your treatment. If your doctor says something you don't understand, ask him about it. Actively pursue drug trials and new treatments. Of course they cost money, but if you don't ask, you don't get.

Unfortunately, different hospitals have different priorities and the one you are referred to may be the very place to go for a triple heart bypass, but not much use when you have bowel cancer. All too often our British reserve and stiff upper lips prevent us from accessing the care we need. The proof? At present, our curative rate is about 38%, one of the lowest in Europe.

Cancer is a lottery, some people win and others lose, but what we must not accept is the man-made variation of odds that are built into our health service. It was set up to give everyone the care they need, when they need it, whether they live in Falkirk or Ayr.

It simply is not good enough to accept that geographical anomalies exist. Each region should have the full range of resources at its disposal, or an efficient and equitable referral system to different centres of excellence, giving everyone a fair chance at survival. This has got to be preferable to sitting at home in front of a computer screen, working out where best to buy a house for your own particular ailment.

Roulette is best left for the casinos. Health is too important for silly games.

12 December 1999

Less is more:

IT took my brother to point out the incongruous nature of my selecting ten luxury items that I should wish for at Christmas for the Sunday Herald's recent festive shopping guide, while at the same time selling all my worldly possessions to raise money for charity. Despite all my protestations and assurances that I wouldn't rush out for that new Audi coupe, he remains unconvinced that I have wholly shed my urban survival outfit and designer-led tendencies.

He might even have a point. I owned a pair of the very fine Armani trainers before the article was even conceived, and I must confess to enjoying a nice cigar after a pleasant meal. Of course my brother Chris knows how important this cause is to me. He has just recently moved out of the family house to his own bachelor pad, but has seen enough of his brother's suffering, both at home and in hospital during chemotherapy, to frivolously dismiss the effort I am making in order to make people aware of cancer. He is my brother and it's his job to take the piss, but he also got me thinking. In particular, I thought about my own faith.

I was brought up as a Roman Catholic but came from a household liberal enough to allow us to question our own faith if we felt it necessary. We could, and did, ask questions, which seem extremely naive in retrospect. It was the asking that was important. This enlightened approach to Catholicism did not sit so comfortably in the unquestioning environment of St Aloysius College. There were some incidents when I was cast as insidiously subversive, usually by the members of the classics department who suspected I was a member of a fifth column dedicated to poisoning the minds of my fellow pupils. But I was a stroppy little so and so. How could you accept certain inalienable truths, which form the cornerstone of the way of life that you choose to live when, technically, you know these facts to be untrue? I know now that faith is a strong belief in something that you cannot prove and am more comfortable when I can set my own boundaries and definitions. Despite the best efforts of man, weather, genetics and God knows what else, I still retain my faith. It is strictly my faith. I doubt there is another person on this planet whose faith is remotely like mine. It has been shaped by my distinctive life and experiences, which are not the same as anybody else's. Which may be bad news for Armani sales staff, but is good news for everybody else.

What annoys me is people who blindly accept what they are told are the right or wrong way to live. Or, even worse, the people who, like sheep in their best outfits, turn out for their weekly feel-good dose of religion. They put on their their pious demeanours and their good shoes, and go along to their place of worship, enjoying a glow of self-congratulation at just how perfect the world is. Of course organised religion has always had its opponents. Some people react to my diatribes by nodding sagely. Ah, they say, that's to be expected, life has dealt him a blow that would lead most people to rebel against their religion. The could not be further from the truth. Since finding out that I am dying of cancer, I find myself with a stronger faith than at any other time in my life.

I have come to the conclusion that the only people who understand the true nature of faith are those who really need it. How can the person who has never suffered or wanted for anything in their life understand how it's possible to trust in something that you cannot prove?

I wish I had that kind of faith, that focus and clarity when I also had my health. I think back and think that I could have achieved anything. But I didn't, because I couldn't, and that's the point. I didn't have the incentive to make that extra effort and I think that effort and faith both come down to the same thing. We have one life here and it is up to us not to waste it.

On that very subject, I can tell you that plans for my "Dead Man Walking" trek are coming along nicely and I am almost at the stage of presenting you, my readers, with the choice of routes available to me. Please ignore all my suggestions for lavish Christmas gifts and start saving your coppers. Prospective corporate sponsors are also welcome to get in touch.

19 December 1999

Royal Appointment:

I NEVER realised how much physical effort there is in a curtsy.

But why would a man want to learn how to curtsy? Only if he was lacking in literary skills yet desperate for a subtle device that would allow him to mention that his invitation to the opening of the Millennium Dome on New Year's Eve had fallen through the letterbox with a gratifying thud.

Please do not try this at home without supervision. I do not want to be held responsible for countless hours of lost productivity due to damaged knees and backs (or, for that matter, entries in Pseud's Corner). You can just take my word for it, it's difficult. Dad will be lifting me in and out of the bath for a while yet. But aching joints aside, it is all very exciting. After filling out a security form designed by a civil servant with little grasp of reality, I realise that I must be deemed worthy, in security terms at least, of meeting Her Royal Majesty. With the form I also had to send away two passport photos in which, thanks to my current course of steroids, I look like a human hamster. But even the idea of mingling with a rodent-featured terminally ill person has not put the old girl off. I have returned the compliment by selecting a special pair of darkened glasses in the event of her Majesty wanting to wear all the colours of the rainbow again. All at once. On one top.

Perhaps I should have waited until my social calendar calmed down before I started my drive to raise cash for charity by selling off most of my wardrobe. But I can exclusively reveal that, on that night, I will be a true Scotsman. Not only will I be wearing my kilt, it will be made in a tartan with special sentimental value. My aunt (who is actually not a relation at all but my mum's best friend who has earned honorary membership of the family by changing endless nappies when I was a baby) has designed and patented a special millennium tartan. She is an inspiring person, who runs a large textile business and has energy left over to do the things that us ordinary people would find exhausting. I will be proud to go to the party in full highland dress, in the millennium tartan, representing all Scottish cancer sufferers.

It's hard for me to thank all the people who have shown me such touching kindness and support, and wearing this special kilt is my way of showing my aunt how much I appreciate her. When I was first admitted to hospital, it was in Glasgow. As my family is predominantly from Ayrshire, I felt a bit isolated, a bit stranded and, to be honest, a bit lonely. After my initial operation, when I had half my stomach removed, I had to stay in for about a month, to recuperate. And while I have the greatest respect for the medical profession, it is impossible not to get bored of breakfast at 8am followed by lunch at noon, as regular as the Greenwich time signal. My pseudo-aunt was a saviour.

Some mornings when I had slept through breakfast I woke up to find a plastic bag at the end of my bed, filled with all the day's papers, drinks, sweets. In short, a survival kit for anyone who is stuck in a ward for 24 hours a day. Sometimes I was awake and, although she could only stay for ten minutes at a time, her visits meant so much to me.

It's great to be able to do something in return, and I'm sure that my new kilt will be more dazzling than any of the designer suits that I have flogged off to help cancer charities.

Now all I need to do is get dad to hoist me out of the bath so that I can have another go at the modest bent-knee drop.

26 December 1999

Athlete's First Foot:

I AM not one of those people who is good at wrapping up presents.

But last year I thought I would surprise Pauline and bought beautiful paper, exotic-looking sheeny ribbons and special tinsel string. The result was spectacular, even if I say so myself. But all I got was "You never did that by yourself! Did you get your mum to do it?" It seems I cannot win, so this year I gave her a tangerine, a bag of chocolate coins and a 50 pence piece. Lucky for her she had been good. Had she been bad, I planned to present her with a bag of soot.

It looks like I am going to reach my next life target, which is visiting the Millennium Dome on New Year's Eve. Just me, the Queen, Philip, Pauline and 10,000 other freeloaders. I am sitting here looking at the brochure they have sent me, full of quotes from English playwrights and poets, but only one of them makes sense to me. It is by Longfellow: "Lives of great men remind us/We can make our lives sublime/And, departing, leave behind us/Footprints on the sand of time." Maybe not the greatest of quotes, but inspirational to me, and to my strategy of taking life one day at a time. Just because I am dying does not mean that I cannot strive to attain the same high standards as everyone else.

This week, I was contacted by a London publisher, who had heard that I was doing a walk for charity, and would I be interested in writing a book about my experiences? Unbeknown to them, I had already decided to start writing a book, primarily as a diary, but hopefully avoiding the trap of penning Bridget Jones' Cancer Diary. I think I could make more money by writing in a diary fashion, but there has been such a glut of literature released in this form recently. Even the once-weedy Adrian Mole has been revamped for Generation X. But how would I approach it? Obviously I don't want to trivialise it but, on the other hand, do I really want to take on the role of worthy sufferer and write yet another reverent tome about the pain and suffering of cancer?

Talking of pain and suffering, I have come off my steroids, and there is always a period of about a week where I feel like a well-kicked football. Suffering from a bout of flu on top, you can imagine how crap I felt. I got a phone call from The Times, which is doing a story on me, asking if I'd mind if they sent a photographer to take some snaps of me on a running track to show what I have lost – my running prowess. I agreed to it as I had already done the interview over the phone (one tip to prospective stars: don't do phone interviews). I met the photographer and we drove out to Crownpoint running track. Rather than just stripping down to my athletics kit, I thought I would be courteous and let the on-duty staff know who I was and what I was doing.

Big mistake. "Oh naw, son, you Cannae do that, you might be a spy, photographing the running track. It's more than my job's worth!" I swear on my life that is what he said. Standing in my running kit, adorned with Scotland badges, I pleaded with the idiot. But my protestations fell on deaf, not-quite-all-there ears, and the jobsworth actually escorted us from the premises. Fortunately, the manager of the Kelvin Hall Sports Arena took pity and let us take our photographs there.My dad has a saying that sh*t always floats. I would like to nominate that jobsworth as the best floater in Scotland.

But in the true spirit of the season, I wish you all a peaceful Christmas and New Year with your families and I look forward to hearing from you in the new millennium. Best wishes.

2 January 2000

Pleasure Principle:

FAREWELL, then, to the season of excess.

For me, Jane Austen had it right when she wrote: ''One half of the world cannot understand the pleasures of the other.''

If she was alive today, I wonder what she would make of one of Scotland's most popular annual pastimes. Would she enjoy reclining on the couch with her needlework and a can of super-strength lager to watch the Old Firm game? Probably not, but millions do and this is but one example of the infinite diversity of human tastes – a diversity that makes the pursuit of pleasure such a vague, fascinating and frustrating subject.

Pick anything that gives you the greatest delight – drinking pina coladas on the beach in Tobago with your partner, listening to Mozart at the Royal Concert Hall, watching Celtic play a blinder, reading Bret Easton Ellis and understanding everything he's on about – and you can be certain that most of your friends will disagree with your selections. There is no universally recognised formula for a good time. But although we cannot agree on the ingredients, there is a common ground acknowledged by those of us who take our pleasures seriously. Nothing as formal as rules, just pointers to delight.

The first and possibly most important of these principles is a break from the modern obsession for instant gratification, the urge to live life as quickly as possible. I understand that for you people with normal lives, a blur of activity is considered desirable; a mark of success perhaps, or the path to personal fulfillment. I do not know, I do not agree with it and it is certainly not my idea of a good time. There are times when fast is good – room service, headache remedies, tax refunds – but if you rush the finer things in life; you will miss most of the delights they offer. Let that great bottle of red breathe, savour that Havana cigar, allow yourself the time to enjoy the artistry that went into that four-star meal. What is the point of civilised indulgence if you are in too much of a rush to enjoy it? It is worth saying that the true pleasure-seeker never skimps. Personally, when faced with an inconvenient shortage of funds, experience has taught me that it is better to go without than make do with a cheaper substitute.

After many impulsive mistakes, I have learned to wait until I have the time and the money to enjoy the real thing. I was educated at one of Glasgow's old traditional schools, where rugby was still refereed in Latin. Cold showers, self-denial and a daily ration of physical discomfort were de rigeur and considered character forming. (Woe betide those of us who had a character already.) Enjoyment was not encouraged, mentioned or given even a corner of the timetable. Instead, it was ruthlessly crushed. Guilt, on the other hand, was compulsory. However, I survived and do not feel obliged to listen to the nag of conscience every time I am faced with a treat. In fact, as a pleasure connoisseur who has to make the very most of every experience going, I think I know the importance of enjoying every tiny thing.

Last year my father and I went to Rome to meet the Pope. Of course we ended up staying and exploring Rome because it is such a beautiful city. Yet all around us American tour groups whizzed past, managing to ''do'' a museum in less than 15 minutes.

So for me a good time is all about taking my time. It is my most precious commodity and I want to use it to the full.

My grandfather's dying words were: ''The roads are icy, take your time''. Some things stick with you no matter how much of a rush you are in.

Jonathan at the Collisseum in Rome

Lack Of Curtsy:

Two days before Christmas, Jonathan underwent intensive Chemotherapy at the Beatson. Immediately after his treatment, he went into Buchanan Street to shop for Christmas presents.

One of the immediate side effects of Chemotherapy is that the white blood cells are greatly reduced, leaving the immune system greatly weakened to fight infection. I can't count the number of times that Susan had warned Jonathan of this danger, and constantly cautioned him not to frequent crowded places, after treatment, where he might run the risk of contracting an infection. Being Jonathan, he ignored these warnings, and driven by the need to complete his Christmas shopping, went blissfully ahead.

When he arrived home, he was unable to get out of his car, he was so enervated, and continually pamped his car horn. I eventually looked out of the window, to find out who was making the annoying noise, and saw his car outside. I ran out and found him slumped in his car. I eased him out and somehow carried him into the house. He had a high temperature and was showing signs of a fever, and as the evening progressed his condition worsened. Eventually, Susan phoned the Hospice, explained his condition, and they agreed to admit him immediately. He was diagnosed as having Septicaemia and suspected Pneumonia. His condition was parlous, and once again he was close to death. He was given intravenous antibiotics to fight his infection quickly, and once again, our emotions were on a roller-coaster ride.

There was no way that he was going to be able to attend the Official Opening of the Millennium Dome Ceremony, an event that he made his goal several months previous. Thanks to the diligent services of Dr.Bass and his Nursing Staff, Jonathan gradually improved, and on New Year's Eve, Susan, Abbie and myself arrived to celebrate Ne'er day with our boy. There were three elderly ladies in the TV lounge watching the Rev.I M Jolly, giving out his usual doleful and deadpan platitudes, they were all sporting new "hairdos" and wearing their best for the occasion. Suddenly, one of them burst into tears and when Susan went to console her, and asked why she was so upset, the old lady replied, that the Rev.I M Jolly brought back so many memories of happier times!

We escaped to Jonathan's room, and put him in a wheelchair and brought him to watch part of the Dome ceremony. As it transpired, the opening was a fiasco, with the invited guests having to queue for over three hours to gain entry. Susan and I were grateful that Jonathan had not been obliged to go through that ordeal. Rather than being in the presence of the Queen, he celebrated the Millenium with Susan, Abbie, myself, and the three elderly ladies. The Hospice Matron had lain on a small feast, and we opened a bottle of champagne and gave Jonathan a sip to celebrate his first steps on his road to recovery.

He spent a further two weeks in the Hospice to recuperate, and when he left, he did get to practice his curtsy, by way of thanks to the caring nurses and staff who had treated him as royalty.

Henry Wilson

23 January 2000

Shop Tactics:

BEING from Glasgow, I naturally hate Edinburgh and all its hideously dressed residents.

Which is kind of funny, because I put my enviable sartorial elegance down to a couturier from Edinburgh, which has just closed its doors. Sure, I worked in the Warehouse in Glassford Street, a famous Glasgow clothing store, but prior to that I served my apprenticeship at Smith's Menswear on Saturday afternoons.

Smith's was an Edinburgh company, sold all the best labels and, courtesy of their talented buyer, always seemed to have the best labels before anyone else. Smith's sold Versace before most wannabe Glasgow gangsters had robbed their first sub post office. So it was a poignant moment when I noticed that they had closed their doors. I felt quite emotional when I looked at the "For Let" sign posted on the shop frontage. Unfortunately, Smith's did not have the cachet of the Warehouse and were always playing catch-up. On a Saturday on the shop floor in the Warehouse, people would come up to me and ask for a job. They would offer to work for no wages. Employers take note – this is how to run a business. (That is a joke. I take the issue of the minimum wage very seriously.)

Coming from this rarefied retail background, it makes me laugh when I hear that Harvey Nichols is coming to Edinburgh. When it comes to fashion, Edinburghers are truly lumps of meat. They have no imagination, no finesse, and one looks pretty much as bloody awful as another. This has not stopped them being immensely excited about the imminent arrival of Harvey Nichols, just as soon as they have knocked down the old bus station. Our less than knowledgeable east coast cousins, God love them, think that Harvey Nicks chose their benighted city on merit, and crow about it at any and every opportunity. Alas, this is not the case. The real story (if you are interested) is that Cruise, that other Glasgow retail temple, now stocks so many labels that there simply wouldn't be enough money to sustain two large high fashion clothing emporia in Glasgow while still making their astronomical mark-ups.

Believe me, the mark-ups are huge. You will always find people who have worked in fashion, shopping at the sales.

I suspect that, even when Harvey Nicks opens in the east, the truly educated suit buyer – male at least – will continue to travel through to Glasgow and buy their suits in Cruise, where the staff (ballet-dancing bleached-haired individuals notwithstanding) can talk knowledgeably about men's fashion without feeling stupid.

The duty of a fashion retailer has always been to provide its customers with modest concealment, protection from the elements, higher social standing and subtle sexual allure. Centuries after the cultured men of Rome hung up their paludamenta (that's military cloaks, for those of you without the benefit of a classical education) after their last toga party, Italian menswear has continued its great march forward. As far back as the mid-1800s, clever blokes were allowed to enjoy the splendour of Italian menswear design. We find it easy to appreciate the generations of dedicated families that are responsible for producing the world's finest wines, cigars, cars and coffee, but we take the traditions of tailoring for granted. Rome wasn't built in a day and neither were its suits.

The godfathers of Italian men's fashion are a unique and intriguing breed. These trusted old school tailors, Ermenegildo Zegna, Corneliani and James Bond's favourite, Brioni, can be egocentric, even downright pig-headed. Never tell an Italian tailor what fabric will work, because their enigmatic approach is the key to the mastery of their trade.

Being a tailor is no longer an enviable apprenticeship – there has even been a noticeable drop in Savile Row – so it's little wonder that the Italians have taken over as the world leaders in men's and women's fashion, with these garments made off the peg rather than made to measure.

Do I hear a voice from the east saying that they can't possibly afford all this when they have a New Town mortgage and school fees to pay? Well, I was going through my wardrobe, selecting what to sell in my car boot sale and clothes which I had bought ten years ago were still wearable and stylish today because of their superior fabrics and cut.

Now you must excuse me. I have sales to go to.

30 January 2000

Read Not Dead:

I WOULD like to apologise, my devoted readers, for disappointing you. Or at least for disappointing the 641 of you who sent me an email when a recent column failed to appear. I am still alive. It was only flu. Only ''flu'' is not entirely accurate. When you have an immune system that is pretty much useless, it doesn't take much for an infection to develop into pneumonia. Starting my Christmas shopping on December 24 at 1pm didn't help much either. I mistook the hot and cold sweats as simple terror at the thought of not getting around the shops in time, when in fact it was the onslaught of the nasty virus.

For me, it's the same every year. Where is the fun in starting your shopping in June while on holiday in Lloret de Mar? ''Darling, I simply had to get you this pink nylon donkey with your name on it.'' And doing the rounds in one day certainly did not detract from the quality of the gifts. Space NK's share price rose as I walked through the door. I now know Ralph Lauren's middle name. I am also on his Christmas card list. Actually, make that his Christmas teddy bear list. Yet even as my credit card was melting, my body was succumbing to the vile flu virus. When you have cancer, you tend to be more in tune with your body than the average person. So when I awoke on Christmas morning, drenched in sweat, I knew something was wrong. The bad news was that it was our turn to host Christmas dinner. Cue loud shouty voices, fights, crying babies and barking dogs. Before the aperitifs.

Whenever I take a high temperature, I have a tendency to talk absolute crap and become delirious. So when the doctor came out to see me, I don't think she appreciated being assaulted by a screaming madman. I was admitted to Ayr Hospice, where they soon confirmed the flu-pneumonia combo. I could handle missing the mince pies and arguments over the ridiculous ''plot'' of Mission: Impossible. What was really worrying me was that I was due to fly down to London for the opening party of the Millennium Dome. As each hour passed, I tried to feign health in the same way some of you healthy people take unforeseen upset stomachs when you want a sickie. Unfortunately my temperature continued to rise and the infection was worrying the doctors so much that I had to have a blood transfusion.

It's a funny feeling. You cannot help but feel a bit apprehensive having someone else's blood inside you. You hear all the stories of people catching secondary illnesses from transfusions, but I guess I am in no position to be choosy.

As the delirium continued, and my vomit turned black with the blood leaking from my stomach somewhere, I admitted defeat. So as well as feeling rubbish, being enraged about missing out on the big party, I felt bad for letting down all the people who had helped me out. My MP, Sandra Osborne, got me the tickets, my Aunt Rose and Uncle Bob offered me their flat in Kensington. My girlfriend Pauline's folks also paid for our flights, and although I begged her to use the tickets and fly down to London with her sister to take advantage of the sales, she chose to stay here and visit me.

So we watched it on telly and read about it in the papers and, to be honest, it didn't sound as if I had missed out on much. I was certainly in no fit state to stand in the freezing cold for five hours to collect a security pass and, more importantly, I could not stand cross-legged in a queue for the toilets. Although as I planned to wear a kilt, and am always on these occasions a true Scotsman, I suppose I could have managed in an emergency.

But I was still most disappointed at missing this once in a lifetime event and, of course, having the opportunity to recount it to the huge circle of virtual friends that are my readers. I still get a kick when people write or email me, even if they think I am dead. Or if they don't realise that the article that ran on this page two weeks ago was not actually written by me.

My grandmother, who I love most dearly, and who is terribly proud of her eldest grandson for becoming a famous columnist, read with interest Aaron Hicklin's adventures in MePa with Kate Moss. She was worried that I had ditched heterosexuality and converted to Judaism all in one week.

I reassured her that I had not moved to New York and still liked girls. I was delirious, but not that delirious. And still very much alive.

6 February 2000

Claws out for Section 28:

BEING a member of a minority group— cancer sufferers— means that one can espouse on any subject, however controversial and get away with it.

For the last few weeks my papers have been saturated with the ''so hot it will burn your fingers'' Section 28 issue. Therefore I feel obliged to get up on my soapbox and voice my opinion. For anyone who has been in long-term recovery from Hogmanay, Section 28 (or 2a, to give it its correct name here in Scotland), forbids teachers from promoting homosexuality as an alternative to ''normal'' family life. Well, this gives me a rash.

Take the term ''normal family life''. Hello. The era of Janet and John, Dick and Clare and Spot the dog is well over. Single parents, whether through divorce or other circumstances, are in the majority. These days, marriage for life is a pleasant thought, a worthwhile aspiration and a goal to aim for, but that's all. I can't see the controversy in producing books and literature that reflects today's society. When the children of single parents are confronted by this unrealistic ''ideal'' family unit, (Mum, Dad and dog) in their schoolbooks, it causes feelings of confusion and inadequacy. Why don't I have a Daddy? Who is mummy's friend who stays every weekend?

Now imagine the same scenario, but in a situation involving Eric and Michael, or Janet and Julie. Who knows what damage could be done if this sort of irresponsible publishing was allowed into the classroom. One sympathetic publishing company is threatening to flood Scottish schools with a book titled Jenny lives with Eric and Martin. On its front cover is Jenny, a sweet-looking blonde girl with pigtails, bringing breakfast in bed for Eric and Martin who are both in bed (together) and asleep. This is the kind of scenario, which is worrying parents, single or otherwise, across the country. While politicians and gay rights groups argue the toss, this important group feels left out of the discussion. Many of these parents, often-traditional Labour voters, who may not live in happy nuclear families, still feel uncomfortable with such a radical alternative. New Labour may find itself losing a lot of support by trying to repeal this statute, but the high heid yins down in England don't seem to be aware of the strength of the feelings they have stirred up.

My own experience was that homosexuality was not even mentioned at school; a strict Jesuit policy saw to that. I know that some people are born gay, and unfortunately they can have a tough time of it in the classroom. But there is a second group – the confused teenager – hormones raging and desperate to fit in. I am all for homosexuality being discussed and explained at school. Gay people make up a large part of society, and their voices should be heard. What is not acceptable is that homosexuality is promoted at school. Then you would have the situation where a confused teenager could adopt the gay lifestyle just because they feel they are different. If teachers advocate homosexuality as an option, a pupil may choose to experiment with the gay way of life. School is for education, but education in subjects that you can't learn in life. We need teenagers who can read or write, not have a working knowledge of The Joy of Gay Sex. So where do we go from here?

Neither side is going to be happy, whatever the outcome, so we have to accept the concept of compromise. Nominated teachers could keep a lookout for pupils who were uncertain about their sexuality, and offer appropriate support and advice.

In a way this is already happening in some schools, where good teachers identify the needs of their pupils and act accordingly. People seem to forget that Section 28 was Margaret Thatcher's knee-jerk reaction to left-wing London councils funding gay and lesbian groups.

Scotland has never really had a problem with gay and lesbian rights. Until now. The Section 28 debate today is the opposite of how it was handled by the Tory government back in the Eighties. Now, as was the case back then, a little tolerance and understanding is needed.

Now, on a totally different matter, I have the three options for my charity event. There are: a 90km trek in Nepal; a 150km bike ride in Egypt or a 120km trek in Canada. Whichever option gets the most email votes by February 10 will be the one that I will undertake. To be honest, I am a bit apprehensive about all three. Will I be fit enough to do it?

There is only one way to find out, so get voting!

13 February 2000

Preaching a Different Kind of Hospital Trust:

WITHOUT wishing to come over all Kelly Cooper-Barr, breathless style lady of the Daily Record, I must tell you that Pauline and I have just spent a lovely weekend in Gleneagles.

Instead of the hotel we stayed in my Aunt Therese's house on the grounds, rather than be cooped up in a hotel room, however luxurious. (This is the same aunt who constantly visits me when I am ill – a true good Samaritan). In fact the hotel was fully booked because of a medical conference. There were so many GPs in residence that the health club had no spare lockers and the beauty spa was fully booked. Believe me, at the prices they charge; only a GP could afford them. I even met my own GP taking advantage of the bargains in the Gleneagles shop, so I knew I was OK if I took ill.

Not that I found the company of so many medics altogether reassuring. The papers were full of Harold Shipman, who has made me re-evaluate my relationships with the doctors that I see on a regular basis. When you have a serious illness that requires ongoing medical supervision the doctor becomes more than someone who shoves a thermometer where the sun don't shine. In fact I see my GP on a more regular basis than most of my family. She knows she doesn't have to ring the doorbell before she comes in, and many's the time I have been woken by her as she travels to her surgery in the morning. In fact I would say she is an honorary member of our family, which is a shame for her. I take any medicine she prescribes without a second thought, because I trust her implicitly.

Many people don't know this, but a doctor's surgery is run like any other business. Targets have to be reached, costs have to be covered and, despite what transpired in the Harold Shipman case, drugs do have to be accounted for. It therefore stands to reason that the patient who is never sick and never needs any prescriptions is the ideal patient, costing nothing to service, but generating income simply being "on the

95

books". So I must be costing my doctor a fortune with the huge variety and availability of the drugs I take. Some of them are controlled substances, meaning I have to get them delivered to my door. This adds to the general feeling of being a criminal, what with the marijuana as well. Actually in preparation for my charity trek, I have abandoned the weed so that my lungs are clear and healthy.

Being afflicted with a variety of ailments means a multitude of tablets have to be taken, roughly 25 every day. I also wear skin patches, which are similar to Nicorette patches, except they contain an exotic mix of opiates, which dulls the pain. Sometimes. I also have to endure three injections a day, which has left me with a backside as tough as an elephant's. Sometimes I wonder if it's all worth it just for a few extra months, but then who could take my place here in the magazine? Living, or should I say dying, vicariously, is quite compulsive. Isn't it?

With the regularity and volume of drugs and treatment that I undergo, the law of averages would suggest that a mistake could be made. In fact it did happen, when I was undergoing chemotherapy at the Beatson Oncology Centre. Somewhere between a doctor and a pharmacist, a drug dose was mixed up and I received ten times the quantity of a chemical that was already particularly toxic.

The result was instant and caused great distress, as well as vomiting, stomach cramps and the shakes. Not that I blame anyone, what with the way the NHS is under funded and staff are overworked.

It would be a great shame if people were distrustful of their doctors because of the Harold Shipman case. The bond between doctor and patient is sacred, with trust on both sides essential. I know I am dying, but I rely on my medical support team to prolong my life within the bounds of medical science. And once all options are exhausted, then I expect my decline in health to be as pain-free as possible, while at the same time retaining some dignity.

But there is no chance of me getting morbid, as I have some serious training to do. You have picked my charity challenge – the Canada Wilds Trek in July, 100km of rocky, mountainous terrain. — Thanks a bunch.

I had better start getting in shape, whatever shape. Whatever someone with cancer can get in.

27 February 2000

Having a Bellyfull:

IT'S almost three years to the day that I awoke in the Victoria infirmary with tubes protruding from every orifice. Including a new one where my stomach used to be.

At the time I was living in town, sharing a flat with my Aussie pal, Phil. I hadn't eaten or moved my bowels for a week and a half, so I decided to go and see my GP. When I left Ayr for Glasgow I had transferred to a new practise, which was, in retrospect, a bad move. My doctor in Ayr was excellent and, as I was to find out, the one in Glasgow wasn't.

Perhaps I am being unfair – after all you don't expect a young athletic man to be suffering from cancer. Anyway, my first visit to this new GP was terminated with a bottle of laxative syrup, presumably to clear whatever blockage was causing my symptoms. It took three more visits, and many, many litres of powerful purgative, until a young trainee GP decided I had something seriously wrong with me and drove me to the Vicky herself. When we arrived, I had my first experience of a phenomenon, which was to reappear at every hospital I have since visited. I call it "every second person who went to St Aloysius is now a doctor". It wasn't long until a guy from my class at school had his finger up my behind. "So, how are you getting on?" he asked. "Fine, fine," I lied. Through firmly gritted teeth.

Mercifully I was taken upstairs, where I got a free bikini line shave. Then an important-looking guy arrived. You can tell how important a doctor is by the amount of people who are following him. This guy had six disciples so I knew he was the head honcho. "Ah, Mr. Wilson," he said in his important doctor voice. "You seem to have an obstruction in your bowel, so we'll open you up and see what the problem is."

Cue panic and fear. Big style. He was talking about operating on me the way Jamie Oliver discusses slicing up a sea bass. And the next thing I knew was a lot of tubes and no stomach.

It all came back to me last week because I was back in hospital. I had been having a pain in my belly for a while, but I tend to ignore aches and pains because, after all, I do have cancer. They tend to come with the territory. This pain, however, was getting worse and not going away. I even called a doctor out, which is unlike me. The pain was as sharp as knives. Scary sea bass slicing ones. Now when doctors examine your stomach you lie down, which is probably why they missed the small knot of hernia-like tissue. I suffered for another couple of days, despite being in the sort of pain which makes grown men cry. I had no choice but to get my little brother to drive me from Glasgow home to Ayr, and if you could see him driving, you would understand what a big deal it was. He is Mr. Road rage.

So I gave in and went to casualty, with all its memories of rubber gloves and old school camaraderie. I waited to see the doctor. And waited and waited and, interminably, waited. And when the doctor arrived, it turned out he was in my brother's class at school. Now I felt old as well as sick but at least this guy listened to me.

I don't mean this to be a criticism, but doctors tend to lump any ache or pain, which alights on me in with my cancer. Sore toe? Ah, that will be a side effect of your cancer. I suppose it is slightly intimidating to be presented with a young man with so much cancer, but I do, and can, suffer from normal illnesses also. Worse luck.

5 March 2000

This Mortal Recoil:

I NEARLY died last week.

Nothing new in that. In all daily walks of life we, in our own way, face danger. We cross the road without looking; we operate or work with potentially dangerous materials, yet as I lay in the ambulance holding my mother's hand, I thought it was the last time. My life did not flash before my eyes, I did not see a light at the end of a dark tunnel, but I was scared rigid and frightened out of my wits.

My day had started normally, grudgingly getting out of bed to go to the hospice to have my blood checked out. Blood contains several indicators as to the health of the host, such as white cell count and liver function, designed to give you an idea as to how your body is dealing with the cancer. Unfortunately, due to the frequency of these ''withdrawals'' coupled with months of tortuous chemotherapy, I have been left with veins reluctant to give up their precious cargo. So when it is my turn to give blood I do so with a heavy heart, for the pain you have to endure as a metal needle is threaded through tender veins is exquisitely horrible. I am quite sure that I have damaged my teeth permanently by grinding them as I try and suppress my cries of pain. I know it is a necessary evil.

So I drove home feeling slightly seedy, but then I never feel 100%, or even 90% fit. As per normal, my mum administered a jab in the butt to control pain and cut down on my ever-present nausea, As the day wore on, my neck started to stiffen up, and by the time we sat down for dinner my jaw was so rigid that I couldn't even put a spoonful of food into my increasingly swollen mouth. This was especially upsetting, as I hadn't had spaghetti carbonara for ages. I asked my dad to call the doctor out. I say asked, but I more or less had to mime it, as by this time my jaw had locked, my tongue had grown and my breathing was laboured. Saliva poured from my mouth, which, along with the rest of my face, was contorted in a mask of pain.

The doctor arrived promptly and diagnosed an allergic reaction to a new drug, which I had started taking to combat my nausea. He prescribed Valium to calm me down and, while he was there, it did the trick. But as soon as he left, my breathing got shallower and more laboured. As my dad held my hand and I tried to concentrate on staying conscious, my mother, who never ever panics, who was the nursing sister in the accident and emergency ward at the Royal Infirmary for years, phoned an ambulance. Something, she later admitted, that she had never done before. It arrived shortly, and I got the full works, oxygen, the lot. I was lying down in the ambulance, holding on to my mum's hand, squeezing once for yes, two for no. I physically willed myself to stay conscious. The last time I was unconscious the buggers whipped half of my stomach out.

At the hospital the treatment was a bit more successful, although the swollen ''fish out of water'' look did come back temporarily. I was kept in for observation, and the diagnosis was that I had a little-known aversion to any drugs containing dopamine. I was lucky this time, my parents handled the crisis and the medical back up was absolutely superb. Both the doctor and the ambulance were at my door in less than 15 minutes and once I was in the hospital, I couldn't sleep for getting my blood pressure checked. Once again, the health service served me well.

'I didn't want to die just then. I still need to do so many things: my trek in Canada, see my sister's impending new baby, my brother's wedding next summer, although I know this is a bit of a long shot. This was my fourth near-death experience, and if it teaches me anything it's how precious life is. I don't feel sorry for myself just because I have cancer, because I am too busy doing the things that I have to do. By the time you read this I will be in New York, and I will get to visit my fellow columnist, Aaron Hicklin, who is putting me up for a few days.

Perhaps we can write about each other?

19 March 2000

New York State of Mind:

SOMETIMES, without thinking, you build a picture in your mind. I had always read the works of Aaron Hicklin, my fellow columnist, with a jealous zeal. Not only can he write a good column with consummate ease, but also he lives in the most exciting city in the world. And he knows it.

Besides writing for the Sunday Herald, he works as an editor on Gear, a GQ-type magazine where he gets to interview David Bowie and work alongside the controversial author Bret Easton Ellis. Yet when Aaron heard that I was planning a five-day trip to New York with my parents, he kindly offered to put us up for a couple of days, to find our feet if you like. It all sounded great on paper. Due to my illness, Icelandair upgraded us to their excellent first class, but any vestige of sophistication was blown when the elastic snapped on my mother's tights and they fell to the floor just as we were passing through customs. Talk about classy. In the airports, I was pushed around in a wheelchair and was surprised by the number of people who looked at me.

Then there were the New York taxi drivers, who did a great job of living up to their reputation. They are, I can confirm, a breed apart. Traffic in downtown Manhattan is so bad that walking is your best alternative. Around 99 per cent of New York cabbies seemed to be from Angola or Korea, and spoke no English, so communication was difficult. The way the streets are laid out – on a grid system – you have to give the intersection of where you are going, not just a street name. Road rage was evident everywhere, with cabbies cutting in and out to find the quickest route. Everyone else in the city seemed to be in a rush. Maybe I have been in Ayr for too long, because I found the pace of life so much faster than here at home.

So it was a relief to be able to stay with Aaron in a less frenetic, tree-lined neighbourhood. It was strange to meet him. I had a mental image from reading his columns, so when he came out to the taxi to help with our luggage, I was surprised that he had such a strong English accent and was a lot thinner than he looks in his picture. His beautiful apartment is furnished with hand-me-down furniture and antiques, as well as one or two modern design classics. And books – lots and lots of books - which left me, feeling intellectually inadequate.

After the comfort and homeliness of Aaron's apartment, nothing could prepare us for our suite at the Paramount. It has a reputation as one of New York's best hotels, with all the rooms designed by Phillipe Stark. All I can say is that he must have had a hangover when he designed them. Black and white were the only shades used and after ten minutes in the room I started to feel sick. If this was a suite, I would have hated to see a single bedroom. It was tiny. I suppose I am spoiled when it comes to decor as my partner, Pauline, is an interior designer, but I got the impression that the Paramount is the sort of place you stay so you can tell people about it afterwards.

We lasted all of 40 minutes. While my mother was downstairs trying to get a refund, Dad and I took turns to go to the bathroom and get high on the decor. We were directed to another hotel in the group, the Morgan, for the more discerning traveller. The suite was OK; in New York you won't get a large room unless you are Madonna. Who, co-incidentally, was in town when we were there. Thousands of kids and, disturbingly, hundreds of adults, thronged the MTV studios at Times Square, holding placards and swearing undying devotion to the queen of pop music.

We decided to do some of the touristy trips, on the basis that if I didn't do them then, I probably never would. I was stunned by the opulence of Grand Central Station – I never imagined a public building could be so well kept and clean. The Rockefeller Center is famous for its Christmas decorations, but even in the spring it was great to see all the kids out skating. There was an old granny on the ice, who was easily the best skater I have ever seen.

Jonathan inNew York.

The Statue of Liberty was a disappointment. I had always imagined it to be large and imposing, since it was the first real sight of New York immigrants got before being dumped on Ellis Island. Maybe after a long boat trip it would seem welcoming. I think I just expected more. In direct contrast, I didn't expect the Empire State Building to be up to much, but the view left me gasping for adjectives. As the lift goes up 88 floors, your ears pop. As you look over the railings at the streets below, you feel quite giddy. I am not scared of heights, but I did feel a little unsure on my feet.

Back on dry land, on our way back from Saks Fifth Avenue, we came across St Patrick's Cathedral, which was the setting for the opening scene of The Godfather III. After an afternoon of rampant consumerism, it was bliss to take in the beautiful cathedral. A short mass steeled us for more shopping. God willing, if I am still around in November, I am returning to New York to do my Christmas shopping. As it was, we had to buy more suitcases to carry all our purchases home, but the savings were astronomical. The excitement of the trip made me overlook the fact that I was quite ill while we were away, but I had to see New York at least once before I depart this earth. It was well worth the nightly visits to the bathroom to throw up and Aaron's hospitality will live long in my memory. I could get used to this.

Do we have any columnists in LA?

Downgrades And Upgrades:

When Jonathan informed us that we were off to New York, he cautioned his dad and I to dress in our finest when travelling. It was his maxim that if you dress the part- you get the part, in other words, if there were an opportunity of an upgrade to Business Class, we would stand a better chance of being chosen. So rather than my usual attire of tracksuit and trainers, I wore a long black coat, flowing scarf and proper shoes- real designer Chic! Jonathan, as usual, was dressed to the nineties, long camel Aquascutum coat, cream silk scarf and a cream knitted Armani hat, complemented with his expensive luggage. In years, long gone, Henry and I have traveled the world, suitably attired, but now dress code is not high on our list of priorities, but to assuage Jonathan, we complied with his wishes.

Since it was some distance to the departure lounge, I had arranged the use of a wheelchair, to prevent Jonathan from being worn out before our flight. So there I was, pushing Jonathan along the shopping concourse of Glasgow Airport, when I felt my tights starting to slip down, being vain I probably had bought a pair one size smaller than required, as women do. Despite my best covert manipulations, they continued their downward spiral, and I finally decided that they had come off straight away. Feigning an interest in a window display of Designer handbags, I stopped and tried to distract Jonathan while hastily removing the tights from around my ankles. Little did I realize that Jonathan could see my actions in the reflection of the shop's window.

He was mortified, "Mum what are you up to?"

Being male and never having worn tights, he couldn't understand that this predicament sometimes does happen- it was a case of – I just can't take you anywhere! Where oh where has this once fashion conscious woman, that used to be me, gone? Although we were near Passport Control, I am convinced that no-one noticed, but that cut no ice with Jonathan, I had broken the magic of the moment, big style! Henry and I thought the whole incident hilarious, but the Boy did not.

Jonathan was spot on about our dress code, although minus my tights, Iceland Air upgraded us to Business Class so that I could give Jonathan his injections mid-flight, in privacy. WE were the only occupants of the Business Class section, which displayed signs proclaiming SAGA. Henry and I discussed the possibility that pensioners must travel in this class due to all the signs, until Jonathan explained, with a roll of his eyes, that in Iceland, SAGA means First Class

One of my long held wishes has been to live in a Brownstone, with a walk up, so I was in heaven when we arrived at Aaron's apartment in Brooklyn Heights to discover that he lived in such a building, One does not imagine New York to have tree-lined streets, but Brooklyn Heights is not your typical New York. Aaron's apartment, was built at the turn of the century and was spacious with high ceilings, and had a balcony to the rear. Despite being complete strangers, he made us most welcome and gave us the run of his apartment for two days. From there we booked a suite at the Paramount Hotel on Broadway, which had been recommended by a colleague of Jonathan. It turned out a ghastly mistake, as the décor and furnishings were more suited to posing than relaxing, and Jonathan did not feel comfortable. To the credit of the Hotel management, they agreed to cancel our registration, gave us a full refund, and recommended The Morgan on Madison Avenue, which had the exact ambience that we all sought.

Things were back to normal, Jonathan was sick after every meal, spent a great deal of time in the toilet, but did not complain. He was enjoying the whole experience of the Big Apple. Each day, he would sleep late and then we would plan one trip per day, which he thoroughly enjoyed. One of the main highlights, was going to the top of The Empire State Building. On a previous trip to New York, Henry and I had endured a wait of approximately an hour and a half before getting to the top. I was dreading a similar wait for Jonathan, but when we arrived, there was very little queuing and the express elevator whooshed us to the viewing deck, in seconds.

Although it was early March, the weather was incredibly warm, with no wind, despite the altitude. The view over New York, from all four sides, was breathtaking, and Jonathan's camera was busy recording the moment.

On the return journey home, I'm glad to say there were no further mishaps with my tights, no slip-ups or slip-downs, much to Jonathan's relief.

Susan Wilson

26 March 2000

Write On:

THE power of the press is a potent thing.

In a recent column, I wrote about an experience I had a while ago. Somehow I received a stronger dose of a drug than was necessary, provoking an instant and violent physical reaction.

This prompted an email from a high heid-yin, wanting to know the exact details of the mistake so that it can be "investigated". I was also branded irresponsible and accused of causing distress and unnecessary anxiety to those about to, or currently undergoing, treatment.

Let me be quite clear: mistakes happen often in hospitals. I receive a lot of email from people who have lost family or friends in tragic circumstances. In today's litigious society, we need to have someone to blame, to apportion accountability. But whenever we introduce the human factor to the equation, there is always a chance of a mistake. It's been suggested that having terminal cancer has made me more forgiving and magnanimous, since death is approaching at considerable speed. I may be tolerant towards human error, but when it comes to ignorant pen pushing, I'm afraid my time is too precious to waste entertaining needless bureaucrats.

I feel rather the same about politicians. My home town of Ayr is just recovering from the recent by-election and it is, at last, possible to buy a pint of milk without the help of Donald Dewar and two film crews. I consider myself a fully paid-up member of generation X: despite enjoying current affairs, I couldn't give a toss about individual politics. I believe anyone who wants to be a politician is self-serving and motivated by what they can get for themselves. It is embarrassing to admit this, but while I was in New York I was following the primaries and thought all four front-runners behaved with at least a modicum of dignity and honour – in direct contrast to their Scottish cousins.

There are exceptions. My family was lucky enough to know Rita Miller, the Labour candidate in the Ayr by-election, before she became embroiled in the turgid backstabbing that is local politics. She often telephones our house, just to see how I am. So it was with great interest that I spotted her name in a Sunday paper. The power of the written word is certainly mighty, even when the words are wholly inaccurate. I read line after line of erroneous reporting, with the sole intention of discrediting a political candidate. Given my inside knowledge of this person, I was furious that a decent and hardworking woman, with a reputation for honesty, was having her integrity besmirched solely on the grounds of her political persuasion. That newspaper will not be appearing in the Wilson household again and I for one was so disillusioned with the whole process that I didn't even vote. I had never seen so many insidious, self-seeking agendas. And that was just the Labour party.

I had cheered up by the time I went for lunch with David Mullane, my old boss from the Warehouse. Without David, fashion in Glasgow would not have flourished to the extent that it has. But his skills have not been restricted to the rag trade. He was on the committee for Glasgow 1999 City of Architecture and is now instrumental in the running of the Charles Rennie Mackintosh society. He did not, however, ring me up because he wanted to talk stained glass windows. David had heard that I was collecting clothes for a charity car boot sale, and wanted to contribute. I was expecting great things and I wasn't disappointed – he handed over three bin-bags full of Boss and Armani.

My car boot sale will have a better range of clothes than most clothes shops.

It was funny that two former fashion victims now find their former world overbearing and self-important. You can only wear one pair of shoes at a time. David also echoed my own recently developed sensibilities about consumption and material wealth. I think the roller coaster ride of the Eighties, when yuppies were king and money was the only measure of happiness, has left many people in their thirties disillusioned with their wide screen-laminated-flooring-four-wheel-drive lifestyle. I feel embarrassed when I look at the sum of my life over the past ten years: gadgets that I have little use for, rails of clothing worn once before being discarded for the next big thing. I am happy to be selling them for the benefit of charity.

I had better get a move on because, on the health front, I discovered a hard mass underneath my belly button. I hoped that if I ignored it, it would go away. Many cancer patients favour this denial approach to medicine and I do know that it is stupid, but it is very tempting to bury your head in the sand when you are dealing with tumours. So I have done the sensible thing and will spend the next week in hospital, undergoing a battery of tests. I am lucky to be under the supervision of Dr John Bass and his team. If you believe and trust in your carers, half the battle is won. The other half ... well, we can wait and see.

Meanwhile I have an appointment at the Harvest Clinic of Hypnotherapy, to investigate alternative therapies. In my condition, you will try anything. I also hope to have sponsor forms for my trek to Canada ready, so any willing volunteers can hassle their workmates, friends and family to help me.

2 April 2000

Science Friction:

I RENTED a video, Gattaca, the other day. Without giving a detailed synopsis, it dealt with an elite space programme, called Gattaca, which you could enter only if you had a perfect genetic make-up. Perfect physique, perfect intelligence and perfect background. One imperfect specimen wanted on to the scheme so badly that he bribed one perfect citizen who was unfortunate enough to have been paralysed in an accident; therefore rendering him useless as far as space exploration was concerned. Gattaca grabbed me for two reasons. I met Jude Law, one of the lead actors, when I was in London filming for Channel 4 last year. He was a really nice bloke, and one of the directors I was working with suggested that I was so similar in looks and build that I could be Jude's stunt double. Unfortunately, cancer excludes me from that particular line of work.

The medical aspect of the film was of greater interest to me, as more and more money is being poured into genetic research. Dolly the sheep seems very old news, manufactured in a laboratory and given specific genetic markers so that scientists were able to predict everything from her sex to her eye colour by using gene technology. I find this particularly disquieting because my cancer is caused by a genetic fault. Doctors have identified the faulty gene that is causing the tumours that are spreading through my body. It can't be long before prospective parents will be given the option of avoiding having a child with a condition like mine, as well as choosing between straight and curly hair. I may have been watching too many videos, but I suspect that the technology exists to provide this sort of service, and it is only our moral sensibilities that are holding it back.

Given the chance, would my parents have paid a little extra for a screening that would have eradicated the chance of cancer? Should the parents of a child with learning difficulties have had their baby screened for genetic defects? These questions are so difficult that it is something of a relief that I will never have to face up to them myself. I truly believe that, as far as my own longevity goes, the candle that burns twice as bright burns half as long. Quality of life is also subjective. When I was at school I looked after what were called, at that time, "handicapped" kids. I found their affection and happiness a real example to us all. Unfortunately, human nature is not as simple as that. I am sure that designer babies will soon mean more than a pop star's brat in Tommy Hilfiger and that the rich and shallow will be courted by genetics companies providing them with blue-eyed blondes. For a price. Of course I was a blue-eyed blonde baby – if they had got me from a genetics catalogue, my parents would be demanding their money back. Some things are best left to nature. To a point. What that point is, I do not know. But I am certainly glad that I was not screened out of existence before I was born.

As I write, the sunlight is streaming through my window at the Ayrshire Hospice. If I wasn't linked to a machine pumping anti-sickness, anti-diaorrhea and painkilling drugs into my system, I could almost compare the experience to a spring break in a top hotel. In some ways, I really enjoy having quality time to myself.

I hate getting visitors, no matter how thoughtful and well meaning they are. I do not include my parents, my brother and his fiancée or my partner, Pauline, but some people come up for the whole hour and expect you to entertain them. How exciting can you make a rectal exam sound? I am thinking of printing a daily newsletter so that everyone can keep up to date with my progress and treatments – "and then he moved his index finger" – without me having to repeat the details for the eighth time.

Not that I could fault the standards of care I've received. Hospices tend to be where cancer sufferers come to see out their final days, and yet the standard of nursing is superb, cheery without being cheesy. The nurses take a real interest and the medical director, John Bass, shakes you by the hand firmly and holds eye contact, which is my own personal way of judging a man's integrity. Dealing with dying people every day must take a toll on all the staff and yet they come in every day and do their best to make you forget you are dying.

I am allowed a weekend pass, but just as I was leaving to go home, there was a fatality. It brought it home to me that a hotel is for living and a hospice, however friendly and pleasant, is for dying.

Gene Genie:

Since Jonathan was diagnosed as having a "rogue" gene, which caused his Cancer to manifest, it was explained to us, that if Jonathan had children, it is most certain that they would have had their bowel removed, at a very early age as his genetic defect would have been passed onto his heirs. The only consoling and effective positive to be derived from this, is that our surviving children: Christopher and Madeleine receive annual screening, by means of a Colonoscopy, to detect whether they have also inherited the deadly defective gene: our grandchildren will also have this done, when they reach a suitable age. This is Jonathan's legacy to his siblings.

When Jonathan's cancer was diagnosed, the surgeon told us that the extent of spread and maturity of his tumours, indicated that the cancer had probably, first manifested in his late teens or very early twenties. When Jonathan was twenty, at University, he was admitted to hospital with lower abdominal pains. Appendicitis was diagnosed and his appendix removed. In retrospect, it is quite possible that this abdominal pain was the initial onset of his cancer, and this is not a criticism of his doctors. Twelve years ago, no one would have suspected cancer in someone so young or so fit, unfortunately it is all too prevalent now. However, thanks to the advances in genetic research, more and more life-threatening illnesses, are found to be caused by defective genes, and if detected early, preventative screening and successful treatment can be given.

I recently read of a woman, in her late thirties, who was diagnosed with a terminal illness caused by a defective gene. Her consultant told her that, in all probability, her genetic defect would have been inherited by her children. Now this woman had a child adopted when she was a teenager. This child, a boy, would now be eighteen years old. After her diagnosis, she tried to contact her adopted son, but owing to the rules of adoption she was unable to do so personally. The Adoption Society, however appraised the adoptive mother of her adopted son's possible condition. This woman, for some unthinkable reason, has decided not to tell her adopted son, for fear of causing him distress.

I sincerely wish that I knew where this woman resided, as I would like to tell her, that she is playing God with her adopted son's future health and longevity. If, in fact, he has inherited this defective gene, then a range of medical tests could be conducted on him. Since he is only in his late teens, preventative measures could be taken to address his condition and ensure his long-term well-being.

Distress, is when you have a loved one diagnosed with a terminal illness, with no hope of a cure. Stupidity, is being aware of such a possibility in advance, and closing your eyes to a possible cure.

This woman is now in the position of condemning her adopted son to a certain death sentence, through her misguided naivety. I truly hope that she reconsiders her stance, if not she will come to regret her decision, and will live with the tragic consequences, unlike her son, who will not have had that chance.

Henry Wilson

9 April 2000

One Small Step:

WHAT is it about cancer and other illnesses that push us sufferers on to attain goals and achieve tasks? This happens to the most sluggish of us, those who, when we were well, would struggle to lift our heads from our comfy pillows and roll over in our superwarm duvets. Are we glory seekers looking to find approval in the eyes of the public? Do I write this column solely to achieve fame, because there is no fortune believe me.

At least three people have recognised me from writing this column, and two of them work at my local post office. That's not to say that media personality status has not come my way since I have started to write. Who could have forgotten my television debut about the legalisation of cannabis? Christopher Eccleston says he still laughs when he thinks about me trying to climb out of the bathroom window when I found out it was a three against three debate with my team being the underdog of all underdogs. With fleas.

Then there was the time I went for a radio interview at the BBC, or so I thought. I am extremely prone to facial blisters, or scabs as my mum likes to call them, but that doesn't matter because it's radio, right? Wrong. Crossed wires led me to yet another excruciating television experience, with every filming break consisting of me trying to separate my top from my bottom lip. Ouch. Now I know how Quasimodo felt when trying to woo Esmerelda. What was unusual about that episode was that my scabby lips only appear when they are due to be used or pictured. They particularly like weddings, funerals and first dates. (I am speaking from memory here – it's been two and a half years since that happened.)

Well, chance favours the prepared mind. Ian Dury knew this. He died the other week having done as much for charity as any one person could. He was part of my cultural landscape; I remember dancing to Hit Me With Your Rhythm Stick at my primary six disco, resplendent in shadow stripe trousers, shirt with matching tie pin and mock piano keys on my tie. I dedicate that tie to Ian, to his memory and to all the school discos that I attended, believing I looked so cool.

I often wonder if I would have volunteered to do a charity event if I didn't have cancer. If I am to be completely honest, I doubt it. Throwing yourself from a perfectly good aeroplane for a paltry sum and still not curing cancer does not make much impact on the grand scheme of things. But these small efforts, these small events all add up and, just as importantly, they make you feel as if you are doing something. Which is why at least 50 of our top companies will be receiving begging letters from me. I don't want to belittle what I am going to do. Hiking in the Rockies would be a stern test for a member of the Fit Family – I am hoping to cover 15km a day when, at present, a walk to the john is an achievement. Is raising money for charity my life's ambition? Am I now a professional charity figure, here to stir your collective minds so that you feel guilty into giving me money for cancer research? I hope so, because my life has precious little use otherwise.

At present I am still a guest of the Ayrshire hospice, and I do mean guest. Three meals a day, delivered when I want them, how I want them. It may be not be Nick Nairn fare, but if he can make French toast like the chef here, then I will whole-heartedly back his crusade for healthier eating, if he will excuse the pun.

This is something of an obsession at the moment. To negate the effects of my new-found tumour, I have been given three mega-injections of steroids. Now steroids are used all the time in medicine, and they are very useful, but they give you the most voracious appetite. If, like me, you have rampant diarrhoea, put the two together and you have one very anxious patient who can cover short distances in a very short times. I also have hair in places that I didn't have places before.

Still, as we say in cancer circles, what doesn't kill you must be good for you.

Jonathan with THAT tie!!!

16 April 2000

Pills, Bills and Bellyaches:

THE battle against pain is an ongoing one.

I try one brand of medication, only to find that although it may help with pain, the secondary symptoms exceed the primary benefits. Injections of morphine, for example, certainly make me feel much, much better. But morphine is such a strong drug that I am confined to the house, unable to drive, and in some instances, incapable of getting out of bed.

This may sound blissful to those of you on the nine-to-five-express, but with time slipping away from me, I can ill afford to sleep for 20 or 30 hours at a time. When my doctor recommended I try a syringe driver, I jumped at the chance. A syringe driver is a box similar in size to a video cassette. It contains a syringe full of the drug of choice, which it automatically pumps into into my body via a needle and tube. Try explaining that to a nightclub bouncer. Now I know the stereotypical image of a bouncer is a muscle-bound ape with no brains but most of the time, once I explain I have cancer and the equipment is medicinal instead of recreational, I get whisked to the front of the queue. Which is ironic, because the mix of drugs I have in the syringe driver is probably a good deal stronger than those for sale in any club.

So it was all going really well, until those side effects raised their ugly heads. I have developed an allergy, most likely to the metal in the needle, which is inserted into my skin. This produces swellings the size of the free-range organic eggs, but looks a good deal less natural. I shouldn't really be complaining about my medication. I know when a new drug hits the market, because invariably I get it straight away. One of the ways I control pain is by using patches, similar to the nicotine ones that help you give up smoking, which contain a gel infused with a man-made opiate. This passes through the skin into the bloodstream. These work very well, but because each patch can only release a limited amount of pain control, I have to wear six or seven at any one time. And as they can only be worn on certain parts of the body – the upper arm or upper back – I tend to run out of skin. The company that makes these patches is currently running trials with the drug in the form of a lollipop. Instead of popping pills or sticking on patches I will be licking lollies. Knowing my luck, I'll need six at a time.

I suppose it's a by-product of swallowing roughly 20 pills a day, but I am not as diligent as I was when it comes to taking drugs. For instance, before I started to write this article, I decided to down a couple of Imodium tablets so that I wouldn't have to run to the toilet every five minutes. I am sure you have seen the Imodium advert, where an anxious father-of-the-bride is worried that his dodgy stomach may interfere with his long after-dinner speech on his daughter's big day. "Don't worry, just take a couple of these," his loving daughter purrs. And all's well that ends well, as the ad cuts to the father boring everyone with his interminable ramblings, as the bride gives her mother an "I told you so" look and wishes she had kept the magic of Imodium to herself.

I cannot function without these little green and grey capsules. So I surprised even myself when I was stupid enough to take two Valium instead of the two Imodium I had intended. I suppose this accounts for my feelings of warmth and relaxed serenity as I sink further and further into this comfortable sofa. This artificial feeling of well-being is not wholly caused by pharmaceuticals. I might still need to go to the toilet, but I don't care.

But it would be wrong to be blasé about it. At the chemist picking up my prescription, I saw two young guys standing in line. When it was their turn to be served, the pharmacist gave them each a plastic beaker filled with liquid, which they greedily consumed. When I got home I asked my mother, a nurse, about the exchange I had just witnessed. Having had a rather protected upbringing, some areas of my life experience are rather limited and I had no idea that what I had watched was two registered heroin addicts getting their methadone rations. This means that they can't resell the drug to other addicts, and use the cash to buy heroin.

Happily, I am still able to control my drug intake myself. As long as you don't include creme eggs as a controlled substance.

23 April 2000

Light Out of Darkness:

I Was disturbed to learn bowel cancer has touched another life – that of Paul Stewart, the 34-year-old son of motor racing legend Jackie.

The disease is one of the most common types of cancer among young men and I am among those afflicted by it. The news of Paul's condition was distressing enough to take me back three and a half years to when I was first diagnosed.

Although its nurses are extremely kind and caring, Glasgow's Victoria Infirmary can seem a lonely, foreboding place when you don't know where you are. I remember, it was about six o'clock on a Saturday night, but because I was in the intensive care unit and all the lights in the ward were off, it was dark. I had been admitted the previous afternoon on the hunch of a young student doctor. Hours later, I awoke in the gloom feeling frightened, especially when I saw all the tubes protruding from my body. I was strapped to the bed for my own protection, in case I rolled over, but the restriction only added to my fear. I had a raging thirst and there was tubing running through my nose and down the back of my throat, which felt incredibly dry. A nurse noticed I was awake and came over to ask if I was all right. I requested a drink, or rather I croaked for one, but because I had recently emerged from a massive operation, that was out of the question.

The nurse left and returned with a small ice cube wrapped up in a piece of gauze fabric, which I could suck without swallowing a significant amount of liquid. I asked her what had happened to me, but she just smiled, told me to rest and reassured me a doctor would talk to me in the morning. An old man in the bed next to mine was delirious, shouting all sorts of nonsense and swearing at no one in particular. The whole experience was surreal and the fact that I was on large doses of drugs to relieve the pain added to the dream-like feeling. I was drifting in and out of consciousness, but in one of my moments of cognisance I awoke to find a doctor leaning over me, checking my pulse.

''Oh, you're awake, how do you feel?'' he asked. He was young, much the same age as myself. I told him of the intense pain coming from my stomach and in what was to become a regular occurrence; I was given a morphine injection.

Just before I drifted into sleep, I asked the doctor what was wrong with me. The pain in my stomach was excruciating and the presence of the pipes suggested to me I had undergone serious surgery. The doctor replied: ''I can't really say. The consultant will see you in the morning, but if I were you I would prepare myself for the worst.''

As long as I live – which may not be that long – I will remember his reply. All sorts of scenarios crossed my mind, but surprisingly cancer wasn't one of them: after all, cancer is an old person's disease, isn't it? The consultant briefed my parents, since apparently this sort of news is better coming from someone close to you. When my mum told me I had cancer, I broke down and wept, thinking ... well, I don't know what I thought, but death was in there somewhere. My future had suddenly evaporated.

Tears pouring down my face, I hugged my parents as if that day was my last. I look back on it as probably the darkest in my life. My Glasgow GP had wrongly told me that I had IBS, Irritable Bowel Syndrome.

Looking back now, I wonder how many other people have been misdiagnosed with the disease, like me. With any cancer of the stomach area, early diagnosis is the key to survival, so it's crucial that you badger your GP into a hospital referral if there is any change in your weight or toilet habits, or if you experience pain or tiredness.

Britain has a high mortality rate compared to other European countries, while Americans enjoy a 60 per cent chance of survival because they tend to have an earlier detection rate. The difference could be down to Americans paying for their healthcare, making them more inclined to use the resources available. It might sound terrible, but high profile cases of cancer like those of Paul Stewart, Celtic footballer Alan Stubbs and the late television sports presenter Helen Rollason, help keep the British public aware of this silent killer.

Obviously I'm a nobody as far as fame goes, but even if one of you is diagnosed early as a result of this column, I will be doing my job.

Sick Joke:

I Am a Big Jessie! A Big Girl's Blouse!

Ever since I can remember, probably since I was four years old and have had cause to vomit, I have always found the need for a parental hand patting my back as I throw up (funnily enough as I was writing that sentence, I had to vault the couch, run upstairs and lunge for the bowl, making it just in time – talk about suffering for my art).

This has become even more apparent over the last two weeks, as vomiting becomes as much a part of my daily routine as breathing. It has become a form of punctuation. Every time I take a new paragraph, that means I've been sick, making my article more reader-friendly, but hardly any fun to write.

I will be 30 years old this year, yet when I run to the toilet to throw up, I still manage a hurried shout to Mum or Dad, whoever happens to be closest at the time. I just don't like being sick on my own. I know how absurd I am. I frequently undergo more distressing and painful procedures yet to me, the mechanical act of vomiting is all the worse if it has to be endured alone. I have stood in foreign countries and looked down at their equivalent of Armitage Shanks's smiling face. It is the loneliest place in the world: on my own, hands on my knees, head angled to project the outpouring into the bowl. How I have wished for a parental hand placed on my back and that reassuring voice telling me it will be okay. For me, a vomit shared is a vomit halved. I can easily differentiate between the "sick" vomit and the casual chuck brought on by overuse of alcohol.

Without elaborating on past misdemeanours, I've lost count of the number of times I've excused myself at the bar, walked with a quickening and determined gait to the toilet, done the deed and returned to the bar. All within two minutes. This is an occupational hazard of bad behaviour and can be done without my mum's intervention. It's only the genuine, legitimate vomit that requires sympathy and company in equal doses. I'm on conventional medicine for the sickness, but as pregnant women know, sometimes the urge just takes you. I was beginning to get a bit downhearted; throwing up all the time does this to you. So when I remembered a letter from a reader offering alternative therapies, I looked out her card and made an appointment.

I lifted the phone as a full-time sceptic but, at some level, I guess I was ready to try anything if there's a chance it would work. So when I arrived at the Harvest Clinic of Hypnotherapy, just outside Glasgow city centre, it seemed all above board. I had an initial meeting with Angela, the clinic's founder, so she could go through the different types of treatments on offer. I took Pauline, my partner, along, partly for moral support, but also because I was apprehensive, especially at the thought of hypnosis. Any of you who have experienced the hell that is a package holiday will have seen the hypnotists who ply the resorts and turn holidaymakers into barking dogs and howling wolves in the name of entertainment. That I did not fancy. But I needn't have worried. Angela explained that the type of hypnotherapy she uses on her patients does not involve a swinging gold watch. It all takes place when the patient is in a relaxed state of mind, but still in control of their actions.

So that I would be more receptive to future sessions, she presented me with a tape to listen to last thing at night to help me relax. It must work because I have tried it three times and have yet to make it to the end of the tape. I also arranged a course of therapies designed to aid body and mind, and will keep you informed as to their effectiveness.

I am all for conventional painkillers and anti-sickness drugs, but sometimes the body can heal itself better from within. It just needs a kick-start. I treated myself to a 40-minute head massage, and I can honestly say that I have never felt so relaxed. All the tension and knots just disappeared and I was on a high for the rest of the day. Research has shown that a healthy mind is important to the recovery of a damaged body.

I am willing to put this to the test.

7 May 2000

We are Family:

'I WOULDN'T say I was a true believer, because I like to remain slightly sceptical, but I am certainly giving this alternative medicine lark a good try.

The other day I had a treatment called The Bowen Technique. As with a lot of these alternative treatments, it is based on the idea that the body can heal itself, it only needs "prompting". I got stripped to the waist – a big treat for the practitioner, I'm sure – and lay face down, not knowing what to expect.

The treatment's inventor, Australian Tom Bowen, was known as "the Mozart of healing. Every musician must place his or her fingers precisely on the strings to produce the desired sound and with the body being an instrument of sorts; I expected to be played a merry old tune. I have been suffering terrible recurring back pain over the last year, which I'm not convinced is related to my cancer, so I was hoping for a result. The therapist made a number of "attunements" to my spine – leaving the room after each one – to maximise the healing effects on my body. The results weren't immediately apparent, but the following day I felt strangely energised and my back was free of pain for a couple of days. I've got another session next week, so I'll be able to tell how effective it is.

One of the benefits of feeling slightly better is being able to mull over the views of my fellow Sunday Herald columnists. Muriel Gray, whose writing is always fresh incisive -and controversial -, recently wrote a piece on family values. The column's hook line was: "You don't really know what life is all about until you have children."

Now I don't have children and never will, but I live in a household that revolves around a two year old and is held together by the archetypal parent figures. I have always enjoyed a traditional family upbringing. If my parents were out working, grandparents or aunties or uncles would step in, but generally as a child, I was surrounded by a loving family.

What really brought that point home to me was watching a programme chronicling the 100 most memorable television events. Of those dating from my era, I was able to say exactly where I was when they happened – and without exception, I was with my parents. For Charles and Diana's wedding, I was in the back garden having a barbecue and the experience was much the same for Live Aid, only with the added pleasure of hearing Bob Geldolf swear live on stage.

Not everyone had the same idyllic upbringing as I had, but I feel being brought up with both parents and a supportive family made a real difference to how I turned out. Single parents have it tough and I admire anyone who manages to hold down a job, raise a child and have a life, but for me, the ideal is a two-parent family unit. My younger sister was an unmarried mum, but she was lucky that my parents looked after her child, Abbie, six out of seven days a week. Being a single parent isn't so much an issue if you have the backing of a supportive family. Unfortunately, having that large, caring family is a luxury few have these days. Where a family once stayed in the same area and visited each other regularly, employment now tends to dictate where people stay. And with life lived at a more frantic pace, people just don't have the time to engender a large family unit.

Simply visiting relatives is more of a nuisance than an advantage. I have long believed the period between living with your parents and having your own children shapes the rest of your life.

You spend your early years living through your parents, but that all changes dramatically when you have your own offspring. The period between these two stages is the only time you have a chance to live for yourself. Unfortunately the responsible society Muriel Gray seeks in her article is in danger of vanishing altogether as families are broken up by the demands of today's fast-paced world. The sad thing is I can't see things getting any better for parents and it is likely that happy, innocent childhoods like mine will become a hazy thing of the past.

After my dose of nostalgia, I must turn my mind to the near future, though – and with any luck, my scepticism about alternative treatment will be proved entirely groundless.

14 May 2000

Life's Great Journey:

UNLIKE Mike Jagger, "Time is not on my side."

I really need to spend what little time I have left with those people who really matter to me. One of my best friends, Marcello, has lived in London for the last nine years, but before that we were really tight. His big brother, Giancarlo, ran the Glasgow nightclub Joe Paparazzi's, so every Friday and Saturday night we were superstars, friends with everyone, and full of the promise of youth with not a care in the world.

We went through broken romances together, managing to convince each other it was better to be single anyway. We saw ourselves as urban heroes, reading all sorts of crazy literature and creating a language of our own. Sometimes we just hung out, but we got bored of the sycophants and phonies that Southside Glasgow social life cast up. Eventually Marcello got a job in London as a financial analyst in the City. We spoke on the phone but letters were our preferred method of communication. Our shared love of offbeat American novels meant we wrote reams and reams, mostly nonsense, but it kept us friends. And in touch.

So with my time becoming more precious and flights to London becoming ridiculously cheap, I planned a visit. Not being any kind of a techno boy it took me three hours to book the cheap tickets on the Internet. And get this – the flights cost a fiver but airport taxes took the price up to £30. Still, a bargain for a return to London. Marcello has a beautiful mews flat in Notting Hill, which he bought before the film made the area mainstream-trendy. He hadn't changed much since our last meeting; maybe put on a little weight, but working 16-hour days does that to you. And it is certainly preferable to the stomach cancer diet. Whatever Marcello does, he excels at it. He always has to be the best. I used to be dragged along in his wake, his excellence raising my game, forcing me to operate at a higher level too. He had planned a party in my honour on the Saturday night. Parties nowadays are good for me: people find out I am a writer with cancer and seem genuinely interested in what I have to say.

We cleaned Sainsbury's out of booze and party food, so when the guests, mostly Cello's colleagues, started to arrive, they were greeted by a table groaning with nibbles and intoxicants. Although Pauline and I were the odd ones out since we didn't work in the City, alcohol soon broke down the social barriers. We were introduced to an-American called Ron, who Marcello described as "a real CIA type". He was certainly the stereotypical clean-cut American, but it was only when he started talking about working in Bosnia for the government that I realised Marcello had literally meant he was a former CIA operative who got tired of rubbish wages and left the service to earn some real money as a broker.

In Glasgow, everyone who works behind a bar is really a model or a DJ. London seems to be full of people slogging in the City while hoping to do something else. Jim is a foreign exchange broker but also has a film production company and has written a screenplay he hopes will make him his fortune. To be honest, as he was telling me about the plot, I had one eye on Ron to make sure he wasn't slipping a secret powder into my drink, so I only caught snippets of conversation. I think the gist was that it's a historical story about immigrants coming to London. Quite topical, really, as Marcello, Pauline and I were the only British people there. I suppose if you are hungry enough and prepared to work in the City, the streets of London are paved with gold. Maybe I would try living there if I didn't have cancer.

And just to make sure I was reminded of my illness, I was as sick as a dog the next day. It wasn't a hangover, which I deserved for guzzling red wine like water. It was the ominous sickness caused by a tumour in my stomach growing large enough to block anything I swallow.

We went to Covent Garden to try to walk the sickness off. Shopping is never a good idea on a woozy sore head and the unexpected heat wave only made things worse. This did not, however, stop Pauline. On our last night, we went to Oxford to check out a Ducati motorbike, which Cello ended up buying. He's a real speed freak, as I was until I realised you get to where you are going anyway, with or without the points on your licence. I worry about him and the risks he takes. We talked frankly about death and I promised to visit him at least once more before I am confined to bed.

Hopefully that won't happen for a while yet. I have a few things to accomplish before I check out.

21 May 2000

The Prodigal Son:

I AM typing frantically while my fingers are still working. I've lost the feeling in my face and my arms all because of that most stupid of Scottish conceits – getting a suntan.

The recent good weather, and when I say good weather I mean anything over 60C and a glimpse of the sun, has prompted me to sit out in the back garden and fry to a crisp. You would think that, with my background of catching any type of cancer going, I would be more careful in the sun, but no. I lie prostrate (don't have that type of tumour yet) and watch as my skin turns thermador. It makes a change from the usual pasty white.

Even though I'm dying, vanity plays a large part in my life. But I'm not alone. Just look at Kelvingrove Park on a sunny day. Even a German would struggle to find a place for his towel. With my parents away to Ireland for the weekend, I have had the house and garden to myself. While I enjoy the peace, quiet and time for reflection, I miss the companionship, which I have built up, with my folks over the last two years. Staying at home means I get to see them every day. Of course it's possible to live at home and be out all the time and never see them at all. When parents accuse their offspring of treating the place like a hotel they are usually quite accurate. Pre-cancer I stayed at home but, due to work and a glittering social life, barely saw my family over breakfast. Now all that has changed. I treat my home like a hospice, where my mother and father provide all the respite care I need. I feel safe there. Virtually the only time I venture out is to drive up to Glasgow to see Pauline.

My younger siblings both have their own homes, so they tend not to visit too often. If I didn't have cancer, I would probably be living in Glasgow too, visiting home once a week, phoning for the odd chat. It would be an improvement on the bad old days, when I left home aged 19 and the only form of communication with my parents was raised voices and constant arguments. I had just started university and was out on the town seven nights a week, enjoying my new-found social life, not for a minute thinking that coming in at four or five in the morning was a tad selfish. In a fit of bravado, after yet another fight, I announced that I was moving out and getting a flat. A lot of my friends stayed in flats and they seemed to manage just fine. But they had two crucial advantages: the support of their family, financial and moral, plus student grants. I had a part-time job in a clothes shop and minimal savings. What seemed like a small fortune in wages when I lived at home suddenly changed into a week's rent, three tins of soup and a kebab after clubbing at the weekend. Fortunately I didn't have to pay to get into clubs, or the soup would have had to go.

My best mate Jack, who had also decided to stand on his own two feet, moved in. When we meet up now we laugh and shake our heads at the poverty and squalor we endured, but at the time the hole in the floor, the rattling windows, the stink of urine and spicy food on the stairs did not seem too big a deal. We regularly ran out of power cards and had to have freezing cold showers by candlelight. The one time we tried to fix the hole in the floor, Jack put a nail through the water pipe and flooded the Oriental Delicatessen downstairs. To this day, I still smile as I drive past the boarded-up shop. I moved back home soon afterwards.

Now I rely on my parents for a lot more than a roof over my head. But a lot of my fellow sufferers don't have this level of support. I was thinking about them this weekend, as I rattled about our house, not having any human contact.

While I am cynical about commercial card-buying opportunities like Mother's Day, parents like mine deserve all the recognition I can give them. I honestly feel their moral support is keeping me alive.

 I was extremely glad when they came back.

28 May 2000

Walking wounded:

IT had to happen sooner or later

In my case, later would definitely have been better. My doctors and the people who were organising my trek to Canada have decided that I am too ill to attempt the Rockies.

I applied to do this walk in December 1999, paid the substantial deposit and started to form a plan of attack: how best to raise the sponsorship money, milk my contacts at the paper for flattering coverage, that sort of thing. Now I find out the Macmillan Cancer Relief Campaign has filled its quota of "fit" people to do the trek, so they don't really need me. I am, after all, a cancer sufferer, and do not fit into a neat little package reserved for fit, healthy charity fundraisers. If I sound a little angry, that's because I am. My time is far too precious for me to hang around being a reserve in case the charity can't fill its quota of able-bodied trekkers.

The ironic thing is that they have lost out on the potential media interest that I would have brought to the project. It's not that my application was unrealistic in the first place. If that were the case, then surely the charity would have turned me down straight away. So here I am sitting at home, blood boiling at the unfairness of it all. Before I had cancer I would have said, "sod it," gone in a huff for a couple of days and then let my anger quietly subside into annoyance. Before long, it would have disappeared completely.

However, I do have cancer. I am a different person now and simply admitting defeat is not an option any more. I could very easily just sit back and let apathy wash all over me; languid waves of acceptance that I should be taking things easy in my condition. But that's not in my nature now. I have decided to do a sponsored walk along the West Highland Way with my friend Michael instead. Distance-wise, it's about the same as the Canadian trek. The weather conditions should be equally inclement. I am optimistic about it. I feel I have progressed too far to let people who do not really know my condition dictate how I should spend my remaining days.

So now the planning begins again: when to do the walk, how many days to allow. The sponsorship requests will now read "West Highland Way" instead of "Canadian Rockies" but I hope everyone who has already offered support will back my decision, and that anyone who has tips, advice or a desire to donate will get in touch. It feels good to have a mission again. I have been depressed recently, which I suppose is to be expected. I feel I still have a lot to offer: my mind is still as sharp as ever, plus I have this amazing self-belief and determination that I wished I had when I was younger. God, the things I could have achieved. But now, all people see is cancer.

I could not, realistically, put in a seven-day week, but there are other options. I was toying with the idea of a book, but am intimidated by the precedents set by John Diamond and Ruth Picardie. I suppose I could write a real rock'n'roll book about cancer: die in the same manner as you were born, screaming and kicking defiantly. I'm still thinking about it.

I print out the best emails I receive, although sometimes their eloquence and poignancy puts me to shame. One recurring subject is that when people are diagnosed with cancer they don't know where to turn.

This is the one thing that puts the seed in my mind to write a book. It wouldn't be a work of art but it would be telling it like it is, tumours and all. I am a bit wary of becoming the poster boy for the new cancer generation – there are over 200 types of cancer and I simply couldn't write a book about them all. The one thing I know I could describe is the roller coaster ride that your feelings experience, from abject dejection at diagnosis to jubilation at a positive blood count.

Perhaps the rejection and lack of faith from my doctors and the trek organisers can be turned into a positive thing. Perhaps that's the trick to surviving cancer, turning the negatives into positives.

I still have a lot of turning to do.

4 June 2000

Tea and Sympathy:

THE life of a cancer sufferer is full of ups and downs, most of them pharmaceutical.

With the range of painkillers I am taking, each dealing with a different pain centre with its own pain receptors, satisfying the varied demands of my body is a fine balancing act. I take an active role in the prescription and progress of my drugs – in a case, as complex as mine it's not fair or correct to leave all the responsibility to doctors. Nor do I expect them to have all the answers. People seem to see doctors as infallible, superhuman professionals, but I know that they can be susceptible to mistakes, misdiagnosis or even pressure from patients.

I have a large tumour on my spleen, and the pain it causes is pretty severe. I know from experience that my painkillers don't quite live up to their name, so I suggested to one of my doctors that I would like to try a course of steroids. They target pain differently and I thought it had to be worth a shout. At first – a result. The pain subsided more than usual and I was spared the pincushion process of endless morphine injections. But slowly, almost imperceptibly, things started to change. For the steroids to work, I had to ingest fairly large doses. Large enough to cause all sorts of side effects. Fancy trying to operate on three hours of sleep a night? It's not easy. Your temper gets frayed and as for your digestion, I can't make head nor tail of it.

For weeks I had been looking forward to a lunch with my writing guru and friend Nick Nairn, at his eponymous restaurant. I have been a fan of Nick's forever: his irreverent wit and inventive cooking style have always appealed. In a restaurant culture that was in danger of moving too far up its own rear end to know that the basics are what count in a good meal, he seemed to talk a lot of sense. Now I'm no great foodie, but I'm always open to new culinary experiences and the invitation to Nick's restaurant caused me a great deal of excitement. Poor soul that I am, I don't get out too much. What I had not factored for was the side effects of the steroids.

One of the main things that steroids do to your body is to give you a voracious appetite. Now that does not sound like the worst thing in the world when anticipating a top lunch. Indeed, for my local Chinese restaurant, it must sound sweet indeed. Every night for the last week I have had to phone for a takeaway because I can't control my appetite.

It's this crazy unpredictability that causes the problems. Eating at 11.30pm plays Russian roulette with your metabolism, especially when you have chronic insomnia and rarely see sleep before 4am. All of which meant that, on the eve of my lunch at Nairns, I had been up all night emptying my full stomach from both ends and feeling absolutely dreadful. I had to phone and cancel which left me feeling really down, another side effect of the steroids.

However you try to control it, pain wears you down. It is upsetting and depressing and throws up all kinds of difficult choices. Who decides what is an acceptable way to go when you have a terminal disease? How long do you keep on fighting? How much of that fight is for other people and how much for yourself?

My recent epidural, a procedure used for women in labour and people, like myself, suffering from severe back pain, has not really worked. So I am trying herbal tea instead. It was recommended by a reader and is blended by a woman called Rene Caisse. It is distributed by a charity, which aims to make alternative therapies available to all, regardless of their financial situation. Many pharmaceutical companies have offered to buy her formula, which does seem to be beneficial to cancer patients, but the charity is not playing.

Have to say it tastes absolutely rotten and is a drag to prepare, requiring endless sterilisation. But if it works, well I won't be complaining.

In the meantime, it reminds me of how much I am looking forward to my rescheduled lunch at Nairns.

11 June 2000

End games:

NO let up in the depression!

My waking hours are peppered with thoughts of death. Even as my life is winding down, I am still a control freak. I find myself planning my funeral in the smallest detail. I am a bit like an excited bride, thrilled at the prospect of her impending wedding. I don't know if it's the pain from the tumour in my spleen giving me hallucinations, but I can see it all clearly and calmly. My family has done their grieving already – the worst thing for my parents is seeing me in pain but being unable to do anything about it.

The recent rash of celebrity departures has further trained my mind on my last exit. When I heard of the unfortunate demise of Dame Barbara Cartland, I had her marked down for the full-fat funeral. A gilded glass carriage drawn by six white horses, adorned with ornate plumage. Hundreds of white lilies and carnations. Thousands of desolate OAPs lining the cortege route, waving copies of her books and throwing flower petals in the path of the carriage, the inside of which would be upholstered in pink satin. And so on. When I read that she had opted for the biodegradable option, the cardboard box under the oak tree in her back garden, I felt guilty and shallow. Her books were slushy so I automatically assumed her funeral would be the same.

Having had a lot of time and, let's face it, a lot of good reasons, to think about funerals, I have decided the bigger the service, the bigger the ego of the deceased.

I'm all for the funeral as a celebration of life – the only tears I want at mine are ones of joy, as people recount their favourite Jono stories. (Please keep the risque ones away from my family, at least until they have had a good skinful.) Wine, good food and singing are all prerequisites of my funeral. My family's roots are in Lanarkshire, where funerals are typically sombre affairs held in a chapel, followed by a graveside service at a windswept cemetery. Tradition dictated that the women gave the graveyard a miss and went directly to the venue for the meal, which would always be a miners' welfare or working men's club, where the dish of the day was always steak pie.

No one ever complained – it was, after all, a funeral. The deceased was never mentioned and the conversation never rose above a murmur. After a couple of polite hellos and a social drink, excuses were made and a wave of relief washed over everyone as they shut the car door. Someone inevitably said," well, that wasn't as bad as it could have been," but secretly inside you shrank from the thought that an impersonal eulogy spoken by a priest who had probably met the deceased twice in his life, and a few words at the graveside, were the sole testament to someone's life.

I have not been sharing these thoughts very widely. Death, like cancer, is a taboo subject, and when you put the two together, most people would rather eat a dog turd. But I've thought a lot about dying; especially this week as I have felt about as close to death as I have since contracting cancer. Sure I've been sick before, but never sick in the head. I feel myself losing the spark and will to live. I am running out of reasons to keep on fighting and find myself with nothing to focus on but my steady decline into a drug-hazed stupor. With increasingly large doses of morphine, it should be an entertaining ride.

And as for my funeral, well, I know my priest. He knows I am no angel, but more importantly, when he talks it will be me he will be talking about, warts, faults and all. As for the refreshments, you can forget shepherds' pie and complimentary glass of sherry. People don't go to funerals for a gourmet experience but some good food and drink always helps to break down barriers. I want my guests, and that's how I think of them, to mingle, to mix, to share stories. Due to my life's itinerant nature, I expect a lot of culture clashes between the guests at my wake. This is where the fine wine should come in.

I really fancy my guests having a right good old toast to my memory. It's one of the images that is keeping me going.

18 June 2000

Some Mother's Son:

EVERY week I receive a lot of emails.

What most of you want to know is this: how does my family get on with living (or should that be dying) with me? So I thought it would be useful if I asked my mother, Susan, all the questions you regularly ask me.

How does it feel knowing you are going to live longer than your son?

Although I have had a while to get used to the idea, I am still taking one day at a time. I first noticed a change in Jonathan's condition when he came home for Christmas dinner. At the time he was staying in a flat in Glasgow, and when he came home he didn't have his usual voracious appetite and he wasn't his usual perky self. Being my usual unsympathetic self, I put it own to his poor diet and fast lifestyle.

Then, in February, he was admitted to hospital to have a stomach obstruction removed. His father and I arrived at the hospital just as he was returning from theatre. I asked the staff what had happened – having being a nursing sister for over 20 years, I could understand any complicated procedures they would have had to perform. I was told, however, that the consultant would talk to us. We left him settled and returned the next day. The consultant was obviously distressed when we met him. Jonathan, he told us, had cancer of the colon, which had spread to his stomach, spleen and liver. He had a son the same age and he was obviously shaken, which shows that even consultants are human. Neither my husband Henry nor myself cried. Henry asked how long and the consultant said the prognosis was poor. We went to the ward to see Jono and told him. He cried and we all hugged. Still numb, we made our way back down to Ayr. We have been numb ever since. I cannot think of him as a child, nor can I contemplate life without him. I really do live each day as it comes. Who knows – he may outlive me yet.

How does nursing your own son differ from caring for a normal patient?

As Jono gets worse, he requires more drugs. Most of these are by injection, which has meant his soft skin has turned into the hide of a rhinoceros. I am in the fortunate position of being able to give my son his medication, which makes it easier to look after him. I think any mother would want to give her child his treatment if she was able to. I do guard my role as his nurse jealously, but thanks to understanding doctors, this hasn't been a problem. Jono will always be my son first and a patient second.

Has your view on cancer changed since Jonathan contracted it?

Yes. I always felt sad when patients would tell me that they had been diagnosed with a serious condition. When they said that they would fight, I encouraged them, but really did not think that it would make the slightest bit of difference. How wrong I was. The goals that Jono has set himself and achieved have definitely helped keep him alive. I have three children and Jono is the last one I would have imagined to handle cancer in the manner he has. We all used to joke that he walked with a limp when he had a cold. Like any normal boy, he hated anything to do with illness.

I think the medical profession should be more positive and encourage people to make the best of their good days. Let them do what they want and be the judge of their own fitness. Patients should also explore alternative therapies, even if the benefit is purely psychological.

How do you think Jonathan handles his condition?

When we told Jono the result of the operation, he couldn't believe it any more than we could. He wept, but I have not seen him cry since. He started to work with his Aunt Therese as soon as he was released from hospital, and between his chemotherapy treatments he worked very hard. It was there he met and fell for Pauline, and has been treated like a son by her family. Jonathan has tried every treatment going, despite the side effects. He has also taken part in drug trials that won't benefit him but will hopefully help someone, somewhere down the line. Acupuncture, herbal teas, hypnotherapy ... you name it, he's tried it. I don't think he could do anything more.

What do you wish for, apart from the obvious?

I wish Jono would complain more and speak to me about what is on his mind. Although I am numb and heartbroken, it is a pleasure to be with him and his courage has taught me never to fear anything that life throws at me. Of course we have our off days but that's to be expected. There are days when he could see me far enough and I do find his stubbornness impossible to handle at times. We are lucky to live where we do, and come under the umbrella of the Ayrshire hospice where they put up with our idiosyncrasies very well. Jono also gets great support from his friends, who have remained very loyal. It isn't easy to be young and have to deal with cancer.

So there you have it, cancer from a carer's point of view. It is always difficult to talk about these things and I was not even aware of some of my mother's feelings. It was as enlightening for me as I hope it has been for you.

Thanks Mum. Maybe I'll even do some work on that stubbornness.

25 June 2000

Message with bottle:

WHEN I look at the written media in Scotland – and I have plenty of time to catch up with my reading – I try to find my peers.

The writers I respect, the ones whose articles make me think, who give the old brain cells a bit of a workout. But what I find is that most of my fellow writers are just that—Writers.

Of course, by definition I am a writer too because I typed these words into my laptop and, via the miracles of electronic communication, you are reading them here. But I write because I have a purpose, a motivation that is more than greenbacks, school fees, mortgage repayments or the inability to stop buying Dries Van Noten. I am dying of cancer and I don't have long left, but I want my demise chronicled to show that death isn't the big monster we all fear. By doing so, when I am in a good mood, I like to think that perhaps I can change some of our perceptions of how we live our lives. Maybe even change how we live our lives. When I am feeling less self-assured, I think that maybe I could just be a good read in the bog.

What I don't want to become is a vacuous chronicler of last week's fave CDs and fluffy shoes. This may seem incongruous coming from someone with a background in high fashion. I know my Prada from my Jil Sander and have worked for top designers as well as trying to sell their products at the sharp end of the business. However, there are fashion magazines and features put together by professionals, so why step on their toes? I have also worked in the entertainment industry, in bars and clubs, behind the bar and as a DJ (a while ago, before everyone and their auntie became one). I travel as much as I can and I love photographing the places I visit. I also have a passion for literature, reading up to three books at once so I don't get complacent.

So how come, when I am so clearly well qualified to talk about men's skincare products and why Budapest is the new Prague, I ended up writing about life before death? Fatal diseases do strange things to your career trajectory. But what I try not to do is to talk down to my readers. Cancer is a delicate and complicated subject, which is often upsetting. Plus there are so many other people who know more than I do. And I know that I'm still a beginner. If you feel I am missing out on a particular subject, drop me an email and let me know. I think I am mature enough to accept criticism. If there are faults in my work they are all mine and I will try to do something about them.

I refuse to be one of those so-called writers who, once a week, phone the newspaper who has decided that their famous face and name will shift copies. They tell them who they met, which clubs they went to, what they wore, and some poor hack has to write an article based on these self-promoting and so-called important ramblings. There may even be some lovely photographs, often with some real A-lister like Giorgio Armani or Liz Hurley wondering who the non-entity from Glasgow is.

No, I write on the basis that people need something they can relate to. If escapism is what they want, I recommend The Alchemist, written 15 years ago by the Brazilian author Paolo Coelho. It's a parable about ambitions, dreams and how to identify the phonies who waste your precious time by holding you back from your true destiny. People like bad writers. Time is precious, too precious to waste reading writing with no feeling. Or writing about handbags.

I will, however, continue to write about the alternative therapies I have also been investigating. My cancer-busting tea tastes slightly more palatable and I also tried a session of acupuncture. I met Dr Rosaleen Beattie when we both appeared on a TV show about cancer and its treatments. She works from the Prince and Princess of Wales Hospice and immediately made me feel completely at ease. We talked openly about cancer and my feelings on the subject. I guess it comes from working in a hospice environment, but people like Rosaleen, and Dr John Bass from the Ayrshire hospice, just seem to know what to say. They gauge people's emotions perfectly and treat accordingly. Dr Bass had the dirty job of telling me that my latest scan shows that all my tumours have grown. It can't be easy telling a young man that the tumours which are killing him are doing it a wee bitty faster. And he has to do this to different patients every day.

So I was a bit apprehensive about being used as a human porcupine when I pitched up at Rosaleen's door, but once she explained how small acupuncture needles are, and how little they actually penetrate the skin, I relaxed. A pulled muscle has plagued me in my back for a while and she inserted a needle. Miraculously, the pain receded. I won't lie and say it has totally disappeared, but it certainly worked better than my recent shiatsu massage.

I certainly feel better after investigating alternative therapies. As far as acupuncture is concerned, I will certainly be repeating the experience.

Now I can see the point.

2 July 2000

The Longest Walk:

I HAVE written under sedation before, but never at this level.

Needs must, though, because after my most recent scan, which showed a worsening in all the sites of my tumours, I am having a sabbatical at the Ayrshire Hospice. The idea is that I have a bit of a rest while they mess about with the doses of my drugs. Which is why it takes me ten seconds to find and press a button. Add this to my spelling shortcomings and you will appreciate that this column has taken two weeks to write. The painkilling injections don't seem to affect the pain. They just play havoc with my cognitive skills. Text written under that kind of chemical duress doesn't read as easily as the fluid, mellow meanderings that usually pour forth when I am on drugs.

One of my fellow guests in the hospice is a young girl in her twenties. Now I think I have problems but Karen is allergic to needles. When you consider that my medication is half-hourly, by injection, you can imagine her situation.

Part of the problem is that you always think you have bigger problems than anyone else. You stand on the bus on the way to work, huffing and puffing about the bank balance, the partner who is pissing you off, what a bad life you have in general. Or at least I used to. But what I can advise from my state of deep sedation is this. Take a deep breath and try to put things into perspective. Do you have to let medical personnel put metal contraptions up your orifices? That is what I now call a problem. I have lumps which I can feel, that I know are going to kill me, but do I let my face trip me? Well, yes actually I do. I went to see a stress counsellor the other day. Apparently moaning and crying and letting it all out is the way to go. It evens out your hormones. So if you see people walking around wailing, well you can leave the blame at my doorstep.

Staying in the hospice for such a long time is like living in a hotel, but with the added benefit of having a doctor on call 24 hours a day. I'm being spoiled with all the attention when I should be doing my homework in preparation for undertaking the West Highland Way. I have got as far as buying the books and the Ordnance Survey maps and some of my "outdoorsy" readers have emailed advice. In fact one woman has offered to put me and my fellow walkers up for the night, which is extremely kind. I decided the best way to go about this was to split the walk into different days. But even allowing for rest days, there will be a couple of days of hard walking.

So I have been getting in training. Residents of Prestwick, don't be surprised if you see something resembling a flailing elephant on the sea front. I decided that one way to get fit quick would be to roller blade, but you could say my rollerblading skills are as scarce as Mike Tyson's feminist fan base. I'm getting there, though.

Absolutely everyone who has heard that I am doing the West Highland Way has nodded sagely and said, almost reverentially: "midges". Larger than an eagle, more vicious than Graeme Souness and in huge clouds along the path, these denizens of the Scottish Highlands are man's greatest enemy. Or so I am told. So I have a plan, one that needs the help of my mother. I don't think she will mind. It's bottle corks, tied to my hat. I would say 15 fine bottles of Chardonnay would do it, although she doesn't have to drink them all in the same day. I have roped some foolhardy friends along for the journey. If, some days, I am too ill to walk, they will have to carry the torch in my absence. Although I have every intention of finishing the walk. As time gets closer I will let you know how to donate cash. I have chosen two benefactors, for two reasons.

The first is the Ayrshire Hospice, providers of respite care, and my sometime home. Secondly, I have chosen the MacMillan Cancer Relief Fund, who not only look after the elderly, but also constantly strive for the improved treatment of cancer. They are treating the problem while looking for a cure.

To be blunt, in my currently sedated state I am worried I may not be fit enough for the walk but as the weeks go by, I'll keep you up to date with my progress.

A walk doesn't sound much until you realise it's almost 100 miles.

Mother Watch:

I don't sleep much at night. I constantly lie awake, listening for sounds of Jonathan. My biggest fear is that he will be sick on his own, an occurrence that Jonathan hates: he likes me to hold his hand, or hold his stomach when he is retching. I often go downstairs to his study, during the night, to find him fast asleep in his large, comfortable chair: generally as a result of his medication.

His readers have no idea of the incredible effort that he puts into assembling an article: they read it on a Sunday without being aware, that the start of a new paragraph means that Jonathan has had to rush to the toilet. This happens at least two dozen times a day.

On one particular occasion I came downstairs at 4am, to find Jonathan sound asleep, slumped over his laptop. In doing so he had deleted his completed current article, which he had not saved. When I awoke him and he discovered what he had done, he was devastated. His deadline was the following lunchtime, and he doubted that he would be able to recreate the missing article, eventually he did, but doing so left him drained, both physically and mentally. I don't know how many times, that I have heard him say that he was unable to do an article for the following week. However, after much coaxing and encouragement he always managed to come up with one. Although it took so much of an effort, he was always pleased to have succeeded, as it meant that he had achieved yet another goal- That's what his life was all about!

Susan Wilson

9 July 2000

Named and Shamed:

SACK Susan Deacon! Sack Dr.David Watts!

Harsh statements indeed, but once you read on, you find yourself agreeing with me. As I write, Dr. David Watts, a GP.from Dundonald, Ayrshire, who is also Chief Executive of Ayrshire Doctors On Call, is probably trying to squeeze his other mint-flavoured size nine into his mouth.

He is the prince who said that if he were forced to choose between treating a pensioner and treating a child, he would pick the younger patient. Indeed, he would rather his own grandchild received life-saving treatment than himself. Elderly groups and politicians have been in uproar ever since his remarks at an Ethics debate at The British Medical Association's conference in London. What we should remember is that Dr.Watt's opinion is strictly that: his opinion. It is not the policy of Ayrshire and Arran Health Board. He should stick to his job and leave the politicking to the politicians, like his boss Susan Deacon. More on her later.

You can almost feel sorry for Dr.Watts. As the NHS's founding principle is free care to all at the point of need, you would expect this to mean equal access and quality of care, irrespective of age. But today this depends on funds available; after all, you can't spend what you don't have. But the irony is that a request to his boss, Susan Deacon would surely have revealed a massive surplus. In fact it was only recently, that Ms Deacon revealed new cash to be spent on Doctors and Nurses in Scotland. For a man of his stature to use his grandchildren as a basis of this argument is naïve claptrap. We would all do whatever we could for our relatives. How many times have I heard my grandmother say that she wishes that she could take my pain away? Alas it doesn't work that way. But the way it does work seems to be deteriorating. There is the postcode lottery, the "Do Not Resuscitate Patients" clause, which I probably fall under, and now age rationing. I wish Dr.Watt's grandchildren all the very best of health, but Chief Executives need to be smart enough to avoid getting caught up in hypothesis and realise their responsibility extends further than their own family.

So what of these famously limited resources? Scottish Health Minister Susan Deacon under spent £135 million, earmarked for the NHS this year. WE get the news of this at the same time as we hear that curable cancer patients are dying due to lack of resources. How can this be? Lack of funds and an under spend in the same week? How can this be explained? Don't bother writing to Susan Deacon, as my mother did two months ago, regarding the mismanagement of Ayrshire and Arran Health Board, as you won't even get the luxury of a reply. Perhaps that would have been different if mum had mentioned that her son writes for The Sunday Herald- a column based on cancer, which is a health issue, in case she or her advisors haven't noticed.

So where is the £135m under spend going? Education? Welfare? -Nope!

Until Deacon won it back last week, £34m was going to be spent on trees and historic buildings, which are worthy enough causes, but surely ones that could be covered by lottery grants. This would also save me from having to do a charity walk to raise funds for cancer care. Britain has one of the worst cancer survival rates in Europe, but I bet we have one of highest rates in tree hugging and monument-visiting in the world.

The problem for someone in my situation is that I'm not going to be around to enjoy all these trees and castles. No matter what your point of view is, people are more important than plants and buildings. Heritage and nature are admirable pursuits but, as I sit waiting in the queue to see my consultant, I don't want to see moss, lichen or the remains of an Anglo-Saxon settlement.

I want to see the man in the white coat, and I want to know that he has the resources he needs to treat me in the way he thinks best.

16 July 2000

Decks, Drugs and Rock'n'roll:

AFTER two weeks as a guest of the Hospice, all that is missing is the piped Henry Mancini music and the matron announcing "medication time" over the intercom as we shuffle up to take our character-numbing tablets.

Actually, I am being unfair. I now look on the hospice as my second home. A stay here also gives my mum a break from the regime of interminable injections, especially useful, as my little sister is about to drop her second baby. Grandparents are great; you just drop off your kids and live your life as normal. Parental responsibility? Not this generation.

While I was in residence, a very generous benefactor gifted a piece of land to the hospice. It used to be an old tennis court, but Karen, my fellow non-OAP cancer sufferer, dubbed it "the secret garden". It's a fitting description of a place that can only be entered via an old gate hidden by overgrown weeds and plants. She had the wonderful idea of writing to one of the gardening television programmes to see if they would be interested in doing it up. Surely Charlie Dimmock, Alan Titchmarch et al would be interested in a genuine charity garden? I am hoping to bump into men in wellies with cameras soon after my return.

Yes, they let me out for a short while, and I celebrated by pointing the car at Kinross and enjoying VIP hospitality, sorted out for me by the lovely Jo from Tennents, at T In The Park. It was not my first music festival. The sister who is just about to go into labour was once a huge Oasis fan. When they played at Glastonbury about five years ago my dad decided he was too old to be a rock'n'roll chaperone. My pal Andy and I were volunteered to accompany her to England. This caused us some paranoia because at the time we were DJs, before dance music was cool and mainstream, so we felt that all eyes were on us, even although we had done our best to dress down and look grungy.

It was a glorious day and, to cool down, we had a couple of beers (shandies for sister Madeleine of course.)

The alcohol must have been stronger than we thought because Andy curled up on the grass and promptly fell asleep. Not an easy thing at a music festival where the speakers were 50 foot tall.

At the time we decided it would be a great idea to cover him with grass. Half an hour later, you couldn't tell where the grass ended and Andy began. He eventually woke up when some hapless person tripped up and spilled their beer all over him. Whenever he starts to annoy me all I have to do is remind him of the time that he and my wee sister had the same amount to drink. She never passed out.

Those familiar with festivals will remember the stalls selling "herbal remedies", natural products guaranteed to keep you awake and dancing. Foolishly Andy and I purchased a couple of packets of these allegedly natural stimulants, took them and waited for the "waves of energy and euphoria" to kick in. I was the first to be affected, running to the Portaloos and making it just in time. Now as a child I was always told to make sure that there was toilet paper in the cubicle, or else move to the next one. But this time I was so relieved to get to a toilet I forgot this golden rule. It cost me dear: a fiver to be exact. A five-pound note was the only paper I had on me.

I have wasted money on a lot of things in my time but that fiver must be one of the most ridiculous, closely followed by the tablets themselves, which only succeeded in inducing a feeling of lethargy and tiredness.

So it was with an ironic smile that I saw all the same stalls at T In The Park. "Dance all night with our herbal E tablets," the stalls proclaimed, and they were doing a roaring trade. People would be dancing all right, waiting their turn for the toilet. I christened the dance "the cross-leg shuffle". I walked straight past, smug in the knowledge that, nestling in my rucksack, was two toilet rolls.

I no longer need to buy pharmaceuticals from dodgy blokes in muddy fields. In the constant battle to control my pain, Dr Bass has prescribed a Ketamine infusion. In large doses, this is used as a horse tranquilliser. It is also used by unscrupulous (as if there any other kind) drug dealers to mix with ecstasy, to increase their profits. But, under medical supervision, it is a recognised pain relief agent.

The treatment lasted four hours during which I experienced hallucinations and talked to people who have died. It was a strange experience but the most important thing is that it seems to have controlled the pain. Slightly. It looks like I may be in the hospice for a while longer while they fine-tune my cocktail of drugs.

At least the people with the white overalls know what they are giving you.

23 July 2000

From Cradle To Grave:

AS I write, I have heard that I am an uncle again.

I do not know the weight or the name. All I know is it was a forceps delivery (deemed painful by those in the know), that the baby is male and that my sister is okay. I thought of her heaving and pushing and in so much pain, trying to squeeze a melon-sized mass out of a hole designed for something much smaller. No wonder they call them stretch marks.

As I cradled my own aching stomach and cried out for morphine, I thought of her and wished for an easy labour with no complications. My mother says the first is the hardest, and when she was giving birth to her own eldest, me, she couldn't care if I was a monkey as long as I got out of her. Contrary to many observations, I looked nothing like a gorilla and could have won many a beautiful baby competition had my mother felt insecure enough to need to put me forward. All this baby commotion has got me thinking about baby care and the other end of the same spectrum, elderly care. The demographics show we are an aging population, with not enough new babies being born to care for the growing older generation. There is no shortage of volunteers to look after young children: grandparents, aunts, uncles all queue up to have a shot of hassle-free parenting. There are few things better than taking a young child to the zoo or cinema only to hand them back to their parents at the end of the day.

I worry, though, about what will happen to my own parents, as they get older, when I won't be around, if and when they can't look after themselves. Private nursing homes are not an option I care to think about. Now, I am sure there are good nursing homes, but in my experience, and from what I have heard from nurses who have worked in them, a lot of them are understaffed television rooms full of old people with nothing to do, the stench of stale urine hanging in the air. Uncaring children who visit once a week or less, as their consciences allow, and low levels of staff who are often under qualified for the jobs they are doing. At the very least we can afford to give our elderly relatives the dignity they deserve. It's not every family that is able, or can afford, to take in elderly relatives, but everyone can take more of an interest, check out the credentials of the nursing home, take their parents out for the day, make sure they are getting adequate care.

The hospice I am in at present provides excellent standards of care but is not fully funded by the government and relies heavily on charity donations and fundraising, as do the rest of the hospices in Scotland. It is staffed by professionals who genuinely care about the patients and their needs. I have only to press a button to have a nurse at my bedside in a minute. It's hard for me not to contrast this with the idea of my parents, or anybody's parents, ending up in a privately run home that is mismanaged, understaffed and does not care for its patients. It seems to be all too easy to set up a nursing home and, as everyone's lives get busier, we just don't have the time, or so we tell ourselves, to visit elderly relatives. But I bet that my sister will not get a moment's peace from all the well wishers wanting to see the new baby. I include myself in this bunch of hypocrites.

I started a new course of medication this week, one I promised myself that I would never take. After witnessing the junkies at the chemist being supervised while swallowing their daily dose of methadone, I promised myself that I would never become that dependent on drugs. But now I find that Dr Bass, the medical director of the hospice, has prescribed me methadone as a painkiller, to work in tandem with the high levels of morphine I am taking.

It impairs my speech and affects my brain function. In fact I find I do have some sympathy for the addicts who dribble as they slowly ask you for spare change.

Perhaps I have found a new way of raising money for the hospice.

30 July 2000

Back To Life:

EACH article I write gets responses or "hits", in the form of letters and emails, and I apologise to those that I don't reply to – I have to ration my time.

I recently wrote about my mother-carer's feelings about my cancer and the response from readers has been phenomenal. The reaction has made me realise that cancer sufferers and carers are not getting the right information, so I've decided to write a plain English, warts-and-all book about cancer, based on my own experiences and with no medical rhetoric.

I realised that my mother could only tell part of the story, so I felt it was only fair to give the Medical profession a say. I chose the doctor who is, to me, the most highly qualified and full of integrity. Dr John Bass, the medical director of the Ayrshire Hospice, works seven-day weeks and is a frequent out-of-hours visitor to my home. He makes decisions I would not entrust to other medics. Only this week I have had ketamine and methadone, both controlled drugs that merit an article themselves. Perhaps next week. Meanwhile, I thought carefully about the issues that mean something to today's one-in-three-will-catch-cancer society, so here goes.

With Britain having an ageing population, how do you think the NHS will cope?

The ageing population will pose an increasing problem. With age comes a rising incidence of illness, particularly cancer, heart disease and strokes. Changes in society mean that fewer old people have caring relatives who will look after them. Families are more scattered now and, increasingly, both partners are working. Therefore a greater burden of care is being placed on the state. These factors, plus advances in medical science with more, often expensive, treatments available will create huge challenges for the NHS.

Where do you see the hospice movement fitting in to the present NHS?

The hospice movement evolved to fill a gap the NHS was failing to fill. Patients were dying with inadequate symptom control, often alone and neglected. Families were receiving inadequate support. Care of dying patients and their families requires special care and a lot of skill and time. Hospice levels of staffing reflects this. The nurse to patient ratio is very high to allow for individual patient care. Skills can be improved with better conditions and training, but the NHS will never be in a position to provide this training due to time constraints, especially in the light of what we were talking about above.

Do you believe in, or advocate euthanasia?

No, never. To legalise euthanasia would undermine the basic trust between doctor and patient. Also, however carefully the legislation is framed, I believe it will, in practice, be eroded. The risk is that what starts as voluntary euthanasia becomes extended to involuntary euthanasia. There is evidence from Holland that supports this view. Finally, with good palliative care, euthanasia should not be necessary. In real life, there will always be very occasional cases when suffering cannot be relieved. However it would be wrong if these cases formed the basis of a fundamental change.

Do you see a cure for cancer?

Not for many years. One problem is that cancer is not just one disease, but one of many. Great strides have been made, and the mapping of the human genome has huge potential for creating major advances in treatment. However, this technology won't translate into treatments for many years. Maybe decades.

Why did you choose this branch of medicine?

I am a palliative physician – what used to be called a hospice doctor. I've always been interested in psychological medicine, but I enjoy physical medicine as well. Palliative medicine is a specialty that nicely combines both.

Do you think that the word hospice has a negative connotation?

Sadly, yes. For many people, the word hospice still conjures up a negative picture. Frequently, people still think of hospices as places where you go to die. They don't realise that many people go into hospices to get better, before returning home. Or that many hospice patients never get admitted but are visited at home by specialist hospice nurses. Or again, that many attend a day care hospice. I cannot put it better than an old lady who said she had gone into a hospice to die but had learned to live again instead. That's what hospices should be about – living with cancer, not dying with it.

While Dr Bass speaks for himself, I reckon most people will find themselves agreeing with much of what he is saying. I certainly did.

6 August 2000

Home From Home:

DURING a rather reckless moment at the hairdresser's this week, I decided against the usual trim and asked for something a little more daring. I left with my tresses cut into different lengths and dyed acid blonde. The new image looks good to me, but everyone else thinks I should have a skateboard under my arm.

It is a world away from my days of chemotherapy, when my long, blonde locks began falling out. I couldn't sleep for the hair that had fallen out tickling my face, and I had to get my mother to hoover my pillow every day. In the end I had to bite the bullet and shave my hair off. Much to my surprise, I discovered that women find bald men sexy, but the benefits didn't stop there. You also get to look tough and no one messes with you.

I have been in the hospice for three weeks now, and while the staff has made it a second home for me, spoiling me with their care and compassion, it just isn't the real thing. I can't just reach out without looking and find my satellite TV remote control, my pillows aren't as comfy and I miss mamma's cooking. The bonus is that my pain seems to be under control, since I am now on methadone. Unfortunately, the drug tends to affect your cognitive and speech abilities. You take the tablets and for two hours afterwards, you find speech difficult and peppered with saliva.

My physical condition is beginning to worry me as my charity walk draws closer. What keeps me going is a belief in the hospice movement, my pig-headed stubbornness and more recently, the advert for the Imperial Cancer Research Fund, which shows three girls playing in a meadow. In an attempt to highlight the statistic that by the end of this year, one in three people will have contracted cancer, we are shown the girls' future careers. One is a lawyer, one is a teacher, while the last, and prettiest, girl is given cancer as her future. Not a very bright one, is it? The advert has reinforced my resolve to do the sponsored walk I've been planning in aid of the Macmillan Cancer Relief Fund and the Ayrshire Hospice. And the effort won't stop there. The owners of The Stand comedy club have agreed to hold a one-off charity night at their Glasgow venue, so budding comedians should brush up on their material and contact them. I'll tell you when the event is as soon as a date has been finalised.

It's strange living in the hospice because everything is done at a certain time – I can expect my lunch to be on the table at 12.15pm. This type of institutionalised living can get addictive: it's probably much like the army in that respect. On the occasional return home to visit my parents, I start to feel a bit insecure after half an hour, and after a full 60 minutes I am desperate to get back. Acclimatising to hospice life was difficult at the beginning, but it will be a much harder job trying to fit into the chaotic world of the Wilson household. Meal times are irregular and you don't get a choice of three dishes, and unless my mother has totally lost the plot, there won't be a tea trolley with homemade scones. I hope I am beginning to paint a rosy picture of the hospice and hospices in general. This stupid idea that once you enter into the domain of a hospice, once they get their claws into you, there is no escape, is a load of rubbish. Granted I've been here for three weeks, but at any time I could have packed my bags and left. But I haven't, because the care and treatment I have received has been excellent.

Now, hopefully, I can get out and get my social life kick started again. Who knows, I may even shave my head and go bald.

13 August 2000

Screen Saviour:

AFTER staying rather longer in the hospice than I intended, I am settling back in at home.

It is comforting to be reacquainted with my ridiculously large television (I wonder whether they say the same about big sets as they do about large cars). Thankfully, my bed doesn't rustle as I toss and turn and, even better, I don't have to get up at 8am if I don't want to. I have found that, with my mother nursing me again, we have grown closer, even though my argumentative manner hasn't waned with my health. My body might be weak, but my mind is still being exercised.

As I look out on the world through my television set, it's difficult not to dwell on the Sarah Payne case, which has saturated the media in the last couple of weeks. The News Of The World has tried to galvanise the general feeling of outrage that the little girl's death provoked, but thankfully sense has prevailed and the newspaper's campaign to identify the nation's paedophiles on its pages has lost its momentum. Sarah's parents, who initially backed the drive in their confused grief, have withdrawn their support. Although well meaning, their efforts would simply have sent paedophiles underground.

While some would say the News Of The World was acting to protect the rights of British children, there is, of course, the argument that the fight to boost circulation was behind its campaign. Whatever the motive was moral or financial, the tabloid press will no doubt be trumpeting another shocking issue before long. It makes me wonder what the next public backlash will be. Personally speaking, my next backlash will be when I turn 30 later this month. That's three decades old, and I'm depressed. When I was 26, I was diagnosed with cancer and given three months to live. I dreamed of having the chance to turn 30 then, but that feeling has left me – I just feel old now. There will be no birthday parties or celebrations, except perhaps with some close friends.

Had I the inclination or the strength to invite a group of mates round to raise a glass to my birthday, it would only cause problems anyway. The various cliques of friends that I have simply don't match. It takes me back to my school days, when I was taught to use Venn diagrams in the maths class. These diagrams showed the difference between various groups of subjects, and the common bond that linked them. The average person might have three different groups of friends, from work, school and the football team, all co-existing with each other, perhaps aware of each other but having one common denominator – you. In my case, my friends are from totally diverse backgrounds. How will my primary school friends, who are now postmen and shop workers, mix with the weirdos I have met through my fashion contacts. And how will the "boys" take to my clubbing mates?

Having cancer has urged me to get in touch with old friends, even the ones I have fallen out with over the years. When we meet, it always becomes apparent that I am much more rounded than when we last met. I never quite know whether that is due to maturity or to the ravaging effects of cancer.

I was pleasantly surprised during my last stay at the hospice to get a visit from an ex-girlfriend whom I broke up with in messy circumstances. She had read my column and decided to make tentative contact with me again. It was fun to rake over old memories together, especially since I seemed to her a totally different personality – not the chancer of old.

On the few times I manage out of the house, I almost always meet someone I know and every face holds a story. I can't help noticing that people look at me as if I'm an idiot, trying to apologise for something I have done up to ten years ago. Thankfully, there are so many larger than life characters in Glasgow that one's own imbecility is camouflaged.

Silliness aside, I am intent on completing my training for my sponsored trek of the West Highland Way, in aid of cancer charities. I am progressing slowly but surely, but if I'm honest, I'm worried that my health will slow me down.

 My days of haring around are over.

20 August 2000

The Real Deal:

THE last time I was in Edinburgh was five years ago.

My old flatmate and good friend Phil was Australian, so he wanted to take in a few shows at the Festival. Being Glaswegian born and bred, I have an inexplicable dislike of Edinburgh and the thought of a day in the capital did not really appeal to me. I went anyway, caught a couple of fine shows, got blind drunk and basically had a great day.

That was in my BC days – before cancer. I hadn't visited Edinburgh since, but my younger brother, Chris, a surveyor, was working in Edinburgh on a building contract, and wanted to see a show called "A Lump In My Throat – John Diamond And Me" by Robert Katz. John Diamond is an English version of me. He writes for The Times and has done so for longer than my tenure at the Sunday Herald. He has throat cancer while I have, well, a fair load of cancer types. Before he was diagnosed, he was a successful television and radio broadcaster, whereas I was a nobody, just a guy with cancer. When someone wants a rentaquote about cancer, they go to John, and sometimes, just sometimes if he is not available, I will get a call.

So Chris bought tickets for himself, me, Mum and his fiancé, Susan. I was feeling surprisingly chipper considering I have been bedridden for four weeks, and we managed a pre-show meal before making our way to the Assembly Rooms where the show was. The idea of performing a written column intrigued me, and the set was quite Spartan – two desks, one heaped with newspaper, presumably to show how prolific John is, the other with a computer, his new method of communication. I have often argued with my mother about which is the worst type of cancer, his or mine. Throat cancer takes away your voice, your ability to eat and taste food and is basically invasive on your life, whereas my cancer just seems to be taking a magical mystery tour of my upper body, causing pain, sickness and other associated symptoms. Incidentally, I emailed John once but he never replied. I felt like a rejected fan, writing to a big pop star, and naive enough to expect a reply. That's why I try to reply to all my mail – it's the polite thing to do.

So we watched the show, my bowels giving me an unexpected interlude, and it was very good – the show that is, not my bowels, which were to take a starring role later. The anecdotes were funny, some were bittersweet, some downright sad, and I could relate to them all. John is a Jew, I am a Roman Catholic, and so we both feel guilty about benefiting in any way from our disease. For instance my sponsored walk will raise money for charity, but it will also be a punishing experience, reminding me of my frailty. The show, deservedly, was a sell-out. It ended much as John's life is at present – unfinished and looking towards the unknown.

Cancer is a word, not a sentence. I contemplated this on the way home, as I forced Chris to make detours via garages with toilets. My stomach was not playing ball, and as soon as I settled into his immaculately plush car seats, I needed the toilet again. My brother, God love him, tries his hardest to keep my spirits up, but even his patience was wearing thin as I requested yet another toilet stop and he watched as I did the "soft shoe shuffle" to the bathroom.

As we pulled into yet another petrol station, the pain almost making me pass out, I ran to the toilet, my muscles ready to release. I saw the toilet bowl, but by then it was too late.

You might think I'm being too candid at this point, but when I started writing my column, I promised myself I would keep it real, if not for me, then for the thousands of other cancer sufferers who have to endure "embarrassments" throughout their lives. I didn't want to paint some sanitised picture of life as a cancer sufferer. That's why I'm telling you about my designer jeans and underwear lying in a corner while I stood washing myself at a sink in a motorway service station.

I had to walk through the shop half naked and thankfully, my Ralph Lauren shirt covered my modesty. People stared as I walked quickly and determinedly towards Chris's car. I could see the uncomprehending look on his face. I laughed along with my mother as I explained what had happened, but my hilarity covered my despair and sadness at what my cancer was reducing me to.

No matter however funny I make it sound, all I remember is the look on Chris's face. I realised then that no one cancer is any easier than another – we all suffer in our own ways.

Laughter To Tears:

It had the makings of a lovely day, as we drove to Uddingston. Chris, my younger son, had managed to get tickets for "Lump in my Throat", being performed at the Edinburgh Festival, it was a play that Jonathan had been longing to see. This was Jonathan's first venture out in four weeks, owing to illness, and he was feeling very "chipper." We reached Uddingston and changed cars, to allow Chris to drive to Edinburgh. Once there Jonathan decided that he felt like having a curry, which we all did. The play was enjoyable, but as we returned on the motorway, Jonathan's bowels started to act up. Chris had to make a quick charge to the next garage with toilets, followed soon after by another stop. A few miles after the second stop, Jonathan asked "How far is it to the next service station, Chris ?"

"About 16 miles, why?"

"I need to go again!" Jonathan said desperately.

Christopher covered the 16 miles in record time, and as soon as we stopped Jonathan hobbled off across the forecourt as fast as he could.

Now, Chris is not the most patient of men, but as he sat, drumming his fingers on the steering wheel, I knew that he was doing so not from impatience; but out of concern and guilt for Jonathan's condition.

Suddenly he uttered, "Mum! Mum! Oh God Mum!"

I turned to him and said, "Chris, one of these days, you are going to have a heart attack. What is it?"

"Where are his trousers?" came his reply.

I turned to the side window and saw Jonathan come walking through the garage forecourt, with only his modesty covered by his shirt, which thankfully was long. Jumping into the car, he explained that he had not made it on time, and had to dump his trousers and shorts in the bin .The other occupants stared incredulously as he was obliged to wash his bottom in the hand basin.

Jonathan made a joke of this and we laughed with him, but when we arrived at Uddingston, Jonathan refused to go to Chris's flat to borrow trousers or shorts. The drive home, all of 36 miles, was the quietest and longest, I have ever experienced. Jonathan did not say a single word.

When we arrived home, my husband opened the door, surprised to see Jonathan without trousers, he asked why?

Jonathan repeated his tale, in a joking fashion, and his father suggested that he should phone the garage manager, and tell him that the CCTV footage of that day would be worth £1000 on "You've Been Framed! When Jonathan went for a bath immediately afterwards, my husband and I discussed our mutual thoughts on what this distressing incident would really mean to Jonathan: It would bring home to him, just how much his illness had brought him indignity and low self-esteem, something that he would not have considered possible.

For the next two days, Jonathan was in a deep depression, and apart from when receiving his medication, made it obvious that he wanted to be left on his own.

From that day onwards, whenever he had to travel any distance, he fasted from the previous evening.

Susan Wilson

27 August 2000

School of Hard Knocks:

I HAVE been humbled by the response to my charity walk.

Never in my wildest column-writing fantasies did I imagine a response so generous and unselfish. Pensioners, children and single mothers have all contributed. From me to you, a great big thank you.
As you read this it will be my 30th birthday. Unlike last year, I will not be celebrating. Not that I am ungrateful. Had you asked me last year if I would see 30, I would have said maybe yes, maybe no. Now I take nothing for granted.

In marketing and advertising circles there is a theory that 30 is the new 20. In the last two decades, if you were 30, chances were you would be married, perhaps have two children, or at least one, be settled in a job and be climbing the property and career ladders. By the time my parents were 30 they had two sons, a house and were property hunting in Portugal, looking for a pub to buy. Compare that to me. I have no partner, live with my parents and earn very little. It is true that I also have cancer, but apart from that, I am much like a 20-year-old. But I see that even people who are healthy are growing up more slowly, living at the family home for longer and, critically, delaying having kids. Children bring a whole set of scary responsibilities with them. You have to have a house, a job (or, failing that, expert knowledge of the social security system) and a willingness to retire from any kind of social life.

With the expansion of the Internet and associated high-pressure jobs, it's possible to gain financial success and accomplish your career goals by the time you're 25. Until recently, you would be hitting 40 before seeing any real cash or job fulfillment. So the kids are too busy in front of their computers to think about having children. When they aren't working hard – most start before 8am and leave after 8pm – they are playing hard. Witness the profusion of new bars in Glasgow, with a shelf life of six months at the most, before somewhere newer and hipper opens. With time being the new wealth, loyalty is thin on the ground. Yet you can have a dream and realise it in one decade instead of four.

This has been on my mind recently because I have been getting emails from younger readers who are worried about their lives and unsure what direction to take. It seems crazy to ask a 15 or 16-year-old to choose a university course leading to a job, which may not bear any relation to what they finally decide they want to be in life. Qualifications are all very well, but enthusiasm, hard work and a stroke of luck will get you just as far, and you can't tick them on your UCCA form.

In Richard Emmanuel's case, they got him right to the top. Richard started in a tiny shop in Pollokshaws, selling mobile phones in the days when they looked and weighed like bricks. As the market changed and expanded, Richard worked 12-hour days and, with brains and a good pinch of luck, DX Communications was formed. Nowadays he jets all over the world. I think he was in Germany when he phoned me to pledge his support for my charity walk.

Just as Nick Nairn and other top chefs are consulted about how the nation should eat, I would like to see entrepreneurs like Richard Emmanuel giving advice to the nation's youth, letting them know it's okay to be unsure about their future, telling them that hard graft and vision are just as good as a piece of paper with a bunch of (unreliable) grades.

When I was at school sitting my Highers, I didn't know what I wanted to be. I was interested in girls; sport, anything but my future. I can't imagine today's teenagers are any different. The American system, where you can be 19 or 20 and still be at school seems far more reasonable.

Now I have ended up in a situation that I don't think anyone could have foreseen, I have a theory about careers and jobs. You can either get a job which you don't like, but which gives you the money to do what you want, or you can get the job that you truly love but that doesn't pay like it should. Those of you who have a job that you dearly love, and pays well, please do not write in and depress me.

The only reason I have this job, writing this column, is because I am dying of cancer. I do not kid myself that I am a great writer – it's my story that is compelling. Ironically, my qualifications are more about issues of life and death than pieces of paper.

3 September 2000

Choose Life:

AS the opening credits roll for Frasier, viewers see the outline of the city of Seattle, where the show is set. To accompany this image is a soundtrack of cool, Seattle-style coffee bar music, hinting at successful professional people at play. I hate it. Why? Because I'm not a successful professional person. I'm a failed middle-aged cancer sufferer.

When I take stock of my life, even accounting for my illness and my mid-life crisis – which I'm having early because my years are being cut short – I really should have done more. I should have visited Seattle, learned to ride a motorbike, mastered more than one language. As my mortality rushes headlong towards me, it's amazing how many small things taunt me, reminding me: "Hey, you can't roller blade", or "You haven't visited Vienna. Or Venezuela".

I don't know if this is peculiar to people who are dying, or to supposed high achievers who have wasted their youth trying to be cool when they should have been trying to be successful. All I know is that when Frasier comes on TV, I feel like a failure.

I am still trying to find the programme that makes me feel good about my life. I have never seen myself as a slacker, but recently I met a man whose background is similar to mine. He is roughly the same age as me, yet he has offices all over the world, a huge, successful company and a beautiful house. He is even a nice guy. I felt like a football fan meeting David Beckham. Perhaps this is how it feels to be in your 30s. For me, general angst about ageing is reinforced by signs of how my illness is progressing. Sporadic vomiting and diarrhoea is now commonplace. When the whole Wilson clan went out for my birthday dinner, my burrito was hotter than expected and I spent my birthday night with my old friend Mr. Shanks: Armitage to his pals.

A rather more alarming signal pointing to the spread of my cancer is my newfound inability to get my finger inside my belly button. I have always taken pride in my meticulous cleansing routine, and now have to use a cotton bud to de-fluff. I didn't expect tumours to be so hard to the touch. They feel horrible, really wretched. They do, however, remind me why I wanted to write a column in the first place – how else could I get to mention intimate body parts in a national newspaper and get paid for it?

With all these physical and psychological reminders of my condition, it's always good to read my emails. Some of you guys should be writers yourselves – your eloquence far exceeds mine. Some messages are genuinely funny, others unintentionally comic. One of my younger readers wrote, in her best e-grammar: "C U in heaven". Maybe one day, but I have no intention of checking out just yet. To prove this, I went out and bought a new, larger, louder television, with all the extras: speakers, DVD player, and the works. When it came to paying for the goods, the salesman trotted out his pitch for an extended warranty and, being a cautious Virgoan, I took it. My new entertainment system is guaranteed for five years. I laughed as I signed the chitty and asked if the company offered a similar scheme for customers. The salesman was obviously not a Sunday Herald reader and the joke went right over his head. What would I give to be around to see the guarantee run out?

As for the sponsored walk, events have progressed at a fair rate. Donations are still flooding in – you really are a generous bunch – and I have also sent more than 100 "begging" letters to companies and corporate ventures.

So far, eight have replied. If only booking accommodation for the trek had been as easy. Fortunately, one of my corporate sponsors is using his business clout to help me out.

To get me on my way there is going to be a charity extravaganza held in a bar in Glasgow's Southside, to which you are all invited. The theme is "Viva Las Vegas" and there will be karaoke, an auction (if you have anything worth giving away get in touch) and plenty of other delights to make the night as debauched as possible.

That's the celebratory part sorted out. But there is going to be more to this charity effort than raising glasses and spirits. The hard work will be putting one foot in front of the other afterwards – on my walk, that is.

10 September 2000

Souped Up:

ILLNESS-WISE, I feel I have reached a new level.

I am finding it hard to keep solid food down, which I find quite upsetting. Along with my inability to put my finger inside my belly button, it is just one of the symptoms rapidly pushing their way into my life. My life is a balancing act, with the invasive cancer symptoms on one hand and the things that normal people do on the other.

My evening meal now consists solely of soup. Despite the amazing array of gourmet varieties available, Heinz tomato always seems to win the day. Sometimes I forget the all-enveloping, sickening, nauseous feeling that precedes a painful bout of gut-wrenching vomit, and try some solids. You can't really blame me. Although she doesn't wear a denim jacket in the kitchen, or have an on-site herb garden, Ma Wilson is no mean cook. Watching what the rest of the family put away for their tea can be olfactory torture. Residing on the west coast of Scotland we are spoiled for choice as far as seafood is concerned. I adore mussels, lobster, crab, monkfish ... you catch it, I eat it and ultimately, rather more quickly than I would like, I deposit it down the toilet.

I drove up to Glasgow the other day, safe in the knowledge that there are two petrol stations with toilets should I need to spend a penny. Or, in my case, a couple of quid. This time, however, I sailed up the M77 without mishap.

I now find myself needing an excuse to go to Glasgow. This time last year, I was driving up every day. My mitigating circumstances this time were to tour SMG's new headquarters, where the Sunday Herald is produced. I was especially keen to be shown around, as I feel somewhat isolated from the news and editorial team. When I write an article I use email to send it in for approval and while it is quick and effortless I do prefer the human touch. And how else can you wangle a free meal? Along with the spinach pancakes I also enjoyed some comfort and reassurance. To be honest, I lack a bit of confidence when it comes to my writing talent. Sure, I have a story to tell, but ask me to write an article about a subject unrelated to cancer and I think I would be struggling. I am not being modest; I know my strengths, namely telling readers exactly what cancer entails. This helps educate those of you lucky enough not to have their lives blighted by this curse.

This is important for cancer sufferers but also for their carers, who work tirelessly and usually without recognition. I am so lucky to have my mother as a carer. Yes, we have fights and arguments, mostly due to being so alike, and sometimes my frustration at being ill and being a shadow of my former self spills over, but I love her dearly and would not be here but for her love and patience. Does she moan as I wake her at 4am for a painkilling injection? No, she puts on her reading glasses, pulls up the injection, gives me the drug and then tucks me in.

I admire anyone who takes in a family member to care for them. Believe me, it is a full-time job. About five or six years ago, one of my mother's old aunties developed senile dementia. As anyone who has seen this disease turn a loved one into a total stranger will know, the distress involved is considerable. Despite the rest of the family wanting this old lady interned in a hospital or hospice, my mother is of the old school. Family is family; you do not just put them into a home and visit once a week. You look after your own. We took her into the house. We all helped out, trying to maintain her dignity, my brother, my sister and my dad taking turns with the jobs that old age and infirmity bring.

So I know how it is from the other side. It was a hard year and a half, but for me the hardest thing of all was the day she died. I was out at work and when I came home she was lying on the bed. As I kissed her forehead, her skin was as cold as marble. Although her body was there, she was no longer the auntie I had loved. I guess that was when the aura surrounding death was lessened for me. It was not as frightening as I thought. People are always fearful of the unknown and now death is only as scary as being born.

I am going to be reborn on my charity gala night at the Cul de Sac Southside on September 23. With the theme of the night being Viva Las Vegas, it would be rude not to dress up as Elvis, the king himself. We are having DJs, a charity auction (if we have enough prizes) and the obligatory karaoke competition. Mix that with cheap drink and the night could get messy.

Viva Las Vegas!

17 September 2000

Are You Sitting Comfortably ?

WHETHER I am getting sicker, or this is just an inconvenient blip, my health seems to be deteriorating. I can't sleep at night, since my bowels keep tricking me into thinking they are ready to work, and then by the time I stumble through the cold house to the toilet, they decide it's not quite the time. I trot back to bed for two minutes' sleep and the next alarm call.

Besides the physical barriers I face, I also have trouble reconciling in my head that diazepam = jellies = valium. Junkies die by injecting jellies into a vein, and they take it regularly as a come down from ecstasy or heroin. Valium is the drug of choice of the upper middle-classes, washed down by a stiff G&T, just to make life that bit more bearable – especially if your husband is having an affair with his secretary. And here I am taking it as part of my calorie-controlled diet. I am popping the drug like sweeties, but it seems to have no effect on me at all. I have been plagued by a form of the shakes, like I am going through cold turkey. I can't sit still, my leg muscles are constantly in spasm, and I sit and rock about in my chair like some demented creature.

But although my inner workings might be malfunctioning, at least my interiors are sorting themselves out. My folks were considering buying me a Lazy Boy recliner for my birthday. The all-enveloping seat that dominates the guys' apartment in the American sitcom Friends has a fridge in one of its arms, a phone in the other and motors to massage tired muscles. Instead of impulse buying, though, we decided to sleep on it – not literally, of course. By coincidence, we visited my Aunt Therese, who is my mum's best friend and the kindest, most unselfish person you could meet. She had what I can only describe as the ultimate chair in her garage. Having moved house recently, she was on a minimalist trip and this chair was not a la mode.

I was delighted to discover it has a control panel similar to the flight deck of an airliner, and the ability to massage almost every muscle in the body. It cost more than my car and looks better too. In exchange, I offered a cushion that straps onto the driver's seat of a car and vibrates to stop you getting a sore behind.

So if you see a woman with an ear-to-ear smile driving a blue Merc CLK, peep your horn and wave to my Aunt Therese.

I might just need that vibrating seat to relax me after some frustrating visits to the hospital. As you might have read, Dr Stanley Kaye, the head of the Beatson Oncology centre, is leaving to take up a post in London. Replacing him is a Dr Chris Twelves, who is supposed to be my consultant at the Beatson. I say supposed because the last three trips I have made all the way up to the Beatson, Dr Twelves has been away at conferences or stuck at airports. In his place, and without wanting to be disparaging, I get to see someone who is younger than me and hasn't a clue about my medical history. This stand-in for Dr Twelves has a cursory glance at my file, which is six inches thick, and says: "So, what's been happening?" Now I am not a violent person, but the twitch in my mother's eye does not bode well for the young man, so I deflect her anger away from Dr Kildare and on to the inaccessible Dr Twelves.

Apparently he only sees you if your case is very serious. Well hello, dying boy sitting here, what do I need to do to warrant an appointment with the fabled Dr Twelves? It has been so long since I last saw him I am actually questioning whether he exists.

We all know how under funded cancer departments are, but it's only when you are at the sharp end like me, where treatment is limited and rationed, that you truly realise the implications. I apologise to the doctors – it's not their fault the hospital is under funded, and sometimes my frustration gets the better of me – but I'm not getting any healthier here.

On a lighter note, my charity night has expanded into a charity weekend. First there is a five-a-side football tournament, then next Saturday, the big night, Viva Las Vegas. Those of you well enough to get up the day after would be stupid to miss a humour extravaganza organised by the comedy club, The Stand, which is sending its best comedians to the Cul de Sac Southside for a charity Comedy Blowout. Tickets are selling fast, so don't miss out. The following day I begin my walk of the West Highland way. Talk about the pleasure-pain principle.

With all this fun and frivolous entertainment, you'd be forgiven for forgetting the hard reality behind it – that one in three of us will get cancer this year.

It is that statistic that motivates me to organise all these charity events.

24 September 2000

Keep On Keeping On:

DUE to deadlines, I will have written this column before the Saturday night that I planned to raise money for charity.

Hopefully a lot of you will have attended, and I apologise for all the hangover symptoms that you are experiencing. A lot of you will have met me for the first time, and I hope I was not too much of a disappointment. I promise to chronicle the night's events in my next column.

I had initially planned one night, a one-off to raise money for my charity walk, but as word grew, more people wanted to help, get involved with the project. So therefore, tonight, which is Sunday, we are hosting a comedy extravaganza called" Dead Man Laughing" organised by those fine purveyors of humour, The Stand comedy club. I never sought their involvement, they came to me, and it has touched me greatly to think of the time, money and effort that people have given up to help the cause. I am also lucky to have an auction tonight, despite the poor response from corporate sources. Among the prizes are signed football tops from both Rangers and Celtic football clubs, a cask of Famous Grouse whisky, which should hopefully attract the connoisseurs out and bid.

On the subject of whisky, I have to thank David Sole, who had a Grand Slam reunion party this year. David captained the victorious Scottish rugby team in 1990 and to mark the occasion, a cask of whisky was laid down. This was given out to guests at the party, but a few bottles were held back and autographed by the whole team. Hearing of my proposed endeavour, David kindly donated one of the bottles to my auction. It would be impossible to put a price on such an item, but its appeal should be considerable.

With the memory of queuing and petrol rationing fresh in all our minds, one of our other prizes, an electric bicycle could prove to be a popular item, ideal for those of us who abhor exercise, but insist on pulling on ill-fitting spandex for the sake of burning up 200 calories. By far the most interesting item on offer is a window casement created in a Rennie Mackintosh style circa 1903, – a truly unique item. I could go on at length about the other prizes on offer, but I won't. Just turn up with pocketfuls of cash and be prepared to be entertained. I want to be honest with you all, because I owe it to you. Every day a huge envelope from the Herald offices is delivered. It is always packed with letters wishing me luck and cheques towards the charities. The walk itself is 93 miles long and I have tried to spread it over the longest number of days possible to make each day a realistic proposition, but I have to tell you, there will probably days where I will not complete the whole stage. I have a large network of friends who are supporting me, but I would be lying if I said I expect to complete the whole of the walk. I hope you will not think any less of me. With all the organisation involved, my training has lapsed slightly. I also have to organise my drugs for the time I am away – could be kind of trippy, the West Highland Way on Valium, morphine and methadone.

It will be a shock to my system being out on both nights in a weekend as I'm usually in bed for 10pm on a Saturday with a good book. Despite it looking different every time, Glasgow is like an old friend to me. You know the type, you don't see each other for a couple of months, but you pick up where you left off without any embarrassment.

My familiarity with Glasgow started when I was sent to school in the city centre. I was positively cosmopolitan compared to old school friends, and to them what seemed strange was normal to me.

I remember the city centre was Central station, the city revolving around it. Now due to development, the city centre is moving eastwards, the only way a growing Glasgow can go. George square is probably the new city centre, but what I can't stand is the attitude of some of these developers and their idea of progress.

You won't see a corner site lying empty for long, before some out-of-town pub\restaurant chain snaps it up and pillages the site with their own inimitable style, ripping up whatever heritage remains. And where will it be in six months? Down the pan, leaving in its wake a shell devoid of the rich history which Glasgow's architecture provides.

It's not all bad news, though. I was lucky to see inside the Corinthian club on Ingram Street, and most of the original features were highlighted rather than obliterated. I was very impressed.

Now my spy in Glasgow tells me of an exciting new development at the old cheese market in the Merchant City; when I know more, you'll be the first to know. You heard it here first.

Now if you don't mind I have some partying to do and some walking to contemplate.

1 October 2000

Love Me Tender:

IT'S official: Elvis has left the building.

The Viva Las Vegas night was a huge success, and we raised more than £1200, so a huge thank you to everyone who attended. At one point, the Cul de Sac was so busy we had to turn people away at the door.

If you did get in, you were probably accosted at the door by my Aunt Therese, who was doubling up as door person/extortionist, refusing entry to those who didn't empty their pockets of loose change. One of the magazine editors, Jane, was especially hard hit, so if my column ends this week you will know why. I was sure that theme nights had some built-in stipulation enforcing dressing up, but alas I have to say I was related to everyone who made an effort. We had three Elvis's and two Marilyn Monroe's, and you can think it was a fix if you like, but I won the prize for best-dressed person there. Copying Craig from Big Brother, I put it in the charity bucket. Not that I'm conceited or looking for applause or anything.

I don't mind telling you, my polyester cat suit was not the most comfortable of attire. The Elvis wig was a bit suspect as well, and I'm sure people were asking what Don King, the boxing promoter with the electrified hairdo, had to do with Las Vegas. (I guess he's been to few fights there.) We also had a karaoke machine cranked up, and when I heard someone murdering You Ain't Nothing but a Hound Dog I laughed my head off. Until I turned around and saw it was my brother Chris, giving it big licks on top of a table. I never even got to sing, having lost my voice early on in the evening.

Without wanting to sound like a big Jessie, it was quite emotional talking to readers who I had never met before, who were telling me how they loved the column and how I was so brave. What do you say to people when that happens? Just for the record, I am not brave, perhaps a bit foolhardy, and just as scared of dying as the next man. It's just that I have to deal with it a bit sooner than planned. What with the lights, the loud music and my flammable costume, I felt really tired and sick and my thoughts turned to my walking expedition. Earlier on in the week I paid a visit to Tiso's, the outdoor specialists, to get kitted out. I didn't have a clue as to what I might need, although walking boots were high up on the list of priorities. One reader who had tackled the WHW had sent me walking socks and a packet of plasters, so I expect the old feet will take a battering.

On entering Tiso's, I was amazed at the equipment they carry: camping stoves, climbing gear and those sachets of dried food that NASA uses. Just add water and you get a three-course meal with Michelin stars. I picked the oldest-looking assistant, thinking that he would have the most expert knowledge, and I was right. Brian had walked the WHW several times and knew exactly what I needed. I also told him I had cancer, if that made any difference. I can be quite indecisive when dealing with matters outwith my sphere of knowledge, such as when I am presented with a wall of hiking boots. Brian was very patient, explaining the virtues of each boot, saying things like "this boot has a 95 per cent protection against water and it has brass eyelets that won't rust".

Way back when I was proficient at athletics, I did have some footwear expertise, but this guy could talk for five uninterrupted minutes about each shoe.

Of course there was a catch: the longer he spoke, the more expensive the boot, but I figured I would need the best. One of my best friends is an Aussie, and so of course a world traveller, so at least I could borrow his rucksack and save £200.

In deference to my medical condition Brian recommended a walking stick. Not any old walking stick, a wooden crafted branch as used by my Irish forefathers, but titanium shafted polyurethane version with a variable spring-loaded end-piece that would take my body weight and then some. So I was ready, all kitted out in the best gear a walker could buy. At least, I thought, I looked the part.

I'm off to do the walk now. I may be gone for some time.

8 October 2000

Stand-up Guys:

AFTER my Las Vegas night, which I told you about last week, I was looking forward to the charity auction the next night.

Sunday afternoon was rather frantic. I was starting my West Highland Way walk the next day and I still had to pack, I had an article to write and I had been out until 3am the night before.

As anyone who has ever packed for a holiday will testify, it doesn't matter how big your suitcase is, you will always manage to fill it with items of clothing you will never wear, but will take along anyway just in case. And rucksacks are no different. I had borrowed one from my Antipodean mate, Phil, who had used it during a year-long world tour, so it should have been ample for my week-long trek. Of course, there I was struggling for space minutes before I was due to leave for the auction up in Glasgow. The hardest thing was making up little packets with my drugs in them. Each was labelled with a day and marked am or pm. It was all very organised and my system should have worked a treat – you will have to wait for next week's column to find out why I was left without prescription drugs for half of my walk. You know me: I like a challenge.

I raced up to Glasgow so that my friend Geraldine was not left to organise the whole night. There had been a five-a-side tournament that day for the charity, the prize being a barrel of Miller lager. The lure of the alcohol had proved too strong for my friends – they waltzed round the other teams to win. Just think 88 pints between five men: would they be standing at the end of the night? Besides the auction, there was a comedy show, performed and donated by comedians under the auspices of The Stand comedy club. I didn't know what to expect, since I had never been to a comedy club, but the offer was too good to turn down. As I get older and clubbing becomes less attractive, I ponder whether I should be going to comedy clubs and venues of their ilk instead.

Much to my astonishment, the bar was hoaching. The poor bar staff are used to an easy Sunday shift, and for the second consecutive night I had the place crammed. With the crowd baying for the evening's proceedings to begin, Susan, the compere, warmed up for the first comedienne to start. Using her Dundonian upbringing as an excuse, she recited extremely funny, but exceptionally rude poems, forcing me to hide from the collective gaze of the oldies' table. My brother, Chris, shielded me from the group, which included my parents, my brother's prospective in-laws and various relatives and friends. I was spared a lynching by the onset of the auction, again compared by the excellent Susan. She was putting in a performance worthy of Christie's or Sotheby's, teasing the crowd with nuggets of information as the bidding slowed up, or more often than not verbally bullying people for more money.

As expected, the football jerseys from Celtic and Rangers fetched the greatest prices. My uncle William had broken off a family holiday in Fife, driven two hours to get to the auction and bought the Rangers jersey, waiting until the compere was closing the bidding before dramatically upping the ante. Then he drove another two hours all the way back to Fife.

This weekend has restored my faith in the human spirit. Fair enough, I expected support over the two nights from my family and friends, but the amount of readers who turned up and contributed was astounding.

There was a point in the evening when everywhere I turned, people were shaking my hand, wanting to congratulate me and wish me luck. I felt elated and dizzy at the same time, and any lingering doubts I had about doing the walk were temporarily banished.

The night was obviously not the best form of preparation for my West Highland Way walk the next day, but what could I do but sit back and enjoy myself. My mum got in on the action, buying an electric bike, which I discovered weighed a ton as I modelled it. Susan got through the rest of the lots, raising a lot of money on the way, and then it was back to the comedians. Luckily for me, their language was not as risqué as their colleague's.

At the end of the show, Geraldine, the weekend's organiser, got me up on the stage. It was a real test of my emotions, what with all these people clapping and cheering me on. I made a small speech thanking all and sundry for their efforts, before a disastrous attempt at telling a joke. As soon as the spotlight hit me I dried up. I mumbled a joke or two and left the entertainment to the experts.

Together, both nights raised between £3500-£4000 thanks to all who contributed money and prizes. We can never raise too much money for cancer charities. On that note, I still have some exclusive whisky prizes left which did not reach their reserve prices at the auction. If you are a whisky connoisseur, or know one, please contact me on the Internet, or at the Sunday Herald. I have some rare bottles of the golden spirit worth collecting still to auction for the appeal.

And what of my drunken friends and the start of the walk – the keg of beer was finished off early in the evening.

Next week, the story of my West Highland Way walk begins – warts, blisters and tumours, the lot.

15 October 2000

Hills, Pills and Bellyaches:

I DECIDED to keep a diary of my trek, as I was sure that I would forget most of my (mis)adventures. I have enough material for two weeks. You asked for it.

Day one did not start as early as I would have liked. The previous night was the Charity Auction. I didn't get home until 4am and I was up at 8am to meet friends in Glasgow. As they had drunk 88 pints of Miller between them the previous night, after one of them called off, so it was just the four of us. Destination-Milngavie: the start of the walk.

Stage One: Milngavie to Drymen, is about 15 miles. It starts in the middle of a shopping precinct, which is not exactly inspirational. Maybe I should have brought my Walkman and the" Chariots Of Fire" soundtrack. When I ran, I used to listen to this before races and it always got my blood pumping.

We started out, and before you could say "post-hangover munchies", we passed a pub serving lunch. This walk being a democratic thing, we took a vote, decided to pop in and got fuelled up for our imminent exertion. This was a plain stupid mistake. My bowels are a finely tuned piece of organic machinery and eating at lunchtime is definite "no- no", unless I'm within running distance of a toilet three hours later. It is that precise. However I consumed a truly scrumptious chilliburger and hoped, no prayed, that there would be a pub or toilet along the way. So we started out again, and as we left Milngavie and snaked towards Drymen the terrain became undulating with the odd steep hill. It didn't take long for the boys to start pulling away from me. Every so often they would stop and wait. We got into this pattern: walk steadily, wait for Jono, resume walking.

The West Highland Way was officially opened in 1980. I remember seeing that famous Scot, Jimmy McGregor, on telly. I was aged around ten, and I followed it every week. The scenery, the camaraderie and his easy-going commentary just made sense. How stupid we are to be seduced by the £250 Package

Holiday- we don-t even see what our own country has to offer. Sure, the weather sucks, and the first section is no oil painting, being lowland, farming terrain, but later on is the scenery that really does take your breath away. My digestion caught up with me about 6 miles into the 9 mile- stretch. Cramps like only girls get. There was no way I could finish that day's hike. I didn't feel that I was letting anyone down, and it was least a further two miles to the main road where I managed to get a taxi. Those two miles were interminable, with stops every 100 meters to handle the pain.

So there I was, having kittens, when the taxi arrived." So you're doing the walk?"
"Yup, except I need to get to the public toilets in Drymen-Now!"
He looked at my face and then hit the gas.
"I do the walk with my brothers every year,"-he offered by way of explanation.
"We can trace our heritage back to William Wallace, so we do the walk in full Highland dress.
Now he had my attention.
"So how long does it take you?" (My own schedule was seven or eight days, depending on my health.)
" Usually about four days, depending on the weather. We sleep rough."
So there he was, James the taxi driver, descendant of Willie Wallace, walking the WHW in four days, which is the equivalent of a marathon, a day, sleeping in a ditch, wearing a kilt and a plaid.
" I usually do it in April to avoid the Midges, but sometimes it gets really cold."
No kidding.

I got to the toilet- major relief- then made my way to the B&B, The Bay Cottage, owned by Elizabeth Bates, which is a concerning name for that line of work, was a delight. The bathroom had a bidet, warm towels and aromatherapy bath salts. When I got up the next morning, the five-course breakfast was finer than the spread in any hotel that I have stayed in (and I don't do cheap hotels). When Elizabeth heard that I was doing the walk for charity, she refused to take my money. We reached a compromise, and I paid part of the bill. I will, however be back.

Day two starts with a climb, one of those where you think you have reached the summit only to find another climb. We could see Loch Lomond, but the terrain became harder. Due to accommodation problems, I had to stay at Crianlarich , which is too far to walk, especially as I was on my own that day. Instead my destination was Inversnaid. A walk is always a good time for introspective thinking. Many things crossed my mind: How long do I have? Who am I doing this walk for? When all is said and done, am I happy where I am?

I think I resolved a few along the Bonnie Banks and I was struck by the friendliness of fellow walkers. The Lodge in Crianlarich was another good choice with a comfy bed and an open fire. I met a lovelyCouple, who were staying at nearly all the same places as me. They were experienced walkers and gave me some good advice. Then I hit the hay early on, as I was meeting my dad the next day.

Day three, I met my dad at the appointed place and we set off to cover Crianlarich to Tyndrum . Every day seemed to start with a hill. Then the heavens opened and the rain poured incessantly. Steep terrain and vile weather started to erode my spirits, I thought that since my dad was a smoker, we would be evenly matched but he started springing from rock to rock like a mountain goat. The incline that was leaving me breathless seemed to present him with no problems at all. After an hour of climbing and then descending, and then climbing again, the ground started to even out. The rain however continued unabated. We ate lunch underneath a tree. From there the path was level but covered in pools of mucky water. Dad jumped from dry patch to dry patch, but I just waded through the pools of water and thanked Gore-Tex for my weatherproof boots. As the light started to fail, I began to fantasise about a hot bath and the Radox that I had brought with me.

But as you will read next week, the best-laid plans have a habit of going pear-shaped.

The Road Less Travelled:

THE first time I met Jonathan Wilson was two summers ago. It was a stiflingly hot day and he was sitting outside a cafe in Glasgow's Merchant City with a colleague of mine. Suddenly she announced she had another appointment and left me sitting there with him in silence, uncomfortable and at a loss for words.

I had been in two minds about his column for the magazine when he first approached the Sunday Herald with the idea. First, this kind of writing is not easy to do, and although he was upfront about not being a writer, Jonathan felt he had a story to tell, that he could be of use and comfort to other cancer sufferers. On this point I felt more assured that it could make remarkable reading. But my greatest concern was that what we were asking of him was simply voyeuristic and exploitative – "media coffin watching" as he came to call it. It somehow seemed distasteful. "I know people tune in every week just to see if I've made it through another week," he later told me.

But on that day, sitting with him in the sunshine, my problem was initiating a conversation. What do you say to someone with terminal cancer without sounding trite, crass, morbidly curious or simply evasive? How do you talk to a dying person? What I learned as I got to know him, however, is that Jonathan Wilson is a person who is very much alive, and that people like me are the ones stuck in their own hang-ups about death and dying and what it means to really live, regardless of what time lies ahead.

Four years ago, when he was diagnosed with stomach cancer, doctors gave Jonathan six months to live. Now they just give him three months every three months, just to be on the safe side. This is a standing joke among his family and friends, but a stark reminder, nevertheless, of the importance of living in the present. Jonathan was always going to get cancer – caused by a faulty gene – it was just his luck, or his lack of it, that it happened when he was 26 and not 76. But his diagnosis ensured that his siblings could be tested for the same rogue gene. So far tests have put them in the clear.

The disease saw him go from super-fit athletic to pain-racked and bloated from bouts of chemo and steroids; from a young man on the cusp of his grown-up life to someone doubting if he would ever see 30. But Jonathan has reached 30, and he has learned to conquer his fear, live with his pain and be positive about his life. This he does by setting himself goals, which has led him to where we're standing today, in the pouring rain outside the Green Welly Shop in Tyndrum, half way up the West Highland Way on an ambitious walk to raise money for cancer charities.

He is much thinner than the last time I saw him. "No more chemo for me," he says, managing a smile as we trudge off through the mud and rain. "The doctors say it won't help me any more, although I have taken part in some unlicensed chemo trials, which may help other people in the future." His options these days are alternative therapies – acupuncture, hypnotherapy, homeopathy and visualisation, and a combination of pain-relieving drugs like morphine. He's in good spirits although he seems to be doing everything very carefully and deliberately. Either he's concentrating on the pain or it's the effect of the drugs he has to take. It sometimes gives him a faraway look, but apart from that, if you were to meet him for the first time, you wouldn't know this was a man with tumours on his liver. He has his good days and his bad days.

Today his friend Geraldine has joined him on the walk from Tyndrum to Bridge of Orchy. Despite the dreich weather, the scenery is spectacular and ideal for walking: steep bracken and heather-covered hills bisected by a nice, straight, flat path and a picturesque burn. Other pals chummed him along the first stretch from Milngavie and his dad kept him company yesterday. Between those days he was on his own.

"It was really important for me to spend a day just by myself," he says. "I just wanted to have a bit of space to think things through, you know? One good thing that has come out of my illness is that I enjoy my own company now. Anyway, sometimes when you feel like shit, it's just easier to be by yourself."

But I imagine that this kind of contemplation must lead inevitably to thoughts of dying. How does he stop himself from being so overwhelmed that the rest of his existence, his relationships, anything he spends time on, is blighted?

I'm aware that I am voicing all my own tightly held terrors, and feel guilty for asking, but Jonathan doesn't seem to mind. He's been there, done that, owns the T-shirt factory. He prefers honesty to evasion. Life's too short.

"When the doctors first told me I had cancer, naturally I was in shock. I cried. I was scared. I was 26 and believed I had six months to live. But that was four years ago. You do learn to live with it. It's not like you have a choice. I'm still afraid of dying, but not the way I was. I think I've conquered my fear, but there are times – at night when I can't sleep or when I'm in pain – that it can get to me."

And then of course he has to deal with the fears of others, of the people who love him. "This has brought me closer to my parents," he says. "They have been so good, so patient with me. My mum administers all my drugs, puts up with my moods, helps me when I'm in pain. She's been amazing.

"You know, at the beginning, all I thought about was me, me, me. It's only recently I've thought about how devastating it must have been for them. To know that they would outlive their first-born son. The day I spent with my dad has been the highlight of my walk. He spurred me on, kept me going. The terrain and the weather were tough going, but it was a good day."

Geraldine, he says, is typical of his small circle of premier league friends he can rely on and not put on an act with. "I hate getting visitors at the house, I haven't got the energy to act the grateful patient. I know that doesn't sound very nice, but I've learned to prioritise my life. Time is my most precious commodity so I don't waste it on people I don't want to see or on things I don't want to do. In that sense my illness has been quite liberating."

As we walk on through the relentless rain that is stair-rodding it down across the ridges of pine and bracken, it strikes me that Jonathan exhibits little bitterness. If I was in his shoes, I would be angry and bitter, raging against the injustice of it all. I wonder if the effect of the drugs mellows his capacity for fury. "I've never been that kind of person. I have to believe that some things happen for a reason. Good things have come out of this – friendships and relationships, finding strengths within myself – as well as bad. Of course I would like to have got married and had children, but I don't feel bitter."

Nor does he feel brave and it irks him when people tell him so. "I'm not doing anything brave, I'm just getting on with it. It's not really a matter of choosing to be brave is it?"

He isn't being disingenuous, but it's hard to agree when you know that he gently broke it off with his girlfriend because he knew it was both stressful and depressing for her to see him so ill. I tell him I think this should have been her choice and not his.

"But I did it for her. I wanted her to have a relationship that was going somewhere. What could I offer her? It wasn't fair." He sounds like a saint, I say. Things like that only happen in the movies. In real life people clutch on to love, if only for themselves. "How do you know?" he says quietly.

I ask him if he believes in an afterlife. "In terms of a place with humans all dressed in white being nice to each other, I'd have to say no," he laughs, mindful of his strongly Catholic family. "But I do believe in the human spirit and in the sense that it can remain with us. And I do believe in God."

I've reached as far as I can go with Jonathan and leave him walking over a bridge towards Bridge of Orchy with Geraldine. She reaches out and puts a hand on his shoulder and he turns to smile at her. The rain is beginning to thin out and as I look back one last time a huge shimmering rainbow arcs over the hills above them. If this was a film it would be a cliche too far, but as it is, this symbol of faith and hope seems entirely fitting.

A FEW days later when he has completed the 95 miles we meet again in Glasgow. Jonathan is very tired and and once or twice his face is a contorted mask. I wince as he grimaces and it hits me how exhausting it must be to constantly fight this endless grind of pain. He tells me it's 70/30: 70 per cent controlled by drugs and 30 per cent for him to deal with himself. Suddenly he excuses himself and says he needs to be sick. It's awful to watch him as he slowly pulls himself up from the table.

But what a different Jonathan comes back. Almost springing into the room, he clearly feels much better. He's elated that he made the whole walk, he says. It's sapped him physically, but left him feeling invigorated in spirit. "When I arrived in Fort William, it was very emotional. I was totally knackered, emotionally and physically drained, but it was a wonderful feeling. Like a burden had been lifted. I felt empty – as if I'd walked out all the bad stuff and was ready to take the next step in my life. It was just what I needed."

Later, when we part, he gives me a hug and he feels strong. I like to think we will be tuning into this boy for a few more columns yet.

Jane Wright

22 October 2000

Plumb Crazy:

SO there I was, fantasising about a hot bath and the Radox bath salts that my mum had sent with my father. We had just walked from Crianlarich to Tyndrum, absolutely soaked. We were staying at the Bridge of Orchy hotel's bunkhouse, which is a youth hostel. As this was showers-only, I upgraded to a double room in the actual hotel. I raced up the stairs and there it was, the bath, calling out to my tired and wet muscles. I ran the water and started to unpack while dad made a trip to the local shop for beer, sandwiches, crisps and other essentials.

With the bath half full, I stripped and stepped in. To freezing cold water. I let it run for another 20 minutes while hunting for an immerser switch. Half dressed, I stomped down to reception, where a cheerful Australian informed me that the boiler "had gone crook" so no hot water would be available. Before I set out I had sorted my tablets and put them into envelopes labelled by day and by am or pm. But after a day in the rain, in a rucksack that was far from waterproof, I was left with pharmaceutical grade paper mache, ideal for Fun With Junkies 101. So there I was, desperate for a bath, facing four days without medication. Still, we had food and drink, a warm room and there was football on the telly to look forward to.
Until the power cut.

Dad went down to the car for his torch. We could hear bottles and glasses smashing downstairs as the staff tried to negotiate a dark, crowded bar. Candles were passed out, but the atmosphere was far from romantic. We sat in our rapidly cooling room, in the dark, drinking beer and eating sandwiches. It was over an hour before power came back.

Dad had to get up at 6am to get to work in time but I slept on. By now the scenery was really opening out, getting pretty spectacular. I felt overwhelmed by nature, the height of the hills, all the different colours. The day did not, however, go entirely to script and at 3.30pm we still had ten miles to walk before dark. Fortunately, the terrain allowed a brisk pace and we saw a lot of highland cattle of the type that decorated the toffee bars I used to eat as a child. The main rail link to Fort William and the Highlands runs parallel to the West Highland Way and, as a train passed, it sounded its horn in salutation, a reminder to me and my friend Geraldine, who was keeping me company, that we were not the only humans around. It sometimes felt that way.

Without my medication, I was soon in pain and my walking style had to change to accommodate the dreaded cramps. I was reading the map every half an hour, to see how far we had to go. As daylight started to fail we picked up the pace and, for the last mile, I had to lean on Geraldine. Surely that is what friends are for? I was sad to see her leave. My mobile phone signal was non-existent and I had no company arranged for the next day. However it was a fairly easy one, 13 miles. Then I had the night to get through. All along my walk, people had warned me to avoid a certain hotel. But my schedule was immovable and I was booked in that night. There was a musty smell in the lobby and a sign directed me to the "Cocktail Bar" to collect my keys. I had forgotten my dinner suit, and hoped I wouldn't stick out too much.
I tripped over the hole in the threadbare carpet as I walked in.

Then I noticed that my fellow guests were not in evening dress but in jeans and sweaters. The place was freezing. I spotted Kevin and Chris, an English couple I'd met before. I asked what was on the menu that was nice. Kevin said the chicken curry was "hot", which sounded just the thing. As far as cocktails were concerned, I could tell this was not a pina colada type of place. I ordered a Budweiser, but it came in a glass that was so dirty that I suppose it was a cocktail of sorts.

The curry arrived. As I tried a mouthful, the sweat started to pour. As I had a second, it fell from my forehead into my eyes, temporarily blinding me. Perhaps this was the chef's plan, as I was pretty sure the pieces of meat were not chicken. Or pork, or lamb. As I downed the rest of my Bud I prayed it was beef. I ordered two more beers and asked to speak to the chef. Now we all know how temperamental chefs can

Jonathan on the West Highland Way.

180

be but I was losing fluids rapidly. "I think you may have made a mistake with the curry powder," I said smiling. "It's rather hot, and it seems more like beef than chicken." He looked up at the menu. "Aye, chicken was last week. I always make them hot. Curries are supposed to be hot, you know." Then he walked up to the blackboard and rubbed out "chicken", leaving the legend "curry" on the wall.

I tried one more mouthful but had to down my two beers consecutively, admit defeat and settle for a packet of crisps in my freezing room. I would have run a bath but it was so dirty I nearly gagged. The towels were either damp or filthy. The sheets on the beds were stuck together.
Abject misery. That's what I felt. Away from home, sore and sick, staying in a pit. I slept fitfully, paid my bill and vowed never to set foot on there again.

The next day started with a climb. I found the infamous Devil's Staircase a real struggle, but it was a light day, only eight miles, and after my early start I soon reached Kinlochleven. The scenery was beautiful and I started to feel that life wasn't all that bad. Kevin and Chris were at the Tailrace Inn when I got there. As we sat and drank some beer, I thought that the camaraderie between walkers was one of the highlights of the whole adventure. If I had done the walk in the summer, it would have been a real hoot.

Rather than eat down in the bar I went to the local chippie and sneaked a fish supper up to my room. I was feeling tired, my blisters were agony but there I was, 14 miles from the end. I knew in my heart of hearts I was going to finish this thing

A Father's Ache:

Jonathan always made light of his trials and tribulations, so I felt that I had to expand on the day that I accompanied him on his walk, to give an insight into what he really went through.

When he announced that he was to undertake the WHW, I offered to do it with him: but he declined my offer, stating that if I saw him distressed or unwell, then I would not allow him to continue.

It was with pleasure and some surprise, when I received his phone-call on the Monday evening, asking if I would like to accompany him, the next day on his walk. He had walked the previous day alone and felt like having some company.

I set off, from Ayr, at 6am on the Tuesday morning, and eventually arrived just before 9am to rendezvous with him at the Public Toilet Car Park (Where more appropriate meeting place for Jono?) in Crianlarich. Not being a seasoned hill-walker, I had brought my Golfing wet suit to protect me from the elements- the rain was coming down like stair rods! Typical Jono, he produced a new, state of the art, all weather Walking Jacket, which he had purchased for me the previous day. Suitably attired, we set off: The first stage comprised of a 600mtr. steep climb, which leveled off and then rose sharply again for a further 600, before reaching a plateau. By this time, my lungs were "hammering", due to years of smoking! Jono was finding the going tough and I was grateful to slow the pace: more for my benefit than his.

The rain fell unabated as we negotiated a treacherous descent of 400 mtrs. Followed by a sharp rising incline once again. Other walkers were passing us regularly, but we maintained our measured pace. The terrain continued to undulate for about six miles: The one consolation was the scenery, which through the rain mist, was quite spectacular. Mercifully we descended our last steep stretch, to see that the path ahead seemed quite level. We stopped and ate our lunch under the shelter of a tree, which protected us from the torrential downpour. We were both sodden and tired, as we set off again. Although the path was flat, it was covered in ankle deep mud and pools of standing water. If anything this stretch was more demanding as the mud sucked at our boots, and made walking an effort. I tried to jump from one dry patch to another, but Jono was almost comatose and ploughed straight ahead.

We eventually reached our destination, the Bridge Of Orchy Hotel, as dusk was rapidly falling, some seven and a half hours after setting off. Jono had originally booked accommodation at the Bunkhouse, which was a dormitory, similar to a Youth Hostel, with communal showers. By now, all he really wanted was to soak in a warm and comforting bath for an hour. So we took a room in the Hotel proper and unloaded our packs. I left Jono and hired a taxi to collect my car from Crianlarich, stopping on the way back, to buy a light dinner and drinks. Jono had to watch his eating habits, so a Hotel meal was out of the question. There was a live football match on the TV, and we had planned, that after bathing, we would take to our beds, have a picnic and watch the "Footie".

However, when I arrived back, I found Jono quite agitated- No hot water for the bath! Upon enquiring, downstairs, he was informed by the male "Aussie" receptionist that the water boiler was "crook", but was expected to be fixed soon: Furthermore Jono's meticulously packed medication, had succumbed to the extreme wet, and many of his tablets had been transformed into a soggy mess.

I offered to phone home, and have his mum, send replacements to his next stop, but he assured me that everything would be O.K.- It was only much later that I discovered how drastic a catastrophe this was! We waited in our room: cold and aching- when suddenly the lights went out, and from the windows we could see nothing but total darkness. We made our way into the hall; there were no emergency lights, and finally managed to negotiate the stairway to Reception. We were met by our "Aussie" friend, (Our harbinger of cheerful bad news), who informed us that there was a power failure throughout the area, but that the Hydro Electric Energy team were on their way to sort the problem. I took a torch from my car, and as I entered the Hotel, I saw that the Bar was now candle-lit: the Management was ensuring that the Bar takings were not affected!

Romantic, it was not!

I'm totally amazed that a hotel, so remote, and at such an altitude, would not have the foresight to have a back-up generator. God help anyone stuck in similar circumstances in Mid-Winter!
We returned to our room and ate our picnic by torchlight, before climbing into bed to keep warm. Just before 10 pm. The power was restored, and rather than wait for the hot water boiler to be "uncrooked", we decided to use the showers in the Bunkhouse. It was sheer heaven to have the warm water cascade over our cold and aching bones. Feeling refreshed and much warmer, we returned to our room and went straight to bed: soon we were fast asleep.

I rose at 6am, the next morning, for my return to Ayr, but as I swung my legs from the bed to the floor, I felt that, during the night, someone had been pounding my body with a Ten-Pound hammer! I looked at Jono, who was still asleep, and could not imagine just how terrible, he would feel when he awoke. I felt like wrapping him in a blanket and taking him home. Driving home, still feeling my aches and pains, I felt proud, yet humbled, that Jono, despite his parlous medical position, would continue his walk.

Incidentally, my all-weather jacket, took two days to dry completely!

Henry Wilson

29 October 2000

Back For Good:

THE last day's walk was always going to be easy.

I knew my journey was almost over. As I followed the path I reflected on what I had done and, for the first time, felt proud that I was going to complete yet another task. I also had time to wonder what I was going to do next. I have always fancied writing a book. A lot of readers have missed some of my earlier work, and that combined with some of the emails I have received would make an interesting read.

Inspired by the scenery, I had walked further than I realised. Suddenly I could see Fort William in the distance and once I crossed the Nevis Bridge I had only a mile to go. It's funny, and I guess it's a remnant of my athletics days, but I expected some sort of finish line, a welcoming party, and the silver blanket. Instead, my quest ended in the middle of a shopping precinct. One of my corporate sponsors had kindly donated a night's free accommodation in a proper hotel. It had clean towels, clean bedclothes and, most importantly, a bath with limitless hot water. My muscles were beyond exhaustion and I was mentally empty. Yet I felt cleansed in a way, as if I had shed a load of excess baggage. Perhaps I was carrying a burden in my mind and in attempting the West Highland Way I was acknowledging that I had limits. Cancer only lives in one way, by progressing, by spreading and ultimately by killing the host. Me.

Bathed and changed I met up with my English friends, Chris and Kev. We felt like celebrating, so I asked one of the bar staff if there was a good restaurant in the area. After one false start we came on an excellent seafood place, the Crannog. I even had a starter, the best langoustines I have ever tasted. A seasoned seafood eater, I am a dab hand with the claw crushers and it wasn't long before bits of shell were flying all over the restaurant. With the great food and good company, it was a treat not having to pack a bag and worry about the next day's hike. My blistered feet were dragging as I limped from the restaurant, well fed and watered.

I gave Kev and Chris a lift to Glasgow airport the next day. As we drove in silence, I wondered at how far I had come. The road to Glasgow passed many of the landmarks I had seen on my walk, and the enormity of it all nearly overwhelmed me. I was desperate to get home and see Mum and Dad, for although I had enjoyed the solitude of my days alone; the close rapport I enjoy with my folks plays a big part in my life. The walk just reinforced this.

My cramps were so bad I kept having to stop the car. The walk had left me a physical wreck and when I pulled up outside the house and my mum was there with open arms, I almost burst into tears. We hugged for about ten minutes. I didn't realise just how much the walk had taken from me, mentally and physically. I had lost a stone in weight but gained 16,000 for cancer research. I felt exhausted but elated. All my doctors thought I was crazy for attempting the walk but I seem to make a living out of proving doctors wrong.

It took me about two weeks of sleep to recover and I can honestly say that my days of charity hikes and other exertions are over. I don' t know if it' s due to the lost weight, but the tumour on my spleen seems to be bigger, plus there seems to be more pain in that area. Maybe this is the beginning of the end for me. I have been thinking of death a lot more recently and I guess it is a lot closer than I would care to imagine.

5 November 2000

Girl Interrupted:

WHAT a week. Karen, my friend and fellow cancer-sufferer, has died.

We met at the Ayrshire Hospice and, as the only two patients under the age of 50, spent a lot of time together. We could speak freely about our problems and enjoy the frankness that shared tragedy brought. The fact that we were both afflicted in our prime gave us comfort in tough times.

Karen was a strong girl, much stronger than I could ever be. She was there for me during wave after wave of bad news. Her time on this earth was shorter than mine and yet she brought joy and laughter when she must have been feeling terrible herself. She raised a large amount of cash for the hospice and always wanted to create a special garden in the grounds. A patron left a piece of land and she talked about asking Ground Force or The Beechgrove Garden for help so we could transform a derelict area into something beautiful that cancer sufferers could enjoy. She never got to see this happen and I feel it's my duty to take up the idea, if only to carry on her brave name.

I went to see her a few days before she passed on. She was a fighter as well, gripping on to life longer than she seemed capable of, defying every diagnosis. Despite being on huge doses of medication she knew I was there. It was so frightening, wondering what I would be thinking in the same circumstances. Then I remonstrated with myself for being so selfish in someone else's time of need. I held her hand. I didn't know what else to do. I gave her a row for leaving me alone with all the oldies. Karen was always scared of needles, which really limited her pain control. I take all types of injections, and even inject myself when needs be. She had started to have some injections by the time my charity night was imminent, but by that time her pain was so great that she was unable to attend. This was the beginning of the end. Six weeks ago she was thinking of coming to a night out. Barely a month and a half later, I was kissing her goodbye. Karen's mum slept in a chair beside her bed for a week. When the phone call came with the news that she had died, I felt numb. How could this vibrant young girl be dead? For the next couple of days I grieved for real. But selfish thoughts kept getting in the way. Would that be how I would go? Would it be so quick?

So I wasn't in the best of moods when my mother and I went up to Glasgow to get our photos taken. We had been asked to write an article for Woman's Journal and the shoot was arranged for the opulent surroundings of a private club, which was once the old court building in the Merchant City. The photographer was a real character, coaxing smiles while entertaining us with showbiz stories. This guy had photographed everyone but he treated my mum like the star that I know she is. Not everyone appreciates her properly so I was truly grateful. He was also mercifully quick, shooting four films in half an hour.

My week was turning into one big lunch date because the next day I was back in Glasgow to eat steak and drink wine with Sunday Herald chef Nick Nairn. We had never met before but had mutual friends and I knew right away I was going to like him. He is just like he is on the telly, very articulate, full of energy and highly entertaining. His restaurant was very busy so he disappeared between courses to help in the kitchen. It's not one of these celebrity restaurants where you think that famous Joe Bloggs has cooked your dinner while all the time he is sitting at home counting the money.

At Nairn's, what you see is what you get, i.e., Nick running around like a madman making sure everything is just right. And it was. The food was marvellous and we were the second last people to leave the restaurant. Nick and I have challenged each other to a race at Knockhill racing circuit. I have warned him not to make bets with someone who has nothing to lose.

My week ended with a trip to the Beatson Oncology Centre. I have been worrying about the speed at which the tumours in my stomach are growing, and I have also been in a lot of pain. And sure enough, when the consultant can measure your tumours with a tape measure, it's a bad sign. He ordered a stack of tests and scans, but all these will show is that my cancer is getting a lot worse. That I am dying. I thought about Karen again, about the speed with which her body failed her. I wondered how long I have left. I suppose we all ask ourselves this, but when you can feel a tumour the size of an orange growing on your spleen, you tend to wonder a bit more.

A few weeks ago, I wrote that I wasn't too scared about death. I lied. Sorry.

Friends In A Secret Garden:

The death of Karen affected Jonathan profoundly. He could not comprehend just how quickly Karen's condition deteriorated. During their stays in the Hospice, they became close friends and confidants. They could discuss the subjects that they were unable to with their families. Although they often talked of their mutual fears about their suffering and ultimate deaths, their time together wasn't always morbid as they shared a love of music and books.

When together, they would occasionally take leave of the Hospice and go browsing through the shop's in Ayr, and on one occasion went to the cinema.

Karen and her family had raised a substantial sum in their Local Community for the Ayrshire Hospice, and it was her intention to have the fund used to develop a "Secret Garden" of tranquility for patients there. With this in mind, Jonathan also pledged his charity contributions to Karen's project, and we were delighted to be advised that the garden project will be started by August 2002, and hopefully will be completed by early 2003.

It will be a fitting and poignant legacy to two young people, who despite their mutual terminal illness, devoted much of their time and energy to raise cash to fund a project for the benefit of fellow sufferers in the future years.

Henry Wilson

12 November 2000

Tower Of Strength:

WITH my illness rolling downhill like a stone, picking up moss-like tumours, I tend to look back at the happier times in my life for a bit of therapy.

I worked in the Caribbean when I was young, carefree and able to live an itinerant lifestyle with no worries in the world. On the cruise ships I was considered a bit of a nutter, pushing the limits of the envelope distinctly outwards. I had the reputation for being a bit of a drinker: well, you had to do something. So we worked hard, played even harder, visited every country in the Caribbean, got a tan and made a lot of friends.

I shared a cabin with one of them, Simon from London. This cabin was the size of a small toilet – and you should have seen the toilet – so you got to know someone really well really quickly. That was six years ago but we keep in touch. He is the type of friend who ignores you for three months and then, when you do get a call, you just pick up where you last left off. No embarrassing silences. So anyway, as I'm a bit of a photo freak who likes to chronicle his sad life when I'm feeling down in the dumps (and cancer lumps), I often look at my Caribbean journals. This time, it inspired me to give Si a phone. Ten minutes later, we had made plans for him to come up to Scotland. And, rather than hangin' at the Wilson homestead, I called in a favour from my favourite aunt. A weekend at Gleneagles for Simon and me. I picked him up at the airport. He hadn't changed much and it was great to see him. He noticed my weight loss – not a good sign. I thought only girls noticed things like that.

The spa at Gleneagles is always packed and I was a little bit self-conscious: a nine stone weakling with an unexplainable lump protruding from under my bottom right hand rib. It looks like my heart is about to explode. Sauna, hot tub, Jacuzzi ... after that lot we were revitalised. I also got a lot off my puny chest – Simon is a good listener. We talked frankly about death, about my funeral. We have been through a lot and if there was an advert for friendship and its benefits, any of my gang could take a starring part. Friends are so important to me as I need support. I need people to be a part of my life and know what I am going through and not be embarrassed or awkward about me pouring my heart out.

I think I am a personable sort of guy but I don't waste time with fair weather friends. I just don't have time for the "how you doing" crowd that prowl Glasgow's pubs and clubs. When you get to my age you have collected a certain amount of baggage, but spare me the fake handshakes and salutary nods. Please. Anyway Simon wanted to see a bit more of Scotland and I was ashamed to admit that I had never visited Stirling Castle. So we went together and if hadn't been for the weather, it would have been an excellent day. Our tour guide could have lectured on mediaeval Scottish history at any seat of learning you care to mention. The circuit was short enough to keep you interested and the castle itself was most impressive. Simon even bought a book from the gift shop, which is a recommendation in itself.

I was pretty tired but we headed for the Wallace Monument with the intention of climbing to the top. But it was too much for me and had to cry off. I felt bad for Simon but he understood and accepted that's the way things are.

My brother and his fiancé joined us for dinner and, for most of the night, I didn't really feel like a dying man. I particularly enjoy situations where I can fit in like a normal person, rare as they are.

That's not to say that there are not positive sides to having cancer. I feel very emotional when I read the letters that accompany the never-ending cheques that arrive for my walk appeal. You are so kind in what you say: if it were all true I would have a lot to live up to. I would be even happier if my effort led to some of you attempting the West Highland Way, or any endeavour that enriches your life the way that walk did mine. I made friends, raised money for charity and learned a lot about myself. Life is so short and it's there for the taking.

There is a favour I need to ask. .
When I found out I had cancer I had nowhere to turn, no point of reference. I am writing a book for people who want a down-to-earth, what-am-I-in-for type of guide. But I need your input: anyone whose life has been touched by cancer should have their story heard.

Get in touch soon.

19 November 2000

A Sombre Tone:

CHEER up, it might never happen!

Well, it will to me but you have a fighting chance to see your next birthday. Those of you who regularly email me have noticed a dip in my spirits. I have often made a big deal out of my positive mental attitude, citing it as the main reason for my long life relative to my illness, but as I know that a lot of my readers have cancer themselves, I have to be honest and say I am struggling. I can put this down to two factors.

The first is the death of my friend Karen, my companion in the hospice. My mother and the doctors tell me our cancers are different and that I am not going to die just because she did. I know that, but her death just made the cancer all the more real. I have been really close to death twice since my diagnosis, but now more than ever I feel terminal. The second factor is my weight decreasing, as the tumours get bigger. Despite eating like a horse recently my weight has continued to plummet.

With these two factors praying on my mind, I have started to phone and email friends who live far away, asking them if they would get the time of their work to attend a funeral. Now I have a lot of worried friends phoning up to ask if things are as bad as my communiqués make them out to be. All I am doing is checking to make sure that I won't have an empty funeral service, honest. It was standing room only at Karen's service. So it could be my imagination, or it could be that I am dying a lot quicker now. I seem to be in a lot more pain and simple daily tasks seem to be getting harder. I had an appointment at the Beatson Oncology Centre, a sort of MOT for my body, and when you have as many tumours as I do the last thing you need to hear is the consultant ordering a new scan because he suspects that I have a new type of cancer. I was actually on the verge of saying to him: "look, just forget it, what is it going to prove?" Then the consultant admitted that, when he saw me last year, he didn't expect to see me back again. My initial prognosis was, after all, only three months.

My mother told me that when doctors find the first evidence of cancerous tumours, the message to their patients depends on their circumstances. As I was a single, childless young male, I was not told just how serious my condition was. It is perhaps a strange quirk of the Hippocratic oath that doctors can judge what is in our best interests. It worked in my favour; I clung to the vestiges of life and have astounded the consultants with my longevity. If the cancer had been discovered when I was married and had kids, then the surgeon would have laid it on the line, giving me time to make the sort of arrangements one would have to make in those circumstances.

I sometimes joke to ex-girlfriends that it's just as well things didn't work out between us, but of course this is all bluster. When you are confined to your bed all week with a cold that a normal person would work through, you realise that much as I try to push cancer to the back of my mind, I get stupid little medical reminders all the time. It takes me five minutes to pee, I can't lie on my stomach and I get at least four injections a day that leave me with skin tougher than a rhino's backside.

It cheered me up, however, when I read that the comedian Fred MacAulay is walking the Great Wall of China for charity. My first idea was to do a walk through the Canadian Rockies with MacMillan Cancer Relief. I was upfront about my illness and they gladly accepted my "deposit" of £400.

I was busy organising car boot sales and charity nights to maximise the money I could raise. Then, without warning, Macmillan wrote to tell me they did not want to take the chance that I would fall ill. I countered that I had organised my own (costly) insurance and that my illness was stable and that I was in training for the walk. But it was all in vain.

The rest I guess you know: instead of going in the huff I planned my own walk of the West Highland Way, raised over £16,000 – mostly thanks to you readers – and gave Macmillan and the Ayrshire Hospice the money. There were no deductions for administration costs or travelling expenses and, with the exception of one night, I paid for accommodation myself. So while I applaud Fred's efforts, and anyone who raises money for charity, I found that making the effort myself was extremely rewarding, enjoyable and helped me find something about myself.

26 November 2000

Tried and Tested:

My consultant organised a new round of tests, including one, which he calls a "fancy" test.

Later, I find out it is the cost which is fancy. I also have to get CT scans and immediately think of the big machine that swallows you up whole, causing big-time claustrophobia.

Before the CT scan you have to drink three pints of a liquid, a dye that will show up on the scan. They try to hide its vile taste by adding diluting orange or lemon but this doesn't work too well and I still have to hold my nose while drinking it. My fellow patients in the waiting area look at me as if I am crazy but I just tell them that I have the hiccups. I am led to the scanner bent double in pain. My bladder is fit to burst. For the scan to work you have to lie perfectly still and perfectly flat but my enlarged bladder is making this difficult. As the machine goes up and down my body, taking photographs, a disembodied voice tells me to breathe in and hold my breath, the machine whirrs and then I hear "Breathe normally". Once the nurse forgot to tell me to breathe normally and after about a minute I started gasping for breath. Then I look to the control room and see two men looking at a computer screen, no doubt showing my body, resplendent with tumours. If I hadn't been so desperate to go to the toilet I would have barged in and asked what they had found, but the call of nature was too strong.

The next day, the expensive scan. No drinking of vile liquids required. Instead I am to get an injection of dye, lie down for five hours and then get the scan. So I'm sitting in a hospital room, the nurse having told me that the injection I am about to receive costs £450. What is not so good is the fact that, due to extensive chemotherapy, my veins have all collapsed. I can understand the nurse's reluctance to play Find Mr. Blood bank. After a couple of attempts, trying to thread a needle the thickness of a pencil lead into my hopeless veins, she gives up and calls a doctor. Doc arrives, ties a tourniquet around my upper arm and tells me to start pumping. After a minute my lower arm is the colour of an artichoke. All feeling has gone. All in vain, although the doctor still has two more goes at threading the needle. Did I tell you how painful it is each time they try and fail?

Things are looking bleak because if I can't get the injection I don't get the scan and then I don't find out if I have a new type of tumour. Eventually Superdoc arrives, finds a vein first time and injects the very expensive dye. It takes time to circulate around my body, so I get to lie down for a while. The scanner itself looks vaguely frightening. You lie down on a bed and a huge Polo mint goes up and down the length of your body. It takes cross section photographs, much like a butcher cutting fillets of beef. Then, only one more test to go, a very simple one. To see if my body is flushing out all its waste products, for this I had to pee in a bottle for 24 hours.

What will all these tests prove? I know I have cancer and that it is terminal. Are there different degrees of being terminal? I don't think it will make a huge difference if the doctor says I have six months instead of four. I will just have to cram more into those four months, although it would be lovely to see another Christmas, perhaps take a short holiday in the sun. What I will not do is feel sorry for myself. I can be afraid because fear is a totally different emotion.

For me, self-pity is a dangerous place and I know I don't want to go there.

3 December 2000

Topic of Cancer:

I HAVE reached rock bottom.

With all the tests I have had recently, I was kind of expecting bad news. I am having fits of pain that would have anyone less used to pain in tears. I can feel hard points under my skin where tumours are growing. I wish my resolve and courage were as firm. I am relying on my mother a lot more. She must have her own problems, yet she constantly tries to lift my spirits. I sit in my room on my preposterously expensive chair and stare at my fire, the flames occupying the dark corners in my mind.

This all started last week with my doctor coming to the house, which immediately put my guard up. Now that I think about it, it must be wearing to constantly have to give people bad news. The scans that had dominated events the previous week had shown up the news that I had been dreading: the cancer had spread to my liver. Cancer of the liver is one of the ones you really do not want to get. Being a vital organ, tumour growth on the liver is a virtual death sentence. We sat in silence, the three of us, taking stock of what had just been said. I could feel tears welling up inside me, which is unusual, as I have not cried since I joined Club Cancer. Dr Bass is a saint. When he talks to you he looks you straight in the eye, and I can call him any time round the clock if necessary. He told me to be brave, that I had been to the brink and back before.

Now I'm facing a rather more prosaic challenge than bearing up while facing down the void: I have to sort out my affairs before I die. But I'm already experiencing extreme lethargy, a side effect of liver cancer. I had thought I was just being lazy, but it turns out this is one of the ways in which the condition manifests itself. I can't emphasise enough how good it is having a mother who is a nurse. The support she gives me is overwhelming, and although I sometimes take it for granted, she knows how much I love her. We recently talked about what was going to happen in the period just before my death. I said I wanted to go into the hospice because I didn't want the house associated with dying. And I want my mum's home to be somewhere she can retreat to, comfortable in the knowledge that I am in safe hands. My mum says she will to take time off work and nurse me at home, which sounds very appealing, but I want to take some of the burden from her.

Talking about the hospice, I recently witnessed how politics can interfere with all of our lives. Being a fully paid member of Generation X, I rarely bother with politics, but this strike involving Unison has left me despairing at the lack of compassion and understanding in modern life. The Ayrshire hospice receives money from the Government to pay the nurses' wages, but they have to find the rest of the money themselves, which they do through fundraising and donations. Every year they have a Christmas fare, which is always a great success and raises a lot of money.

This year, however, the fare was threatened because Unison members staff the venue. You would think that exceptions could have been made for a cause as good as this one, but no. I'm from a working-class background, and my family has always been a staunch supporter of the unions, but I've got no hesitation in saying that those shop stewards who denied the hospice the opportunity to raise money should be named and shamed. If they or one of their family members ever needs to use the hospice, they should be told to sling their hook.

Obviously, I'm not in great shape myself, but I'm always saddened to learn of serious illness in others. I'm sorry to hear that Alan Stubbs, the Celtic footballer who had testicular cancer last year, is sick again. Like me, he was a fit young man in his prime, and has been struck down unexpectedly. The exact nature of his new bout of cancer has not been revealed, but with cancer, it is usually the secondary tumour that causes the most damage to the body and it could be that it has spread to his stomach.

It was odd to see the player in the newspaper, head shaved in readiness for it to fall out. When I was getting chemotherapy, my hair came out at such a rate I had to vacuum my pillow every morning. Rather than have odd clumps of hair in patches all over my head, I went to the barbers and asked for a number one all over. I then went home and Pauline shaved the rest off with a razor.

I was making a statement that cancer wasn't going to beat me. What's more, I enjoyed all the attention I got for going bald, and the only downside was having a cold head. I hope Alan is in the same frame of mind, and I am sure that everyone, even Rangers fans, wish him a speedy recovery.

After all, it takes something like this to put football and life into perspective.

10 December 2000

Shirt Tales:

ONE benefit of my impending departure is that clothes I wore when I was 18 fit me again.

Now I know most of you were not privy to my haute couture upbringing, and unlike me, were probably glad to consign your wing-collar shirts and polyester knitwear to the bin. The difference is that at 16, I discovered the world of fashion when I started a Saturday job with Smith's Menswear in Glasgow.

The environment was highly sales-oriented – we had a team talk before we opened the doors. Each person was given an area, which we were to stick to religiously and sell from voraciously. Smiths always had the best labels long before anyone else. I have a Ralph Lauren – which, by the way, rhymes with thorn – top from that time. It is 15 years old, yet I could easily wear it out clubbing tomorrow, with envious looks galore. When I discard clothing nowadays it's because it is worn out, yet I am loath to throw anything away. Every top has a story and I'll be damned if a frayed cuff means goodbye to a favourite shirt. So I have decided to start a new fashion trend: comfy chic. This is the antithesis of the "ned" uniform of a starched button-down collar shirt and freshly pressed jeans. Instead, I advise you to raid your father's wardrobe and steal all his cashmere sweaters and expensive work shirts, swerving only to avoid anything related to golf. Buy the most expensive clothes you can afford. Trust me, I have been doing it for 15 years and there is a reason why some shirts cost more than a car. It's because they last longer.

Forget the gangsta chic promoted by Versace and, as a general rule, try not to wear more than 14 colours at once. Charity shops are prime hunting grounds. The most important thing I have learned, having worked in all levels of the fashion business, is that if you are comfortable in what you are wearing, you feel good about yourself. This builds up your confidence and the chicks – sorry, ladies – become a whole lot more approachable. I go out and see all these guys wearing Prada suits and Helmut Lang shirts standing at the bar trying to do sexy and cool but really looking like an expensive suit on a hanger drinking a G&T. The best girls go for confident, funny guys who don't worry about creasing their trousers. So I can get into all my suits, yet I'm still dying of cancer. Even the loose waistbands remind me. Everything reminds me. Sometimes there is good news: with child cancer, more than 70 per cent of sufferers are now surviving, largely due to use of chemotherapy, and a more friendly, down-to-earth approach to the disease. Where once a diagnosis was a death sentence, it is now tempered with hope.

I received three pieces of bad news this week. A boy I sat next to at school, John-Paul, has died of cancer, the same type I have. He was a well-built chap and worked on and off as a doorman at various nightclubs, which was fortunate for me. Many was the time I was escorted into the night air for being the worse for wear. Even as I am wondering how it is that cancer is slowly but surely infiltrating our society, I get an e-mail from a girl who I also went to school with and guess what? Liver cancer. With complications. And as if this was not enough, one of my first dates at school, with whom I have not been in contact for years, has also had problems with cancer.

So I get thinking, this is an abnormally high occurrence of cancer in a control group of youths. In today's InfoTech, we-live-so-fast society, we tend to put off visits to the doctor. Sore stomach? It's either Irritable Bowel Syndrome or an ulcer – drink less coffee and eat more bran – but I wonder just how many of you actually have cancer, perhaps one which manifests itself slowly and surreptitiously.

In our eagerness to get on with the small stuff, we ignore the warning signs. Maybe we should all listen to our bodies more. Or perhaps I'm just getting morbid.

The news that I now have liver cancer has sent me into a spiral of depression. I am struggling to get out, but it's like one of those parachute accidents where the parachute doesn't open, just spins out of control. My family and friends have rallied round and done their utmost to cheer me up, but I guess it's up to me.

I am going to try every potion and mixture ever rumoured to do people with cancer good. I was seeing a great hypnotherapist in Glasgow and hope to see her again. If the mind is willing, the body will follow. My doctor has told me that he feels helpless, with my liver working at less than half capacity and the high levels of pain control leaving me exhausted. And all in time for the Christmas rush. I know what he means. So if I miss a column, I apologise in advance, but I really am beat.

Take care.

17 December 2000

La La Land:

I DON'T know, whether it's just my cocktail of morphine, methadone and opiates, but when I get up in the morning and turn on the TV I find the Teletubbies strangely soothing.

They also make perfect sense. As they dance around hugging each other, I feel safe. I also think about my own family, how close we are, how much time we wasted before my cancer brought us closer.

It's no secret that I depend on my mother: she is the rock on which I crash when it all gets too much for me. I always looked up to my dad. One of my earliest memories is of my first day at school. I couldn't tie my school tie, so my dad stood me in front of the mirror and showed me how. Then he put on his aftershave and sprinkled some on me. This ritual took place for a couple of years. I could tie my tie by then but I found it reassuring. I felt like a man, like my dad, with my freshly ironed shirt collar holding my tie in place, smelling of Pierre Cardin. Now if my dad goes out for dinner, I will give him one of my ties. I've caught him trying on my aftershave too. With my dad working, I don't see him too much but we'll watch the football together. Whenever I am sick he provides the same compassion, and probably feels the loss as much as my mother.

Every day now, as the cancer grows, a little piece of me dies. I was warned that one of the side effects of liver cancer is tiredness but I didn't expect this. I sit in my chair and think about going to the toilet, or making a cup of tea, but the tiredness makes me feel like a lump of lead. It takes the prospect of a visitor to rouse me from my chair.

My brother comes to the house a lot more now. He stays with his fiancée, Susan, quite a distance away, but he still manages down. Even though he won't admit it, I know it's because I am dying. When we were younger we were inseparable, sharing childhood adventures, but as we grew older our paths diverged. I became a party animal and social butterfly on the Glasgow scene; Christopher got his head down and worked. I think I even embarrassed him then, being a shallow and vacuous person, worrying more about how I looked than who I was.

I always wanted the best for my younger sister, Madeleine. I wanted her to be a doctor or lawyer, some career that would let enable her to make the most of her undoubted intelligence. Adolescence took her down a different path and she is now married with two beautiful kids, Abbie and Daniel. My folks act as surrogate parents while Madeleine and her husband work. So I see the kids a lot and have watched how children nowadays are forced to grow up too soon. My parents protected Chris and me so that we had an innocent childhood. I remember being heartbroken when I found out Santa Claus did not exist. Who drank the milk and ate the cookies that we left out on Christmas Eve?

My mum worked at the Glasgow Royal Infirmary, on nightshift, and Chris and I would put our coats over our pyjamas when my dad gave her a lift in. After we dropped her off, Dad would drive around George Square so we could look at the Christmas lights. When I think about it, I had the perfect childhood.
As a family we have tried to prolong Abby's innocent days. It's not easy. She is currently writing a letter to Santa asking for a doll called Amazing Ally. Ally talks, recognises commands and has, it is claimed, "lifelike emotions". Perhaps she also has a fly cigarette when left alone, or swears when she doesn't get her own way over something.

Maybe she will come supplied with the pill, even though she is under 16.

I find myself reminiscing about all the great Christmases I have had because this will be my last one.

I intend to enjoy it. Exhaustion, Amazing Ally and all.

24 December 2000

Timely Reminders:

A COUPLE of months ago, I wrote an article about my relationship with my mother for Woman's Journal. Last week it was published, with huge photographs, in full colour.

There is a counter in the perfume hall in Frasers where they have a machine, which magnifies your face so you can see all your dirty pores. I think the photographer borrowed it to photograph Mum and I, such is the magnification involved.

When I agreed to do the piece I added the fee to the charity account. I had no idea my paltry story would be of sufficient interest to be syndicated to any other publication, never mind getting a two-page colour spread in a Scottish tabloid the next day. I am sometimes recognised while walking through the streets of Glasgow, or in a shop. People ask: "Are you that cancer guy?" I have to admit to being a bit under whelmed by all this celebrity status. What would be good would be to receive £1 every time someone told me I was so brave. Nobody knows how they would react in a given situation and, for me; cancer is just a faster route to something we will all have to face. I often wonder if that's why older people walk around with a world-weary look, why they reminisce so much and revisit their old stories.

Since being diagnosed with cancer I have found myself looking at life in different ways: as an elderly person, a handicapped person, as someone who is recognisable as a face from the papers. One thing that annoys me intensely is that, because I am young, people assume I can't be handicapped. You know who the worst offenders are? Traffic wardens. They see an orange badge on my car and assume that because I still have my own hair and wear Prada, I am using, or should that be misusing, someone else's badge. If I am feeling awful, which is pretty much most of the time, I take great pleasure in telling them to p*ss off and do some job more fulfilling, like picking up dog litter with their bare hands. Almost, but not quite, as annoying as these failed policemen are the people who tut and give me dirty looks for using disabled toilets. What do I need to do to make people recognise my disability? Perhaps an orange T-shirt issued to all us invalids would be appropriate. I could pull mine up and show them the tumours.

With my illness progressing, I get small reminders of how my life is changing. With the pain becoming unbearable, I undertake a vigorous pain control regime, which leaves me absolutely shattered. It is the kind of tiredness where you just cannot keep your eyes open. I can sit for hours. I didn't realise how inactive I was until I looked at my watch. It's one of those ones, which does not need a battery; it gets its power from your own body movements. Well, my watch had stopped. Which just goes to show that even money cannot stop time, the most precious of all commodities. One of my correspondents, who also has cancer, remarked that as cancer sufferers, we possess an inner knowledge about life. I agree: since being diagnosed I see life a lot more clearly. I often laugh at the problems my friends have. In their lives they may seem significant, but in the grand scale of things, I wish their problems were mine.

I was never a hyperactive sort of person but I have definitely chilled out since having cancer. I just do not seem to get worked up about trivial things when I have other matters on my mind. Why should I? It's not going to do any good.

I am so sure of my newfound insight that I have left words of wisdom for some of my friends and family, to be distributed at my funeral. If I can suggest what I think would be an improvement, I will not hold back. And what gives me the right to do this? Simply a strong feeling of what is right and what is a waste of time.

And the idea of getting the last word at my own funeral. That's priceless.

31 December 2000

Strawberry Heals:

A FRIEND in Australia, a writer, sent me the following short story:

A man was walking through the bushlands of Africa when he was suddenly confronted by a hungry looking lion. He turned on his heel and ran away. In his haste to escape, he fell down a ravine. Fortunately, he landed on a ledge half way down. Above him was the hungry lion; below him was a sheer drop. He was trapped. It was then he noticed a bush on the ledge. Growing on it was the largest, juiciest strawberry he had ever seen. He picked the strawberry, sat back on his ledge and ate it.

A simple story, but an important message: don't lose sight of the strawberry. The strawberry, of course, can be any part of your life, which is particularly memorable. This approach to life was neatly summed up in the film Ferris Bueller's Day Off. The character's attitude was that life moves pretty fast and if you don't stop and look around, you may miss it altogether.

As I sit about thinking of life, I can recall many strawberries. Years ago, I was in Glasgow shopping with my parents. We went into Frasers for tea, at the time the store's restaurant was quite posh and packed with those ladies who lunch – i.e., women who don't work for a living but shop every day and drink coffee with their friends.
One such lady at the table adjacent to ours went to the toilet to powder her nose. As she walked back through the restaurant to her table near the entrance, the room went quiet. Then suppressed laughter broke out. She had tucked her skirt inside her pants and strolled through the restaurant showing off her ample derriere. When her friends told her what was causing such hilarity, she mustered up as much dignity as she could and tucked herself in properly, to a rousing round of applause from the other customers.

Of course there must be a flip side to these unforgettable episodes. Let's call them gooseberries: events that were unpleasant at the time and painful to remember. I have plenty of these too. A reader recently

205

asked why I put myself through so many horrible tests and scans. The answer was that I wanted to see how the land was lying. After I had finished my West Highland Way walk, I had lost a stone in weight, so I needed to know if it was just this immense effort, which had resulted in the extreme tiredness and also the increased prominence of the tumor on my spleen. It feels as hard as a rubber ball and is tomato-like in size.

Something in my mind was niggling me. Although I have a very high pain threshold, I was requiring more and more morphine injections. No one knows my body as well as I do, so I had inkling something new was amiss. Hence the tests. I have already tried to describe the pain of having a needle threaded through a defunct vein but to be honest; I am not a skilled enough writer to properly describe the agony one experiences during this procedure. Enough to say my eyes welled up with tears. A gooseberry indeed.

Other readers have noticed my depression and despair. One actually suggested I change the name of the column because dead man writing is too downbeat. But I feel it describes the reality of life with cancer. Being told that the cancer has spread to my liver was a kick that really got me down. I am only human.

My appeal for stories relating to cancer, from sufferers, carers and relatives, has yielded the most amazing cache of tales. There are blunders by consultants, miracle cures and families overcoming their collective stiff upper lips to join together in difficult times.

One theme I find runs through all the emails is the lack of information available at the time of the first diagnosis. Sometimes when you hear the word cancer all you think of is death. Doctors tend to err on the pessimistic side and when they do talk, favour medical gobbledygook instead of the plain English, which the patient needs. I hope the collection of experiences I'm compiling fills this void and shows that cancer is a word, not a sentence.

Happy New Year.

7 January 2001

Brave Heart:

I AM scared to open up my email, as I know that there will be at least 500 letters to reply to.

Not that I am boastful or ungrateful; I love all your communications and some of your letters put my efforts to shame.

This week I tried to make an effort shake the lethargy, which has plagued me recently. I could be sitting talking to someone and then the next thing I would feel would be my mother nudging me – it is so bad mannered yet I cannot help myself. I honestly think I have narcolepsy. I wanted to try and spend more time with my friends. At present I am spending quality time with my parents, so it was my friends' turn to get some attention. I no longer have a season ticket at Parkhead, which was one way I bonded with the boys in my previous life, so now I have to watch the big match on television. I must admit I am reluctant to leave the safety of my house, knowing my mother is only a shout away.

Still, come Saturday evening, the pain was not too bad, and I made the decision: I was going to drive up to Glasgow and have a night out with my mates. We congregated at the Cul-de-Sac because one of my friends was DJ-ing and needing moral support, and we were looking for drink. To record the last months of my life, I have splashed out on one of those cameras that give you an instant photograph, so I took a picture of each of the lads, each one a gentleman. I don't need to tell them how crap I am feeling, they know. Cherish your friends and the times you have with them – the good nights out, the shared jokes and confidences. One of my friends, Paul Walker – younger brother of Andy, the Sunday Herald sports columnist – was telling me of a quest he was intent on undertaking. For the benefit of the Beatson Oncology Centre, Paul is going to do the New York Marathon, a mammoth challenge. Paul and his family have lived with the spectre of cancer, so when I talk to him there is a level of understanding.

It's funny, but there is an unspoken compassion that exists among people whose lives have been touched by cancer. What with my page three story in a Scottish tabloid I was getting double takes all night. We ended up going to a nightclub called the Shed. I was quite apprehensive because on two previous occasions, I have been turned away from the door because of cancer. The first time was for having a baldhead and presumably looking too mean and tough, the second for having a syringe driver – a device that dispenses drugs – strapped to my belly. I was honest with the door staff about my condition, but even so, I was judged undesirable.

This night was different. I got to the door, got the cursory glance up and down, and was admitted to the hedonistic multi-level entertainment palace that is the Shed. I guess in days gone past, I would have got a drink, danced to the music and eyed up the talent. In fact, without sounding too big headed, I wouldn't have had to try too hard. Good looking (if I do say so myself) with an easy confidence, I don't use chat up lines, but I've always found that if you can make a girl laugh, that's half the battle.

I still see my last girlfriend Pauline regularly. She was my partner and best friend for two years, and you don't flush that down the pan just because of a break up.

I don't think I have truly expressed my love for her in this column. Despite living more than 40 miles away from me, when I was ill she came to visit me on a regular basis. We finished up because of my deteriorating condition. There was never going to be a happy ending – no marriage or kids. It was finished with a heavy heart, funnily enough one of the few organs in my body that is still working.

I would have asked her dad for permission to marry her like a shot, if I thought we'd had a chance at happiness. Alas this was never going to be the case, and we decided to change our relationship to that of friends. At first she wouldn't accept it. Stubborn to the end, she never wanted to give up on me. When I think of the times she looked after me when I was sick, I feel so grateful – that was the type of girl she is, always loyal.

If life is a voyage she was my north, and some guy is going to be the luckiest person in the world. I'm still very much a part of her life and her parents still treat me like a son. They never questioned the fact that their daughter was seeing a guy with cancer; I was just plain old Jonathan to them. I owe them a lot and love them dearly.

I thought of all this as I was out on Saturday at the club looking at all the girls. Who was I kidding? I am now down to eight and a half stone and have a sickly pallor. Even the best of my smoothie lines wouldn't have made a difference. Have I had my last kiss before I die? Possibly. Still, it won't stop me going out with my friends – I'll just have to live vicariously through them. So come on lads, pull some crackers for me.

As the night ended, I drove home alone, knowing there was a woman at home, waiting patiently and faithfully for me: Mum, with an injection to take away the pain that I felt, at least physically.

14 January 2001

Loaded Questions:

HOW opinions and perspectives change when you have a life-threatening disease.

I was perusing the latest issue of one of those male magazines, you know the type – glossy, cover shots of half naked nubile females and banner headlines screaming guarantees of hitherto unpossessed sexual prowess and financial muscle. A friend had bought it for me when I was going through a period of inactivity, and – in the absence of quality reading material – I was soon immersed in a land of laddism, where men are kings and women are rated out of 100, based on looks, figure and their ability to pout suggestively on their website. It's basically a no-brainer publication, ideal for the magazine stand in the toilet, for those of us who spend long periods in the toilet.

I was perusing some article about Hollywood, and there was a picture of Brad Pitt, out of focus. The caption underneath read "Michael J Fox tries his hand at photography". I was outraged, and I had to reread the line to be sure of what I had read. As you may or may not know, Fox, the star of Spin City and the Back To The Future movies, suffers from Parkinson's disease, one of the symptoms of which is trembling. However, my outrage was soon replaced by guilt. When I was younger I was the sort of guy who took an event or circumstance and made a joke out of it. If you ever wondered who was quick enough to have thought of a witty riposte out of a world disaster or the death of someone famous, that was me. First thing Monday morning, I would be in at school or work, entertaining people with crass jokes and tasteless witticisms.

Now sitting here with cancer, the jokes do not seem so funny anymore. It's too easy to take the cheap shot. By the way, before I go any further, I should say that I still have whisky to sell for charity, please can someone buy it? Then I can finally have closure from the West Highland Way.

Anyway, my festive celebrations (or holidays if you are American) went well. I guess it's no surprise that I think this will be my last Christmas and New Year, so I wanted it to be a bit special. The money I had put aside for rainy days became money for presents. I really wanted to spoil the family, so the credit cards got a real melting. Just for the record, my mum is always bashing on about how she could be a vegetarian, so I decided to put this to the test, and booked her on a weekend course of how to cook vegetarian food at my friend Nick Nairn's cookery school. I'm down to one meal a day now and dropping weight like an advert for Weight Watchers, so I had better see some tasty veggie and organic meals or I am chasing Nick for a refund.

We actually have a mutual friend, Gianni Romano, who threw a Christmas party this year. Nick and Gianni are cycling freaks, and Gianni's younger brother Marcello is one of my oldest friends. There is a small circle of friends I feel comfortable with. I do not need to tell them where I disappear to for half an hour, they know I'm off being sick, or giving myself an injection. It's different in new company – I start to get anxious and worry what they are thinking. This leads to me avoiding situations where there is the chance that I am going to have an upset stomach, and let's face it, that's most of the time. Still, I cannot hide myself away and that's why it was good to get to Gianni's party. I met fellow writer Beverly Lyons there, and we both lamented how our articles pigeonhole our reputations. Me as a sick, dying, cancer suffering young man, and Beverly as the clubs reporter for the Evening Times. Sometimes success has its limitations.

At Hogmanay, I'm a bit of a traditionalist, and like to see the bells in with my parents. This year was a bit more special, just the three of us and a bottle of Veuve Cliquot demi-sec. When I think back to all the other New Years, they don't mean that much if you treat your friends and family contemptuously.

I gave my mum and dad the biggest of hugs. After all, this time last year I saw in the New Year at the hospice, barely recovering from pneumonia. Before I went to my bed, I looked back at the year, and all the trials I faced, and of course, all the good things too.

I will leave it at that for now. It's too early to be making resolutions. To do that you have to know you'll be around to keep them.

28 January 2001

Public Enema:

IF at this time last year you'd said I would still be alive, I would have thanked you graciously while thinking, what are you – some kind of a nut?

I have laboured and crawled through the past year, never knowing if I would be here the next week. There have been some highs: raising thousands by walking the West Highland Way. And there have been lows: losing my friend Karen to cancer and the spread of the cancer to my liver, a virtual death sentence, being just two of them.

When I started writing this column we knew how it would pan out. I think I was supposed to be dead by now. From the start I have laboured and struggled each week to make it interesting to non-sufferers as well as supportive to those of us whose lives have been affected by cancer. This year I guess I will be chronicling my body's failing condition, although my spirit will always be strong.

One of my New Year's resolutions was to try any and all types of therapy. A reader offered something that sounded hopeful, where sufferers had gone into remission for years after their doctors had given up on them. The idea was to boost the immune system by following a diet. I was very interested. I had heard Steve McQueen had given it a try but found the regime too tough to follow. With my strong will I was sure I could give it a real bash. Then I received the diet sheet. The "diet" side of it is probably similar to all those crazy regimes lots of women talk themselves into and I was perfectly confident. Until I read the word "enema". Now I am of the opinion that some orifices are for one-way traffic and the thought of chamomile tea and coffee enemas is enough to put me off my cafe latte. No wonder Steve McQueen couldn't manage it. He probably didn't know whether to drink his coffee or stick it where the sun don't shine. But I am going to have a go anyway.

I probably need it after the festive season. To prolong the New Year party, some of my friends went down to Portpatrick, on the Dumfriesshire coast. It's the sort of place where everyone knows everyone and, before long, word had spread of a bunch of boys from Glasgow, drinking the bar dry in one of the pubs.

On the way down in the car, my stomach started playing up. With my friend Frank driving as fast as he could, we roared into a small hamlet right on the sea shore. I desperately looked round for a pub where I could use the facilities when I saw a sign proclaiming WC. I couldn't believe my luck. Being a public lavatory veteran, I keep a roll of toilet paper in the car and carry a packet of hankies in my pocket but nothing could have prepared me for the horror that was this toilet. You remember the scene in Train spotting where Ewan McGregor has to rescue his drugs from the pan from hell? My sanitary saviour was akin to this. It hadn't seen a cleaner in years. Even the graffiti was filthy. Still, I managed to get out without skin touching porcelain. Somehow.

As soon as we arrived at the hotel I showered all memory of Satan's restroom away. Then it was time to hit the bar. When it comes to all-day drinking, I used to be up there with the best of them. No longer. My bladder just can't cope with pint after pint of beer. So I move on to spirits, but because I have lost so much weight this just gets me instantly paralytic, causing early retirement from the male bonding ritual.

It was a different story when, due to the kindness of friends, my travelling nurse Susan (aka Mum) and I deserted cold, rainy Scotland for warm and welcoming Tenerife last week. I kind of got the feeling that this was be my last jaunt abroad, so I made the most of it. I even booked a wheelchair at the airport, so that I didn't have to walk for miles.

Maybe I should have booked one for when I got legless in Portpatrick.

4 February 2001

In Sickness and in Wealth:

HOW do you pursue wealth while living in a good, Christian way?

How do rich people like Sir Tom Farmer maintain their Catholic faith while being the tough-talking boss of a large company? By helping the needy and less fortunate, donating to charity, doing good by their fellow men? Lying by the pool in Tenerife gave me time to give this question some serious consideration.

I was the grateful recipient of the gift of a holiday, plus spending money, from friends who know they can't cure my illness with money but can certainly make it easier by helping me out whenever they can. So I spent a week with my mother in the Canaries and, for those seven days, was fit and healthy. I felt like a normal person again. Who says money can't buy happiness? My only wish is to be able to give something in return. Something more than my love, thanks and the short period of good health that I enjoyed. Something inside me, however, says for them this is enough.

As Glasgow Airport's international departure lounge is a mile from the check-in, Mum organised a wheelchair so that I did not need to walk too far. Her tights even managed to stay up this time. On a previous trip, the elastic snapped just as we entered customs.

Once again I was aware of people's prejudices as I caught them sneaking a glance at me in the chair. I had tried to book a seat close to the toilet, with a bit of leg room, but there's always someone who knows how to manipulate the System and get the best seats, to the detriment of genuinely sick people. Of course there are people who abuse their illness and wear it like a badge. There was one woman, also in a wheelchair, who instead of getting out at the bottom of the stairs and walking up, insisted on a mechanical hoist to lift her, chair and all, up to the plane's door. She then walked to her seat. Throughout the flight she was pressing her call button: her food wasn't warm enough, she was too hot. Then she insisted on moving to the little bench where the cabin crew sits, produced an inhaler and started using it to control an attack of

213

wheezing more akin to the sound of pigs grunting. For the benefit of anyone in hearing distance, she described her many illnesses. It's bad enough being ill without making a huge meal of it. Why spread your misery to other people, especially those going for a break?

Our hotel was splendid. King Juan Carlos uses it when he stays in Tenerife so it was more than adequate for Mum and me. Every day was sunny and, despite being blonde, I do tan. Mum, being a nurse, had packed the factor 75-sun cream. I put it on my lips to prevent cold sores and when I put my lips together they stuck. I had to re-read the label to check it wasn't cement.

We settled into a daily routine. Up early for breakfast, then back to the room where we had our own balcony which led, via a spiral staircase, to our own private roof terrace with plunge pool. I would then lie prostrate the whole day in the warm sun. I do not know what it is about the sun but I felt content and carefree – I sound like a tampon commercial. At night we would go out for dinner, or not, depending on my unpredictable bowels, and then have an early night. Being on holiday with your mother might not be for everyone, but I am so close to her we're like best friends and did not argue once. Her snoring was the only bone of contention.

We both enjoy people watching. Every morning, at the sumptuous breakfast buffet, which featured champagne and salmon with caviar (although my mum wants to stress that she never indulged, at least not in the champagne) an elderly English couple, resplendent in their finery, would sneak food into napkins and then into carefully placed bags.

As my grandmother says, the rich stay that way by watching the pennies. Or, in this case, the croissants.

One day we went to a market. There was a South American band busking, the type with the panpipes, flutes and drums. They were playing away when a holidaymaker lost her footing on the rough ground, tripped and fell, taking out the whole band. There were pipes in the air and guitars on the ground – you can imagine the mayhem. Only one thing remained unmoved and that was the music, which kept on playing. The rats had a CD playing and were just miming along. One of them quickly turned it off but their con was exposed.

The journey home was spent clutching a three-ply sick bag. (When I'm sick, one bag is not enough.) We landed in freezing fog, just to remind me what a great week we had just enjoyed. Later on, as I was throwing up, I realised there was not going to be a happy ending or miracle cure and the best I could aim for was a painless, sick-free period of rest.

Mother Courage:

IT'S no good. Whatever I do, I can't raise my spirits after coming home from the sunshine island of Tenerife. The weather is so depressing that I am convinced it is the reason behind my sudden attack of vomiting.

Also, I had a real fright this week. My mother had been complaining of pins and needles up her right arm, but she just put it down to poor circulation. As the days went on the situation did not rectify itself and she started having chest pains. I had to literally hold the phone to her ear and dial the number of the doctor.

Nurses make terrible patients. When the surgery said a doctor was in the area and would call round, she nearly had kittens. The doctor arrived and he was a really nice guy. Due to the nature and location of the pain I left them to it, but I did listen at the door, as I knew my mum would not take advice that would affect the running of the Wilson household. As I heard the doctor getting his stuff together, I entered the room and asked what the prognosis was. Without blood tests and cardiograms he would not say for sure, but he put his money on angina. He phoned Ayr hospital to speak to the admitting doctor and was just about to phone for an ambulance. Mum looked ready to have the vapours. An ambulance? I managed to placate both physician and parent by saying I would transport her to hospital myself.

I was already regretting this decision as we drove up to casualty. "I'm fine," she repeated, as much to persuade herself as to reassure me. It didn't really work; I was really worried. Mum has a tough life just now. She looks after yours truly and while I only require only two injections a day, the psychological pressure of looking after a terminally ill patient is considerable. And I know I'm not the ideal patient (wonder who I get that from). She also looks after her granddaughter, Abby, who is three years old, loud, boisterous and basically a handful. I don't know how she does it, but she does and she holds us all together. So I waited in reception and eventually a nurse led me to an admitting room. Mum was lying on a trolley, hooked up to various machines. Most worryingly she looked ... well, she looked frail and although she will not thank me for saying this, she looked her age. All she wanted was for me to leave as I was stressing her out by being there. To be precise, she did not want me to hear what the doctor said as I would insist that she stay in hospital if that was what he ordered.

So I went home. Dad phoned, and I put a spin on her condition that could have saved Peter Mandelson. No point in worrying him when she was sitting up and bossing me about. But even after my toned-down account he said he was on his way home. You have to know my dad to know that this was truly a big deal.

Then Mum phoned, looking for a lift home, so I relaxed – until she told me that they wanted to keep her in overnight. She had used me as an excuse to say no. I felt like a millstone round her neck, her own health problems taking a back seat to my own.

As well as feeling guilty I was beginning to see a pattern develop. People are scared to have, or even talk of, illness in front of me. It is as if they don't feel they have a valid complaint because I have cancer, therefore their aches or pain can't be that bad.

When I consider it, I can't think of the last time someone complained of illness in front of me. I have to virtually torture mum to get her to tell me how she feels. I don't know how I can convince people that their ailments are as valid as mine and that it is okay to share their worries.

Anyway, Mum seems to be slightly better, but she is terribly tired. So the patient has had to become the caregiver. That's if making cups of tea and doing the shopping counts as care.

It's hardly a fraction of what she does for me.

18 February 2001

Popping Pills:

IT'S not often that I go off on one: I try to live my life in a relaxed way, not allowing the inconsequential details in life to rile me. Why bother? I have enough to worry about.

Recently, however, a character in a television programme has really bugged me. I cringe whenever I see his face or hear his self-righteous claptrap. I am talking of course about Darius Danesh, the bigheaded, big-voiced singer on Popstars. From the start, the cameras lingered on this egotist and his quest to become a pop star. He actually has a decent singing voice but this was ruined by his arrogant sound bites. "I feel a lot of love and energy in this room." "I want to change the whole pop business as it is pretentious." The latter comment was especially ironic as I have never seen or heard someone quite as pretentious as Darius.

When the judges finally got around to telling him he was not going to be in the band, I rejoiced. Justice had been done. Darius was not, however, finished. He announced to the remaining candidates that he had written them a song. What he really meant was "I've written a song about me for you." He was then caught offering one of the grubbier tabloids the line up of the final band. Of course, it backfired, but not before Darius got himself maximum publicity. And even though I can't stand they guy, you've got to admit some grudging respect for someone whose ego is so big he can say: "My singing voice is a gift. It would unfair not to share it with the rest of the world." He's the new Nasty Nick. No doubt he'll go a long, long way.

You watch a lot of telly and read a lot of papers when you're ill, so I pounced on an article with the headline "Cancer wonder drug could become 21st century heroin." I keep my eyes peeled for any advances in palliative medicine, drugs that control pain, as I am desperate and willing to try anything that will give me some sort of quality of life.

I was disappointed, however, by the sensationalist way that the story was presented. The drug in question is OxyContin and it is given to patients who can't tolerate the side effects of morphine. The writer went on to say that in America, it is rivalling crack-cocaine as a dangerous recreational drug.

I asked Dr John Bass, the medical director of the Ayrshire Hospice, if he had heard of it. I was surprised to hear that it has been used in Britain for a couple of years now. Surely if this drug was the scourge of the medical establishment, it would have hit the headlines before now.

In America, OxyContin is available by prescription only. It's the same here in Britain, but due to our stricter controls, it is harder to abuse the prescription system. I found the whole article slightly alarmist. It sensationalised what is sadly a fact of life – any drug can be misused. The most valid point, that cancer sufferers will associate the drug with crime and heroin addiction and so will not want to use it, was relegated to the end. The article's simplified message was that all drugs used in the pain relief of cancer sufferers, including OxyContin, could be abused and lead to addiction and overdose. Experts in the field, however, fear that patients who have to use these strong drugs will believe they are drugs of addiction. When used under the direction of a doctor, these drugs are in no way addictive. They are effective, safe and very important. Without proper pain control, quality of life is awful. Believe me. I know.

Another concern is that health care professionals who are less well informed may develop fears about these drugs and with these misconceptions, adversely influence others.

As I see it, we should re-emphasise the crucial role drugs such as morphine, OxyContin and Methadone play in pain control while putting in perspective the very small number of people who will try any drug for a high. This episode taught me a valuable lesson in how to read newspapers: the writer's viewpoint and breadth of knowledge can easily influence an article's direction. If the reader chooses to accept it verbatim, they are accepting the writer's views and prejudices.

I will watch out for this in the future.

25 February 2001

Running Man:

"And for those of us who know the pain, of Valentines that never came".

IT'S a song, one that I have never needed before because I have been seeing someone around Valentine's Day since I was 15. In those days it was just a card. As I got older, the pressure was on to provide a more materialistic romantic offering. A card and a rose. A card and a bunch of roses. Dinner and roses. Dinner, roses and a present, usually perfume.

So this year, being single, I was quids in. I also enjoyed listening to my friends moan about the high cost of partner maintenance around the middle of February. Not that I am a skinflint or unromantic, but it has been refreshing to view the whole event from a neutral standpoint. There can be nothing worse than those huge cards with the red furry hearts. How can that be viewed as romantic?

I have often thought of Valentine's Day as a cynical marketing exercise by the card companies but the first card-free February 14 for two decades did remind me of my first love. They say it's the one you never forget and I'd certainly go along with that. Your emotions are magnified; you examine and interpret every small nuance and action. I was a late starter when it came to girls, my first real relationship occurring when I was 19. I was struck dumb in her presence. It took me two months to work up the courage to ask her out and the relief and elation when she said yes was immeasurable. I can still remember our first date vividly. We walked around Glasgow. I was happy simply to have this goddess on my arm. We went for lunch some place, and when she smiled I swear my heart beat faster.

The only event that overshadows this explosion of adolescent feelings is when love breaks down. The end of a relationship is a tortuous time. I have a friend who bolted to Dublin; such was the pain of his broken heart. My first real relationship ended when I lost my girlfriend to an older man. He had a job, a flashy car and the money to impress a young girl. I was a poor student, drove a VW Beetle and couldn't afford to compete for the affections of a material girl. It took me about three years to get over this. As you get older, you look back at your behaviour and smile ruefully at how intense your feelings were. Not that I would swap them for anything. The memories remind me of how alive I felt at the time.

I have been revisiting the past a lot recently. My Alma mater, St Aloysius College, invited me to present prizes at their annual road relay athletic race. This was quite an honour on two fronts. First, because the headmaster usually presents the prizes. Second, because this event is a big deal in the athletic calendar, with teams from all over Great Britain coming up to Kelvingrove Park to take part.

I used to be an athlete of some note, and at one stage represented my country abroad, so it was with some interest that I viewed the young runners on display. Everyone who competed gave 100 per cent and, as anyone who has visited Kelvingrove Park will testify, it is not the flattest of places. Arms and legs were pumping and flailing all over the place and when you're knackered, you don't care if your face is bright red and covered with spittle. It took me right back.

I came across an old friend in the park. He used to be an outstanding athlete but now has a blood disorder, which is serious enough for him to have given up running. If I did not know better, I would have to say that running is bad for you, with both of us seriously ill.

Then he had another surprise for me. He has taken his vows and is now a man of the cloth. You could have knocked me down with a sweaty running vest. Here was a friend, just a regular guy who liked a drink, was a hit with the girls and had a successful business. One day he decided he had had enough of life and felt the calling of God. He had joined the Jesuits, the group who originally founded St Aloysius. As a brotherhood it is quite an extreme branch of the Catholic Church, with additional vows and criteria. My friend had to make his way around France and Spain with no money, begging for food and lodging. We parted company with me promising to buy him a dinner soon. It is the least I can do.

As for the prize giving, I had my speech all planned. I was going to tell the assembled group of kids to make the most of their school days as they turn out to be some of the best times of your life, but also to enjoy life in general because you never know what is round the corner. My own cancer would be the example that proved the point.

But as I went up to the lectern to speak, I looked up and saw the collected faces of youth, all innocent and full of promise. How could I tell them that something as horrible as cancer had blighted my life and could easily happen to them? So I mumbled a quick thanks to all those who had competed and who helped organise the day. I just couldn't bring myself to darken all the good performances with my own sad story.

I met a few of my old teachers, who seemed to have aged well – like fine wine, I told them. The school was more or less the same as when I had left and I presented prizes to guys who weren't even born when I was a pupil there. I know it was an honour, but it made me feel old. Returning former pupils are supposed to be famous and glamorous. Not peely wally and sick.

4 March 2001

Live and Let Love:

I HAVE relationships on my mind again.

I know it's pathetic dwelling on romance, but who doesn't want to be loved? Looking back over my past, remembering the good times, I realise it's probably for the best that I am where I am just now: single. I recognise how old fashioned I am; I assume marriage is the normal course that a relationship takes.

Of course many people are not married yet happily stay together and have children. I have a friend who is close to giving birth and I am enjoying all the preparations for the arrival of the baby. It's exciting watching the family crowd around the expectant mother in some sort of ancient protection ritual. Just as you read about my experiences to see what cancer is like, I can build up a picture of life with a child through her. With my mother babysitting her grandchildren as well as looking after me, I get to participate in bringing up children. I often wonder whether it would be different if the kids were mine. What would it be like to have children? How would I explain cancer to them?

I have a six-month-old nephew, Daniel. You should see this boy – guaranteed to win any bonnie baby competition. I try not to have favourites, but I can't help myself when I see him, he is such a wee angel. I wonder if he will remember me when I am gone. I make sure there are loads of photographs of the kids and me, so they will have at least a reminder of me, in the same way that I've left lots of little reminders for my close friends and family. Nothing too morbid, but I want to give them something they will look at and think, that was Juno's. Is that vain? Do people who are about to die feel compelled to do what I have done? I have never been to a funeral where "gifts" were handed out. Perhaps I will start a trend.

I am sure everyone has possessions with a special emotional value for someone close, yet in the awkward period after a funeral it's often a case of first come first served, usually starting with whoever helps with the clearing-up period after a death. When my grandfather died, there were objects that marked a close bond between him and me, yet they disappeared. All I have are the memories of the things we shared when I was growing up. I do not want that to happen with Abbie or Daniel. I want them to have something tangible, something they can touch when they look at the photographs and wonder about me.

Perhaps it was fate that I never married. I have friends who have been married for shorter periods than I went out with long-term girlfriends. How do you know when it's the right time? Does society dictate what is an acceptable amount of courting before you take it a stage further? Maybe I had reached that stage but was unable to see it. And if I ever was at that stage, is it not a stroke of luck that I did not get down on one knee? Imagine if I had got married and had children. The newspapers are full of stories about people with cancer. Married people with cancer. Married people with kids with cancer. I know how hard it is for my immediate family to deal with cancer. My last girlfriend Pauline knew I was ill when we started dating. They say you can't choose whom you fall in love with, but splitting up with her was like sawing off a leg. I had to let Pauline find someone else, have children, the full show, and all the things I couldn't give her.

I'm not brave, or especially chivalrous, but I didn't feel I could trade my short-term enjoyment for someone else's long-term happiness. Some people have said to me, forget about doing the "right" thing, just pursue your own happiness, and that philosophy has its attractions. In the end, however, I choose to be remembered for allowing a friend to search for her own happiness.

This week I have been invited to a (rather late) Burns supper in aid of the Ayrshire Hospice. I am embarrassed to say that I am no expert on Ayrshire's most famous son but the organiser, Bob Morrison, is a past president of the Alloway Burns Club, so I will be in good hands. Bob, a man of great humour and speaker of some distinction, has been all over the world with Rabbie Burns, including a VIP dinner in Stockholm where he addressed a room full of ambassadors. I am sure he will be thoroughly entertaining.

Quite where I am going to put the five-course dinner, however, I do not know.

Jonathan and Pauline

11 March 2001

Dream On:

I CAN'T sleep!

It's reasonable enough to expect the odd nightmare, given the amount of drugs I am on, but every night this week I have awakened, covered in sweat, having had the most frightening episode imaginable. I get up to go to the bathroom, do my business, then go back to bed. But once I get back to sleep it's straight back into the nightmare, as if I have paused the video.

The subject of the nightmare and its characters change, but there is a common thread to the plot, namely that I am not strong or fast enough to prevent whatever horrors befall me. The message is simple: I am not the person I used to be. Once I was fast and strong, now I am weak and slow. Trips to the bathroom are an effort; I drag my heels up the stairs only to enjoy the head-rush of the downward journey.

These days, I take my little pleasures where I find them. One of my tumours has made it difficult for me to enjoy a bath. My mother is extremely adept at interior design, and ideas thereof, so we decided to turn our downstairs bathroom into a shower room, with handles on the wall for me to hold on to and a foldaway seat should I get too tired. The idea is great but whenever we have tradesmen in the house everything goes wrong, and I mean everything. I have seen walls demolished and floors ripped up, all for the sake of a single wire. So when the contractor told us the job would take three days, Mum and I gave each other a knowing look. Still, we held on to our enthusiasm, daring the job to go well.

The first day passed. The old bath was ripped out and new tiles were laid. Perhaps this time it was going to be different. Perhaps no structural pyrotechnics would be needed; perhaps the god of builders and DIY-ers would smile upon us. Perhaps ... nope, not this time. On the second day the electricians arrived and spotted the problem. Bathroom at the back of the house, electric box at the front. Cue ripping up of hall floor. My poor mum was close to a nervous breakdown but the electricians, to their credit, had their wires laid and floor back down before you could say Handy Andy.

Day three dawned and there was no sign of the workers. Were they going to let us down again? Surprisingly, no. At 10.30am the full team showed up. Much banging and drilling later, we have our shower. It works well and my faith in tradesmen has been restored. Thanks, boys. Now I can have a really good wash without witnessing the tennis ball-sized tumour on my spleen.

Apart from nightmares and electricians, my main problem is lethargy. I have tried to maintain some sort of timetable of short naps I could stick to, but after a couple of days I am forced to admit defeat. So this is cancer: the gradual taking away of health and faculties.

I am keeping my food down and this has led to my weight remaining constant, although by no means ideal. I thought I should try to keep my looks as I had a letter from the television show Trisha, asking if I would be interested in appearing on a programme about cancer.

My view is that if doing a TV show promotes the opinion that cancer kills too many people needlessly, I'll do it. Otherwise, it's not worth my precious energy. Not being a regular viewer of daytime television I didn't know my Trisha from my Montel Williams, so I sat down and watched it. It was basically a free-for-all, along the lines of Jerry Springer. I could not envisage a serious debate about cancer when the producers seemed to be concentrating on father-in-laws sleeping with the next-door-neighbour's postman. Sorry Trisha, I'm going to have to pass.

I much prefer the letters and emails that readers and well wishers send me. One offered me a prime seat at the Old Firm match. Here was someone big-hearted enough to offer something half of Glasgow craved. I will never work out what compels people to be so generous to someone they have never met. Incidentally, the brakes need done on my car.

Only joking

18 March 2001

Self-Preservation Society:

I GET a lot of calls from journalists writing about cancer, looking for a clever comment to dress up a story. If you are Scottish, you call me. In England, you call John Diamond, or at least you did until he died earlier this month. He died primarily of throat cancer but mostly just of cancer. Trust me, it's a cancer thing.

I always derived a little comfort knowing John was down in London, doing his thing, writing his column, most importantly, being alive. It is funny, because I know a lot of my readers turn to the back page just to make sure I am still alive. I did the same thing with John's column and now he has gone. I was always going to be a poor man's John Diamond. He was the numero uno cancer chronicler. I had always tended to Ruth Picardie's poignant column, "Before I Say Goodbye", for warmth of writing and heart-felt comment and I defy anyone to read her account without weeping. But as a cancer virgin I bought John's book "C: Because Cowards Get Cancer Too". It is required reading for all new members of the cancer club. I have still to finish it. When I was diagnosed I was scared and had nowhere to turn, to ask silly questions, to have a point of reference. It was not what I needed then.

On the other hand, "A Lump In My Throat", the stage adaptation of John's book, left me with a huge lump in mine. The playwright, Victoria Coren, skillfully put John's words into the actors' mouths and conveyed the roller coaster of emotions you ride when you have cancer. I was close to tears. Maybe some of it was self-pity, I don't know, but I felt a bond had been forged between me and Diamond. I emailed him a couple of times, but had no reply. I understood he must be busy – I mean, I get over 200 messages a week. What must he have found in his in-box? Perhaps he thought one cancer writer was enough. Naturally I don't agree with that. I know I'm not the first to write about these experiences, but I still think my column is worthwhile. I hope that, in some small way, I connect with readers, whether they have cancer, or are looking after a loved one with the disease. It helps so much to know you're not alone.

Maybe I have a chip on my shoulder about John's skill as a wordsmith. He was a professional writer and broadcaster while I am just a guy with cancer and a word processor. Sometimes I am frustrated by my lack of skill and I struggle to find the right words to express how I feel. John could base a column on something wholly insignificant, such as setting the video recorder. I secretly marvelled at how he handled having a wife and kids, responsibilities I do not have and couldn't cope with.

I know that this column, like John's, can only have one ending, no matter how long I string things out. I wonder if, like me, he had a final one written. It is terribly vain, writing your own eulogy before you die, but that is one of the advantages of having cancer – and there aren't a lot of those. I rewrite my last column constantly, each attempt slightly different. It's a bit like those disks they send for your computer. Each new version is slightly better than the one before. I am on version 7.0 at the moment. I hope to be around until 20. At least.

As much as I admire John's cancer articles, I'm glad I can remember him before he was ill. I watched him on Newsnight one night. God, he was sharp. The unfortunate Tory on the receiving end was begging for Jeremy Paxman to ravage him instead.

It was odd to put a voice to the column that, for so long, was reduced to a guttural bark.
At the end he could only be understood by his wife Nigella Lawson, the food writer and television chef. He also leaves behind two children, Cosima, seven and Bruno, four. I think it was good that they saw their dad with cancer, because it makes his achievements all the more special. They never doubted his love, even if he could not put it into words the rest of us would understand.

I love that he held a party to celebrate his tenth anniversary of being with Nigella. I could relate to that. You look out for any chance to celebrate an event, to mark a date because it means you have lived that little bit longer.

A week is a long time with cancer.

25 March 2001

Backs Against the Wall:

I KNEW cancer was not going to be easy but this is hell. Hell on earth!

I am pumped full of drugs: methadone, morphine, opium, marijuana, and the whole lot. But does it help? Not a jot. I have a pain at the base of my spine that is destroying my soul. I have prayed to God. I have made pacts with the Devil. I have drunk concoctions that have me gagging between gulps. No good.

There is nothing as lonely as sitting at the end of your bed, sobbing through pure pain. I am no wimp. I would face off with anybody, I never back down once I have set out my stall, but this is backbreaking. What hurts me just as much is trying to hide the pain from my mum. She has put her life on hold to look after me but, for all her expertise and love, cancer just has us both beat. I wonder if this is it, the slowish descent to my demise. I am reduced to taking a mid-afternoon nap. Imagine the scene: a nursing home or hospice somewhere. It's a bright day and the sun's rays are streaming through the window. Next to the window is an armchair, on which an old man sits, dozing quietly. Except the old man isn't old.
He is me.

I can't sleep at night and the tiredness during the day is devious. It creeps up on me. I could be sitting reading a book, and then my eyes get tired so I rub them for a second. But that second they close is so nice and I think, well, the book can wait. It is not going anywhere, whereas I am going to a nice warm, comfortable place where I am safe and get to meet friends I haven't seen for years, relatives from my childhood and situations that can only take place in your dreams. I love my dreams. Sometimes I prefer my dreams to real life. Is that sad? Maybe I should give up now. Sometimes I let the good days get away with me and I slip into a normal life routine. The eye-opener is not the pain or discomfort – what really brings it home to me is when I try to move outside the envelope that cancer has stuck me in and my mum says, ''but Jono, you're sick''. She knows me inside out and to hear from her that I have a killer disease, that I am dying and that death will be sooner rather than later really stings.

I really enjoyed watching coverage of Ellen MacArthur, the 24-year-old who sailed around the world single-handed. Now that's brave, whereas sitting here with cancer, typing a magazine article, is not. All I can hope to be is entertaining. What have I done to be special? I consider walking the West Highland Way without the help of drugs to be the ''bravest'' thing I have done. I learned a lot about myself that I would not have discovered otherwise. I also found out how to lose a stone and a half, and that you can achieve whatever you set your mind to do.

I counted my toilet breaks today. Thirty-eight. There goes my chance of a job in a call centre, since their toilet visits are monitored. As regular readers know, I like my mum or dad to be present when I am yakking up. During the night I was ill (it was worth it, fish suppers down in Ayr cannot be beaten) and vomited bright red blood. My mum says not to worry, that I have probably just burst a blood vessel. If it was serious, the blood would be dark brown. What happens next? I retch up a load of dark brown liquid. Then limp back to bed with my thoughts. What is Mum thinking? Has she given up? I can't ask because I'm afraid of her answer. I know I am living on borrowed time.

I got a phone call from an old friend the other day, someone I grew up with. He is a respectable businessman now.

When we were young we terrorised Glasgow's nightclubs, drinking, carousing and doing a lot else I can't mention. He stays in London now, so I need to visit him soon, because my windows of opportunity to travel are closing. We talked about the good old days and my mum looked in to see what was causing the raucous laughter.
It's good to know that all over the world people are thinking of me.

Early last year I stayed with my fellow columnist, Aaron Hicklin. Aaron is one of those rare people who has a great life, but deserves it. He gave my parents and me the run of his beautiful apartment while he worked crazy hours at his ultra-hip magazine, Gear. I happened to mention my favourite book was American Psycho, the satire on Eighties yuppie life, by Brett Easton Ellis. Yesterday a package arrived from Aaron containing a signed copy of the book with a message to me from the author. It reminded me that no matter how caught up in our lives we are, how intense things get, you really can make a difference to someone's life.

Thanks Aaron.

1 April 2001

Save a Prayer:

WHERE to begin?

The pain in my back that has been plaguing my life had reached critical levels. You come to expect pain when suffering from terminal cancer but I was walking around the house in the early hours of the morning, trying to tire myself out. I read somewhere that if you can't sleep then stay away from your bed, so that you associate your bed with sleep. I tried to read a book. I even tried to write an article. All it did was make me crankier. As I passed each mirror in the house I caught sight of what looked like a ghost, pale and tortured.

Back pain is much underrated. I know that when people want to skive off work they go to the doctor with a supposed sore back. It's virtually impossible to prove or disprove. Well, I wish all you malingerers one minute of the pain that I am suffering just now. I promise you that you would soon find a new bogus ailment

So it was time for an epidural. Now I know women giving birth get this procedure without a hitch and I have had two before. I have no real reason to worry about it. But the thought of a needle going into my spine still frightens me. The day before the epidural I starved myself because it paralyses you from the waist down and I did not want any little accidents. Knowing my apprehension, my mum came along to hold my hand. Yes, that's right, big brave Jonathan, not scared of anything, has to have his mother to hold his hand. This is not in any way a reflection on the skill of the attending physician who kindly performed the procedure, but I cannot lie to you. I was lying on my side, whimpering, gripping on to my mother's hand.

Of course everything went fine. I went into the recovery room and slept for an hour. When I woke up, my mum was over talking to some lady. It turns out she was a reader and loves this column. Cancer has touched her family and she took strength from reading it. She is also a lady of great faith, carrying with her a relic from Padre Pio, the Catholic monk who is in line to be canonised. I don't talk much about my faith, as it is my business and perhaps not as interesting as my fight against cancer. But I get a huge number of emails and letters from people who are Christians — not just Catholics but Church of Scotland, Seventh Day Adventists and the like. When I examine my own faith, I look deep inside myself and ask what I really believe. I am not one of those pious persons who attends a service once a week. For me, worship is not a supermarket with a loyalty card for regular attendance.

I am exasperated by people who self-righteously proclaim how strong their faith is, when they have never had to test it. There cannot be a day goes by when I do not question the validity of my faith and my religion. Why did I catch cancer and have to undergo its various afflictions when there are loads of people of dubious virtue — drug dealers, paedophiles, and murderers — who seem to sail through life without a hint of struggle.

Still, I do pray, and while I would not say I am your average card-carrying Catholic, I do possess my own brand of Christianity. Last week two of my closest friends, a married couple, needed every ounce of help and support they could get. They had to undergo a real trial of faith, a life or death situation, and despite not being able to help physically, I prayed to who or whatever entity there is up there that they would come through it okay.

Fingers crossed, things look like they are going work out. Now maybe there is no afterlife, and my midnight entreaties were a waste of time, but I do wholly believe in the power of positive thought.

Lots of readers tell me they have been offering up their own version of a prayer that my illness will not carry me off too soon. I really believe, despite all the different denominations at work, the sum total of all the favourable thought must be doing me some good. Would I have survived this long without the power of positive prayer? I don't think so.

So, do I believe in God? To a degree. Perhaps I was destined to contract cancer so that fate would land me a newspaper column where I could write about the disease and help readers understand its vicious nature.

8 April 2001

Count Your Blessings:

IT'S 1am. I can't sleep.

All my nerves are shot, my legs are jumping and my mind is racing. What is it like to die? Will it be ... sore? I am on new medication — lollipops infused with opiates. Whenever the pain gets too much, I just do a Kojak. One "Who loves ya baby!" and I'm flying. Perhaps you can tell.

It's the psychological side of dying that's getting me down. There are no textbooks or manuals to refer to when you have a terminal illness. This is the motivation behind me getting a book together, so that cancer sufferers can have a handbook to help them through. John Diamond, God bless him, wrote what he thought was the book to help cancer patients, but for me that was a hard book to get into. Two out of three of us will either have cancer or know someone with cancer, and not all of us have a university degree to help us digest a clever but complicated book.

When it all gets too much I know I can take a Valium to calm me down, but I don't want to become addicted, popping pills whenever life gets too much. I have so little left that I want to be fully compos mentis, to try to enjoy it. I am getting new pains every day, which probably signifies the spread of the disease, and I am scared of the whole concept of death. Nobody can tell me what it will be like. My mum, who has worked as a nurse for years, says she has never seen someone die in pain, although it must happen. Most people who have witnessed death talk about a release, a look of contentment that comes over a person. Perhaps we do move on to a better place.

I don't think I've thought about dying as much as I should. Perhaps by not thinking of it, I put off the huge psychological impact it should have on me. What if there is nothing on the other side, just a void, and by dying we are simply signing up for the longest sleep of all?

I have already lasted far longer than the consultants expected. They said three months and that was four years ago. I like to think it's because, although I have cancer, I live life to the full. Despite having days when I can't get out of bed I still try to play the cheeky chappy, to live a sort of normal life. I enjoy football, I eat too much take-away food and, whenever possible, I go out with my pals and get drunk. So what's your excuse for sitting in and feeling depressed? I would give anything to have my health back and some of you have the audacity to complain about your terrible lives. Give yourselves a shake. On an average night I have to go to the bathroom 20 times. I can only sleep in half-hour snatches because I am constantly woken up by my insistent bowel and bladder. Then the cycle starts all over again.

I really do not want you to feel guilty about my predicament. I'd like you to step back and take stock of your life. Maybe you are married, perhaps with kids. I never had that choice. Your job might be fulfilling but if it is not, do something about it. I am lucky. Despite my cancer I have this column and while I know I am no great draw when it comes to writing, I feel that what's here is honest, it is from the heart and it is real. I do not doubt that if I wasn't writing, I probably wouldn't be here. This column is one of the few plus points in my life, along with the love of my family and friends, and it has given me the strength to carry on.

As you will have noticed, it has also given me the idea that I'm a qualified lifestyle coach. But it's hard not to notice people wasting opportunities when your own are melting before your eyes. So why not do something this week that will make a positive difference to your life: phone an old school friend, take your partner out to dinner, and take the kids to the cinema.
Something.! Anything!

I promise you'll feel a whole lot better about yourself.

15 April 2001

Personal Services:

EVERYTHING is customer-focused these days.

Not just shops and bars and restaurants and all those other people-contact jobs. Doctors and nurses now have a code of conduct, which requires them to deliver the goods, not only on the hospital ward floor but also in liaison with patients and relatives. They have to be 'people persons' on top of all their other responsibilities.

On my last overnight visit to the Beatson, the ward I was in was embarrassingly under-staffed. We are all aware of gross under funding and staff shortages — and the staff on duty were doing their best. The main problem was not a lack of nurses, but of cleaners and support staff. That left the nurses rushing around mopping floors and serving food. Which is not their job. It's not like that at the Ayrshire Hospice. Here, the nurses do the nursing, while other duties are taken care of by other staff members. Your jug is refilled on the hour with fresh iced water, your meals are served with a smile and the whole experience is more in keeping with a hotel than a medical facility.

Of all the responses to this column, the ones that give me the best insight into my writing are those from doctors and nurses. I do not mind telling you how good it makes me feel having the support of (some of) the medical profession. Your emails tell me how my articles are discussed in official circles. Trainee doctors and nurses are given copies, to let them see what the average cancer patient thinks about levels of service, about attitudes to cancer patients, about drugs and about the whole cancer experience. It is my dream to see this column included in the syllabus for student doctors and nurses. That would make all my work really worthwhile. I suspect that it would be far more use than the customer care workshops they are required to take as part of the new-style NHS, a quantifiable and justifiable industry. I believe doctors should be trained to think about the well being of their patients, and that nurses have an important part to play in that process. They should be trained to work as a team, with the comfort and recovery of the patient given the first priority.

Doctors are held in high regard in our society. They study for six years and then work ghastly hours in a hospital, sometimes on duty for three or four days, without proper sleep, in conditions of extreme stress, carrying the responsibility for their patients' lives. The immense pressure that even junior doctors have to cope with is scary. We know nothing about their training and experience, yet we take their word as gospel. One of the most difficult aspects of a doctor's work must be having to break bad news. How does the training for that go? Head tilted to one side? Earnest gaze at that point at the bridge of the nose, to avoid proper eye contact? Affected enthusiastic tone of voice to give just the right amount of hope? Or the old classic — flip through the patient's charts for a totally meaningless blood result?

My own consultant, Dr Bass from the hospice, could teach a master class in how to break bad news with the right amount of dignity. He always starts any meeting with a firm handshake and fixes you with his gaze.

He is part of a small group of men for whom I have total and utter respect. (Others include my father, my brother and my ex-girlfriend's dad.) If I had the option, I would choose to have their virtues.

Dr Bass manages to combine humility with humanity and while he never exactly makes me feel good about having cancer, I feel that together we can make the best of a bad deal.

This is not a common trait in oncologists, or other doctors who deal with death on a daily basis. I have had meetings with doctors who do not maintain eye contact, do not shake hands and keep their heads buried in my unbelievably thick set of case notes.

Dr Bass never raises my hopes — I do not have the right to expect any — but we speak frankly and when he leaves the house I feel, well, content. I am dying and saying so gives me a sense of freedom.

You people who are well and alive would not understand the freedom I feel. Soon I will be dead and exploring other pastures.

I'm not ready to check out just now, but stand by.

I will be soon.

29 April 2001

The Getaway:

I HAD some money put by for a rainy day.

But since every day is pretty much overcast in my life, I felt there was no reason having money in the bank when I could use it for better purposes. Such as a holiday with my mum and dad. I went to Tenerife with my mother in January, but my poor old father had not been on holiday for a couple of years, so I decided it was time to return for a break, just the three of us.

Our holiday in January was a gift, one that, to be honest, we could not afford. Our hotel, the Sir Anthony, was quite simply lavish, easily justifying its five stars. The hotel's British representatives only work with independent travel agents. You won't find its brochures in Thomas Cook.

This time, I decided to play a joke on my parents. Rather than let them know we were heading for another week of five-star indulgence, I said I had got us a cheap deal on the internet — a small, one-bedroom apartment with a camp bed in the living area, about a kilometre from the beach. God love them, they put on a brave face.
'Perhaps there will be a pool,' said Mum. 'Any holiday is a good holiday'.

I don't know how I managed to keep a straight face, especially as I watched Mum packing. Usually she is so careful that when her clothes come out of the case there is not one crease. This time she just chucked everything in, hoping there would be an iron in our apartment from hell. Meanwhile I was making secret phone calls to the travel companies, reminding them not to give the game away if they had to phone me. When the time came to leave, I was almost ready to burst. The travel agents were as good as their word, as there was a wheelchair waiting for me at check-in and we were seated in the front row of the plane, next to the toilet. I was glad to be flanked by my parents and not a stranger. My dad doesn't mind that I dribble when I sleep.

When we got there I had to pretend to go and get a taxi while mum and dad attended to the luggage. In fact the hotel sent a car to meet us. Our rep, Jean, remembered me from January. I quickly told her of my secret plan and she joined in, pretending to my parents she was there with someone else, but was good enough to arrange a taxi for us. She wished us a great holiday and winked at me.

Then the driver took our bags, not to some little rust bucket but to a stretch Mercedes. I thought by then my parents would have clicked, especially my mother. As she puts it, you have to get up early to catch her out. But dad just remarked on the high standard of taxis on the continent. As the car slowed outside the hotel, mum pointed it out to dad, saying that we had stayed there the last time. Then the car stopped. My folks looked confused. I burst out laughing. For the first time in her life, my mum was speechless.

The porter took our bags up to the rooms, which were really suites. As well as a balcony, we had spiral steps up to our own private terrace and plunge pool, so there was no real need to use the hotel's four main pools. Dad did venture down one evening when no one was around. He didn't want everyone looking at his trunks, which are spattered with paint. (And you will have to ask him how he got paint on his swimming trunks.)

The next day we met Jean again. What a gem. Originally from Dublin, she married a Spaniard and has lived on Tenerife for 15 years. She knew I had cancer and asked if there was anything I needed. I remarked that it was strange for a five-star hotel not to have tea-making facilities in its rooms. That same day she went out and got me a kettle, as well as an iron for mum. She also recommended the best restaurants and, as a special treat, arranged for champagne and hand-made chocolates to be sent to our rooms.

So what did we do? To be honest, nothing. We sat in the sun all day and went through ten books each. I made plans for my book. We ate out every night. Our favourite restaurant advertised that it used South American beef but, as we found out, Argentina has its own problems, so we stuck mainly to fish. Of course, it would be rude to go to Spanish territory and not have paella.

Our balconies looked out onto the promenade and as people walked past and looked up enviously we felt like shouting 'We're normal'. Mum and dad had a great time people-watching and played spot the drug dealer. This wasn't hard — they were all Versace-clad young men, talking into tiny mobiles, accompanied by tall blondes dripping with gold and dresses up to you-know-where.

All too soon it was time to go home. There was a huge queue at the check-in desk; kids crying, couples arguing. Then Jean appeared with a bouquet for mum. 'Our customers don't wait in the queue,' she announced. We could have kissed her. Actually, we did. She took our bags and checked them in herself.

Back on the flying cattle truck, our seats were at the front but I felt a bit uncomfortable. Going from the marble splendour of the hotel toilets to the messy cubicle on the plane, I decided to wait until we landed. Of course as soon as the suitability sign flashed up, my bowels posted a notice of intent. I sat for 30 minutes with my legs crossed, eyes closed in concentration. One of the hostesses asked if I needed a sick bag. Only if it clips around my waist, I felt like saying.

It was freezing in Glasgow and I can honestly say I wasn't glad to be home. With bargain holidays on the Internet, I could afford to go away again next month, but I don't think I will.

At my stage, camp beds in the living room are not really a joke.

6 May 2001

Showtime:

THESE days, whatever I wish for I seem to get.

People are so considerate, wanting to help me any way possible. William and June were our neighbours when we stayed in Blantyre and over time became great friends — people you could really count on. After we moved to Ayr we stayed in regular touch. They were as shocked as anyone to discover I had cancer and I will never forget their offer of support to my parents.

The other week they came for dinner and many bottles of champagne were consumed. As we sat and talked about life I happened to mention I had never been to the theatre to see a big show. I felt a bit embarrassed and uncultured, especially as my parents have seen many shows, including Evita with Elaine Paige, and Blood Brothers. William and June had seen some impressive productions too. Then, out of the blue, William asked if I fancied going to London to see something. He didn't need to ask twice.

We were to fly business class with British Midland and stay at the Ritz. I have stayed at some pretty special hotels in my time, but the Ritz has a certain reputation. To be honest, I felt a bit daunted. The confirmation fax reminded us we had to wear a collar and tie if we chose to dine in the restaurant.

I had to be up at 5.30am to be at the airport on time. I was absolutely shattered, wearing a Burberry cagoule and a pair of sunglasses to hide the bags under my eyes. When people looked at me I'm sure they wondered who the pretentious git was. Then I felt a tap on my shoulder — it was my friend and fellow contributor Nick Nairn, on his way to Leeds. I needn't have worried about looking tired. Nick appeared to have fallen out of bed and straight into his clothes.

We decided to take the Heathrow Express into London. As we arrived at the platform, a train was about to pull away, so we dived on and sat down. The seats were comfortable and roomy, the storage space was ample and there was a large television showing the news. It wasn't until the conductor came round that we realised we were in first class. Piccadilly Circus seemed to be the closest tube station to the Ritz and it was a bright, crisp day so we decided to walk. I thought I had packed light, but my bag was becoming increasingly heavy until I was really struggling. Just as I was about to collapse, William said, 'There it is.'

A doorman in a topcoat and tails welcomed us and led us into the lobby, which was opulent to say the least. During our two-day stay we kept remarking on how familiar it was. It finally dawned on us that this was how the Titanic was depicted in the film: the band playing at night, the marbled walls and art deco furniture. Our room was no less breathtaking. Only the view let it down, but that's London for you. There was a vast bowl of fruit, a huge television and a video. The bathroom was the size of my bedroom, and full of Bulgari toiletries.

We decided to take a taxi to the matinee show rather than walk. William had chosen "The Witches Of Eastwick". In the film Jack Nicholson played the Devil but here the role was taken by Ian McShane of Lovejoy fame. I was amazed at the strength of the actors' voices and the on-stage pyrotechnics.

At one point the female stars were flying over the audience on invisible wires. We had fabulous seats, right at the front, so each thunderclap or noise had me jumping out of my seat. Despite my early start and the exertion of the walk to the hotel, I enjoyed the whole experience.

We went for a stroll after the show and ended up in Leicester Square. It was packed for a film premiere but we didn't hang around. Let's face it; our teeny bop days are over. Instead, we went to the pub for a quick pint. William is easy to talk to — a great listener. I'm glad my parents have friends like William and June — I guess they will need them in the future.

We were getting hungry. Back at the hotel we had a look at the dinner menu. I know it would have been an experience to dine at the Ritz but to be perfectly honest; the menu did nothing for me. It was all quail eggs, pheasant and other rich food. So we jumped into another taxi and headed off to one of my favourite restaurants, the Hard Rock Cafe. Call me common, call me predictable, but the atmosphere is spot on, the service is good and the food always tasty. Afterwards, it was William's turn to crash out early. I had to have a go in the massive bath, just for the experience

I had two fabulous days, living like a king, or at least a Tory MP. You have to pay for the sake of comfort and ease of travel but great friendships cost nothing.

13 May 2001

Trick or Treatment?

I SEEM to have become a bit of a charity figure, which is an honour.

This week I was in Hamilton, accepting a cheque from a group, chaired by June, a good friend of my mum, which regularly holds "old-time" dances. I tried to give a speech, but as this is my weakest link I was rescued by my friend Willie, the useful guy who also took me to the Ritz in London last month.

He began by listing my meagre achievements, starting from the initial prognosis of three months and moving on to my disastrous parachute jump and my walk of the West Highland Way, deeply embarrassing. Then I thought it would be appropriate to go round the tables thanking everyone and I was touched by all the words of support. It was humbling to watch these couples doing all the waltzes and old-fashioned dancing. They had real style and grace, Especially compared to the big box/little box jerking of today's movers and shakers. I wondered if it was a natural progression or whether the fast, ferocious pace dictates today's dance rhythms of life, as if people need to shake all the excess nervous energy from their bones. Not that I have any excess energy. I am shattered if I have to climb the steps to the toilet.

I used to attend a fabulous hypnotherapist who also recommended other helpful types of alternative therapy. We lost touch when I went through a rough patch. I could use her help now, with the research for my book coming along nicely I am drowning in information and wondering what to put in and what to leave out. Maybe once I get a book deal, the publisher will guide me. God knows, someone has to. One of the reasons I want to write the book is to address the complacency of people who believe that, if you or someone you know has cancer, you can be assured of the best treatment going. I don't want people to look at me and think, 'Well he was given three months and lasted four years so I'll be fine'.

There are reasons I have lasted so long. First, I am stubborn. If intractability makes a difference, then I have a fighting chance. Second, I question every decision made by my doctor. I have an excellent doctor,

Dr Bass, who checks up on me weekly, but he is from the hospice. Not every patient is so lucky. Third, I have a nurse-mother who is on call 24 hours a day. Not many people enjoy the level of care I receive, so do not feel sorry for me. I have it easy.

I still have dealings with the Beatson Oncology Centre, which has been in the news again. It is supposed to be a centre of excellence, but all it seems to do is generate bad press. I guess if it was doing well, you would not hear about it. The last time I was there, I waited two hours for an appointment. There were people sitting on the floor because it was so busy. I know that everyone must be sick of me spouting out the statistic that two out of three of us will have cancer, or will be related to someone who has, but it's true and we all need seats while we are waiting. It was due to the volume of cancer traffic that one of the scanners broke down that day. These scanners detect tumours and are our front-line defence in the fight against cancer. What I find stupid is that we have these super-duper machines but the staff who operate them are strictly nine to five. The scanners are perfectly happy to work around the clock, so surely it makes sense to have the qualified staff on shifts, so that the machines can be used more efficiently. Doctors and nurses are under pressure. They want to help but their hands are tied.

Rather than wait for ten weeks to see if a tumour has grown, some doctors admit to carrying out disfiguring operations instead. Surely this can't be right?

As more and more people contract cancer, the resources seem to have stayed the same. All that's growing is the waiting lists. Through my sources I have also found out that the Beatson clinic is moving to Gartnavel, only months after a £1 million plus revamp to make it look more trendy and consumer-friendly. I shook my head in disbelief after hearing that one. This is our health service and we need to get more proactive. It is all too easy to sit back, feeling healthy and saying, 'I'm alright Jack; I will not be needing any treatment'. That was what I believed about myself. I was a non-smoking, light-drinking athlete. Is it going to get any better? Not in the foreseeable future.

Acting head Dr Chris Twelves said recently: 'I do not expect to see light at the end of the tunnel for another three years.' And as he admits himself, many of his patients do not have the luxury of being able to wait that long.

20 May 2001

Nursing by Numbers:

I AM always going on about how lucky I am having a mother who is also a nurse: injections 24 hours a day, having someone in the house should anything go wrong.

It has brought us together but it has also meant that my dad has been a bit left out. It must be hard for him, seeing his eldest son waste away and not being able to do too much about it.

But I have found an activity where Dad can help. All the injections to my legs mean I have hard areas of tissue, which frequently ache and keep me awake. My persistently sore back is not cancer-related but can be traced back to my parachuting accident — my main parachute did not open and I had to rely on the back up. I hit the ground so hard that my feet sunk into the earth. Add the aftermath of this to my bothersome thighs and, to be honest, I was struggling.

A friend had bought me some aromatherapy oils so I decided to ask Dad if he fancied massaging my legs. A life of hard work has given him rough hands but they felt blissful on my poor legs. I had to cover my face to hide my pain but it was good pain, if you know what I mean. I did not want him to ease up because I knew that, in the long run, it is good for both of us. It's important for Dad to become involved in my care as I do not want him to feel ostracised and I love him dearly. I have no favourites when it comes to my parents but I talk more to my mother as I spend more time with her. Not everyone has such good care available at home. The lack of coherent planning within the NHS makes me feel as queasy as my tumours. Here's one example. At present, if you phone your doctor out of hours, you are referred to a 'doctors on call' service. You are then connected to a trained nurse or nursing sister who will ask about your symptoms and assess what kind of illness you may have. They will then ask you to come to the centre, or send a doctor or an ambulance. They may also decide that your condition is not urgent and tell you to hold off until you can see your own GP.

The process is called triaging — a phone line version of the battlefield medicine where medics decide whose life is worth saving. It sounds brutal but it seems to work. It has been in place for roughly five years in Scotland and is considered a great success. Here in Ayrshire the set-up is held up as a model of excellence, referred to by other health boards when planning their own service.

The disturbing news is that instead of trying to improve and streamline this process, Scottish health boards must now adopt a new service (snappily called NHS24). It has been running, badly, down in England, for 18 months — with many glitches and procedural errors. It will be phased in over the next three years here. What worries me is that this new NHS24 service will do away with local services and centralise itself in a glorified call centre in Clydebank. Now I know Scotland has a great reputation for call centres, with our soft accents and natural friendliness, but this is healthcare, not life insurance.

Some £5.5 million has already been spent on the introduction of NHS24, with select groups of nurses and nursing sisters attending courses at Airth Castle Hotel to learn the new computer system. Instead of using their experience, training and instinct, they are being taught to use algorithms. When someone calls in they will be asked set questions to identify what their illness is. Is the patient male or female? Is the patient conscious or not?

Phoning one of these centres will be about as personal as buying car insurance. And, with the centralisation of these call centres, all local accountability will be lost. At present, when you phone up the on-call service, a GP from your own surgery may well be on duty, someone who knows you and your family. And when chancers phone up begging for methadone, someone who knows them will be able to deal with them quickly and get on to the next, possibly urgent, caller.

My mother is really worried about these changes. When they were first suggested, last summer, she visited MSPs all over Ayrshire. Not one MSP knew what was going on. She also contacted Susan Deacon, Scottish health minister, but did not even receive a reply.

When you look at hospital waiting lists for hip replacements, scans for cancer and the general underfunding of the health service in Scotland, £5.5 million seems an awful lot to spend replacing a system that seemed to be working perfectly well.

27 May 2001

Semi-Detached:

SO there I am waiting for my new hi-fi from Dixons to arrive.

Alas, they forgot to bring the speakers — kind of an essential and integral part of any hi-fi. I was told they would arrive in something like two weeks. This was no use to me at all, so I decided to return the whole thing and get a refund.

In the car, ready to take it back to the shop. A parking warden told my dad to move his car as it was in a loading zone. He explained that he was unloading a hi-fi asked whether, since I had terminal cancer, he would give us two minutes. 'I don't care what your son has — move your car,' he said menacingly as he fondled his Germanic moustache. My father was quicker than me and managed to hold on to my mother and her already-aimed fist of fury.

We probably saved his life, but nothing could deflect the torrent of abuse that emanated from my mother's mouth, words I could only dream of knowing, never mind saying. I feel very proud of my mother, her colourful vocabulary and her protective maternal instincts, always on the surface.

These are the thrills in my life. Writing from the protective bubble that is the Wilson household, my copy does not have the show business, wall-to-wall star quality that my fellow columnist, Aaron Hicklin, can offer. I mean, he's met David Bowie. I do understand my need to write and I recognise the cathartic nature of my work. If I write about death enough it won't be so scary, but because I am starting to get increasingly housebound, perhaps I am distorting the nature of cancer. I don't want that.

Obviously anything I write is flavoured by my personality. I just don't want people to rely on my experiences. When people contact me and say nice things, like I help them to cope with a relative's cancer, what they have to realise is that it's my cancer I write about. My experiences only. These situations make me frustrated at my lack of writing talent. I wish I could use flowing prose, rather than the hesitant, jilting style I have adopted. Denial plays a large part in this column. If I am writing, then I am not dying. If I stop writing, I will die faster. Does that sound stupid? The column gives me a purpose. Without it I would have a huge hole in my life.

Cancer is as real a subject as a writer could choose. It is personal; it is relevant to everybody. I try to find the funny side — there is only so much melancholy a reader can take. This is where Mum usually comes in; she does not realise her comic genius. But, hilarity aside, I am a professional, expiring writer and that's how people will see me. Jonathan Wilson. Occupation: dying writer.
Kind of catchy in a funereal way.

What do I get out of sharing the end with you? I have an inherent need to cope and writing helps me exorcise my fears. Sometimes I wake up, feel the large tumour on my stomach and ask God, or whoever, why? The tumour is large and it sticks out by about two inches.

Writing the truth can hurt — it can especially hurt the people who are close to me and are likely to feature: Mum, Dad, Pauline my ex, my family. Sometimes it is easier to write something on a computer screen than it is to say it — and I sometimes dread Sunday mornings, in case I have hurt someone inadvertently.

 Occasionally it's a burden, my own cross to bear, but it was me who started this ball rolling so I can't moan about it.
What I gain is a degree of detachment from life. Each column is like taking down an old wall, brick by brick. I sometimes wonder if people will read my column after I die. That would give the work a purpose and me great pleasure. Posthumously of course.

I could have adopted a different persona but, narcissism aside; I felt I was interesting enough just as I am. Anyway, was I not someone special at one time? We all have delusions of grandeur. Now I live vicariously, through my friends, laughing at their misdemeanors. Wishing, just wishing.

I don't think it's morbid to talk about my death and funeral. It takes a weight off my shoulders, but more importantly off my parents' shoulders. To protect them, I have disconnected myself slightly from life. Most nights I think about how much I have achieved in my short life. I also enjoy dealing with all your emails. With death imminent, I talk freely with my mother about it, I accept it. So must others. If I was unhappy with my life, death would be harder to accept, but with all this love around me I have few pangs of regret or bouts of remorse.

I would say I am more of an honest person now. I enjoy the freedom that the knowledge of my imminent cessation gives me.

At least I am not a traffic warden.

3 June 2001

A Little Perspective:

MARTIN Luther King once said that if a man did not have something to die for, then he should not be living.

I often think of this quote from a great man — in fact I thought about it before I had cancer and wondered what in life could be so valuable. I know now that everything is worth dying for: family, friends, happiness, and my own peace of mind. I could go on. I often get so caught up in my life that I forget that other people's lives exist.

I found out, quite by accident, that a very close family member had visited the Royal Infirmary because she had found a lump in her breast. This relative is strictly of the old school, brought up during the Second World War, never going to the doctor unless it was a major emergency. She went to the infirmary herself, had the mammogram (which I understand to be a fairly traumatic experience) and then waited for five hours, without so much as a cup of tea or coffee, only to be told to return the next week for the results.

So she has to walk the Green Mile until her next visit. Only this time my mum and dad, veterans of dealing with the health service, will be there with her to make sure no time is wasted and that she is not shunted into a dreary waiting room to spend an afternoon staring at posters warning of flu, TB and the like. I do not blame the nurses or ancillary staff. The problem lies right at the top of the NHS.

Just seven months ago, the Scottish minister for health, Susan Deacon, announced a scheme to extend breast screening for cancer for the over-65s. This programme has now been postponed for at least two years, a piece of nonsense when you consider it could save around 250 women's lives per year, by screening thousands of women in the target age group. Instead of going right ahead, the Scottish Executive decided to set up a taskforce, to examine whether this was achievable. Is it just me or does this seem stupid? Would it not make more sense to have the taskforce examine the validity of the proposal before going public with such a grand statement of intent? This smacks of electioneering gone wrong to me, and further erodes the health minister's reputation.

The taskforce report recommends that the extended screening programme should not begin until at least 2003, well after the election. From being an apolitical slacker, I am becoming a well-versed politics-watcher, able to discern spin from substance. It is a medical fact that older woman are more prone to breast cancer, so would it not make sense to screen from the other side?

This is a tried and tested method for screening cancer, the stuff of life and death, and it shouldn't be used as a political pawn. Yet these recommendations come just months after Susan Deacon used the breast cancer-screening programme as an election promise, supposedly a key measure in the ongoing fight against cancer.

From my point of view, cancer is not a political football. It's a daily reality and decisions like this affect my family and me. Deacon looks to me like an ideal mouthpiece for headline-grabbing electioneering, but when it comes down to the actual implementation, to staff, machinery and investment, she has yet to deliver.

Away from politics, I had a reunion with two friends whom I had not seen since our school days. It was funny to hear about how their lives had developed since we had lost touch.

We all had aspirations of university and then a good job. I wanted to work in London or even further afield, perhaps New York. We all had big plans but, to be honest, how many people know what they want to be when they are 15?
This week I met a nice guy who has always wanted to join the police force. He is now on secondment in Arran, one of the island's police officers, but he is one of very few people I have met who knew what they wanted to be and actually followed it through.

At the age of 15, when you are forced to choose your subjects, you are just too young and immature to make the career-shaping decisions that are foisted upon you. In our school magazine, after your photo they listed your intended career. I would love to know just how many of us made it to our intended career. I know I didn't.

The American system, where you are basically in high school until you are 21, is a far better option. After last year's debacle with the grading process, would it not make sense to revamp the education system, so that teenagers can make an informed choice about their future, rather than a decision based on pipe dreams influenced by friends, television or parents?

Despite having cancer, I feel that now, aged 30; I would be mature enough to choose a career. The only problem is that not many vacancies exist for terminally ill candidates.

No matter how smart they are.

10 June 2001

Trials and Tribulations:

I THOUGHT I would try anything in the name of research until a reader sent me a newspaper article about a new study asking volunteers with cancer to be injected with the Aids virus as part of a new gene therapy trial. HIV evades our immune system's defences, which makes it ideal to carry new genes into cancer patients' bodies.

But I must admit I would be apprehensive about taking part in such a trial. My blood count is dangerously low anyway and I have already had a blood transfusion, which is not one of my favourite medical procedures. The transfusion did go without a hitch though, and, so far, touch wood; I seem to be responding favourably to it. For the medical trial, the virus will be made harmless, modified so that patients do not have any ill effects. I developed cancer due to a faulty gene. Scientists now believe they can replace malfunctioning genes but the process requires a carrier to transport the new gene into the patient's body but the immune system will always attack this carrier gene. Modified HIV can avoid an immune attack for a considerable time, which is why it's so deadly, but which is why it's so ideal for this type of research.

I have become involved in clinical experiments in the past — not that it can help me, but some years down the line it may do someone some good — and at the moment my symptoms and side-effects are OK.
I still have irritable bowels though and sometimes the pain keeps me up at night. However, it's a common complaint that is causing me problems right now. It's my back. My doctor thinks it's probably sciatica. The pain slowly works its way down my legs and is unbearable. I am like a cat on a hot tin roof, walking around the house in the early hours of the morning, struggling to type because my hands are shaking in agony. It really is a pain in the backside.

I contacted my hypnotherapist about my new ailment last week and, as soon as she has come back from honeymoon, we will work on it. I can only pray she has a remedy. So I went to my GP, who is quite a progressive doctor and a bit of an expert on alternative therapies, He even practices acupuncture. And believe me, it's a pretty painful way of relieving my aches. I could see how the Chinese Secret Service use it as an instrument of torture. The pain was unbelievable, but with the agony I am experiencing just now, I think I would advocate amputation if it relieved the pain.

Unfortunately, I was feeling too ropy to make my weekly journey to Arran and I definitely feel the worse for not having gone. I really do feel the benefit of getting away overnight. I think it's because you have to get a ferry to Arran, that it makes it seem like you're going to a foreign country. Then, when you get over there, it has this concentrated Scottishness. Fred MacAuley put in in a nutshell when he said Arran was Scotland in miniature and that is exactly what it is. I get the feeling that everyone who lives on the island knows everyone else.

Last time I was there, I noticed an advert for a Masseur/Reiki practitioner on the ferry so, with my sore back in mind, I decided to book a massage. This lady was fully booked but kindly gave me another number. So there I was, ready for my massage, stripped down to my undies, only for my newly discovered prostrate problem to intervene. It would be funny if it wasn't so sad.

Guys will relate to this better. You stand at the toilet, all ready to go, and ... nothing. So you turn away and then you need to go again and ... nothing. You can repeat this ad infinitum, but it meant that I was unable to go ahead with the soothing massage on my leg.

There was a bright spot to the night though. I found the most amazing Chinese takeaway, which is not something that you really expect to come across on Arran.

The next day we drove all the way round the island and I kept being distracted by the "pretend sheep" in the fields. By pretend I mean the stand-up, one-dimensional sheep, in the field next to real sheep.
I thought perhaps it was some kind mating ritual to get the sheep going, but apparently it has more to do with history and money than anything else. Intrigued? Let me explain. In the olden days, the tax collectors didn't come ashore to count the sheep. They just rowed out, stayed in the boat and counted the sheep from there. Who said we Scots aren't canny?

Anyway I'm off for some torture therapy. Keep me in your prayers.

17 June 2001

No More Hero:

WHEN I was in my teens I was seriously into athletics, training twice a day, following a strict carbohydrate diet.

I was racing at the highest level; I even had a self-hypnosis tape to build up my confidence so that I had all aspects of a competitive athlete covered. Even when I watch athletics on television today, I still get that nervous feeling I used to get at the start of a race. My mouth goes dry; I get fidgety and feel like I need to go to the toilet. I guess I will always love athletics.

Of course I had my heroes. British athletics was fairly successful, with rivalry between Seb Coe and Steve Ovett. Ovett was the runner's runner. He came from the north and had a chip on his shoulder, which he used to drive him on and on to higher acclaim and faster times. He was short with the press, which did not endear him when it came to the races with Coe. Seb Coe was the exact opposite: polite, eager to speak to the press, yet sharing Ovett's will to win at all costs. He was the darling of British athletics and he was my favourite.

Fast forward to now and it seems that he is still successful, a baron and close aide to William Hague — even if he lost his seat in 1997 and last week failed to secure victory for the former Tory leader. Wherever we saw Hague campaigning, kissing babies, two steps behind him was Coe. I do not hold anyone's political allegiances against them, but when Sebastian Coe spoke roughly to an elderly couple, when they were trying to ask William Hague a question, I abhorred his arrogance. I was disappointed that one of my heroes was actually a bullyboy in a suit. Sad.

I've cheered up, however, since seeing Angela Trainor, my alternative therapy counsellor. Although we only planned out my future sessions, I feel better already. We didn't have time to start any treatment, but just talking helped. I was making a positive move, taking control of my own health. I am getting Indian head massage, which I now rate as a treat and allowable vice seeing as how I do not drink, smoke or chat up girls any more. Then I'm getting Reiki, followed by the Bowen technique, and finish off with Hypnotherapy and Visualisation exercises. I will tell all when I have had the treatments.

So I left the clinic feeling good until I saw a huge pool of water under my car. I opened up the bonnet and saw that one of the radiator hoses had split. Without a toolkit or membership of one of the rescue companies, I had to resort to some DIY mechanics. I drove slowly to the local garage and bought a bottle of water, except they had run out of normal water, so I had to buy a bottle of peach water. How trendy am I? Forget pot pourri in the ashtray.

As I limped home, driving cautiously with the waft of fresh fruit coming out of the heater vents, I had a brainwave. Why not sell flavoured water for your car's water supply? It would negate the need for those horrible sickly trees. Any venture capitalists out there willing to try my idea out, just call.

When I was younger, I would always be thinking of ideas, ways to be successful. I had my life in front of me. But today I realise my best days are behind me.

I was thinking about the West Highland Way. How did I manage it? I've been invited to the Leukemia Research Fund's annual "Bikeathon" on June 24. It's 26 miles long and takes in some beautiful scenery. It starts and finishes in Kingussie, via Newtonmore, Laggan and Glen Truim.

There are no great hills, and the course is well marshalled. I would love to do it but I just cannot realistically see me lasting that long.

So in the space of one year, from walking 96 miles, I am too scared to enter an event a quarter of the distance and it's on a bike, and therefore a lot easier.

24 June 2001

Open Your Mind:

CONGRATULATIONS, to all the women who ran (or walked) the Glasgow 5k in aid of Cancer Charities. Among the runners was Elaine C Smith, who is very generous with her time when it comes to cancer and frequently drops me a thoughtful line, telling me, to keep my chin up. Pauline, my former partner, also took part and has been bitten by the running bug. There is a 10k run at the end of the summer and she is now training for that. Even if you just walked the 5k, it is five more than I could, so well done.

I have been upsetting people again. A couple of weeks ago I mentioned that a close relative was upset after a mammogram. This caused a flood of emails defending the need for mammograms and the good work done by the trained staff who operates the machines. May I apologise for any distress this may have caused but the traumatic part was not the mammogram but the horrible long wait, when she did not know if she had cancer or not. I never have a bad word to say about nurses, who I feel carry the whole burden of the NHS on their shoulders, which must grind down their morale.

On my last visit to the hospice in Ayr, I discovered that one of the nurses who treated me on a regular basis had left to join the police. I feel this is a terrible loss and she will be sorely missed.

I have written a lot about the inadequacies of the NHS in Scotland recently but I was still surprised to see my story appearing in a Scottish Sunday tabloid. Someone decided to follow up one of my stories. It also must have rankled with the Scottish Parliament because nurses themselves are usually barred from speaking to the press.

I had a weird dream the other night, involving my first real girlfriend. They say you never forget your first love but, to be honest, my last love has been by far the hardest to get over. We are still friends, but as her social circle widens and she meets new people, new boyfriends, I sit in my room and wonder 'What if...'

I have friends who still love their first girlfriend. I was really upset when my first relationship broke up and I lost the girl to an older man with his own place and a fancy car. I was struggling at Uni, lived with my parents and drove a VW Beetle. No contest, if you are into the whole money thing. It took a while to get over being dumped but, as I grew older, I realised that I was still in love with the person I met all those years ago, but that that person did not exist any more. Once I got my head around this, I no longer had a broken heart.

This would be my advice to those teenagers dabbling in romance for the first time: it's fun, great while it lasts, but there are plenty, and I mean plenty, of fish in the sea. Unfortunately my particular ocean has no fish. It must be the pollution or something.

Meanwhile, there is a storm brewing in the world of cancer treatment. On one side you have the doctors, consultants and even patients who decry and abhor 'alternative' therapies. They feel that chemotherapy, radiotherapy and surgery are the only options open to cancer sufferers. On the other side, but not so dismissive of conventional therapies, are the practitioners of these so-called alternative therapies. There seems to have been an explosion of people claiming to be therapists; Reiki, Reflexology, Kineseology, Aromatherapy and Acupuncture, to name but a few.

There was recently an alternative medicine fair in Ayr town hall. I went with a friend and was astounded by all the different methods of healing on display.

Did you know that your 'life-force' could be photographed and displayed as a colour? Or that there are crystals, which re-align your body's energy? You could have spent hundreds of pounds on all the unusual wares on show.

As I have tried both approaches, I am sitting firmly on the fence. I can afford to: my GP is also an acupuncturist and my alternative medicine consultant also sees the benefit in conventional medicine. I trust both of them implicitly and reckon this lets me attack the cancer from two angles. I just worry that the charlatans that are springing up will colour the reputation and integrity of genuine healers.

As it is, my recent course of acupuncture seems to have helped my sciatica. No more tormented midnight walks through the house, no more frustrated tears of pain. I have another appointment tomorrow.

Fingers crossed...

1 July 2001

The Real Big Brother:

THE last target I had set myself was to attend my brother's wedding.

When I received the itinerary of his stag weekend, I knew I didn't have far to go. Being of limited drinking capacity, I decided to only get involved in Saturday's festivities, and so travelled down with my dad Henry, the father of the bride, Dougie, and a couple of Chris's mates to meet up with the rest of the party at the hotel in Liverpool.

As we got there, the rest of our party in the car park met us. At first, it looked like they had been ejected from the hotel after a mad night out but it turned out that they just needed a little fresh air after the previous night's drinking session. Now, the law of the stag party clearly states that what goes on tour stays on tour, but being a dying writer allows me an exemption. Sorry, guys.

Kenny, best man and trip organiser, had booked us on a go-kart session. The format of heats, semi-finals and then a final sorted the men from the boys. Kenny has never sat his driving test, which would account for his performance and chalk-white face. Everyone had to wear a crash helmet, but you could still tell Kenny by his ghostly pallor and the Driving Miss Daisy approach. My younger brother, Chris, was a little too determined to win at all costs and received the dreaded black flag for confusing go-karting and the dodgems. I half expected him to shout, 'Scream if you want to go faster' and throw his arms in the air.

As the numbers were whittled down, I found myself in the final, cancer not affecting my hand-to-eye co-ordination. Alas, fate dictated I had no chance to win. Everyone had to run to their kart, much like the grand prix races. As the flag waved us to start, I tried to run but my legs buckled under me, so I had to walk to my kart. I could see the pity in my group's eyes. 'So this is cancer,' they were probably thinking.

The rest of the drivers were halfway around the track by the time I got to my kart, so I drove sedately round the course, trying not to move my neck, which ached from being repeatedly bashed about by the motion. But it was a good start to what was to be a good night.

Smelling equally of alcohol and motor oil, we went back to our hotel. I had wangled a room to myself, but my dad had to share with the father of the bride. Don't know how I managed it but I did. Some time later, there we were, freshly washed and pressed and ready to hit the town. One of the running jokes of the night was that all Liverpudlians were 'scallies' and you had to watch any financial transaction in case they tried to 'do' you. With our hands in our pockets, we headed off to Pizza Express. I guess that's the only place that would take us. The beer and wine flowed but the pizzas were disappointingly small compared to the Glasgow branch. Still hungry, we hit all the pubs that Liverpool could throw at us.

I had noticed that Kenny was disappearing at points throughout the night. What was he up to? Yes, you've guessed it, he had managed to organise a stripper in what I can only describe as Liverpool's largest pub. To my brother's embarrassment, the guy who accompanied the stripper alerted the whole bar to her presence then she launched into her act. I was surprised how much she took off. I've seen plenty of strippers in my time, but Kenny got his money's worth with this girl. After some harmless (undressed) fun, Chris 'won' two bottles of champagne.

Then the hastily redressed girl left, leaving a photograph that, if I am not mistaken, would do as evidence in a divorce case. All I could think about was that Chris looked like Frank McAvennie, the footballer famous for going out with topless models.

We then found an Irish bar with a band playing, so the requests went in and, before long, the pub was reeling to the sound of The Fields Of Athenry and suchlike. At this point, I have to rely on hearsay, as I was knackered and returned to the hotel. In the taxi on the way back, I asked the driver to stop at a petrol station so I could get a drink. He started to moan, so I gave him a fiver to hold, as my hotel was just round the corner. I went into the garage, but when I came out, the taxi had gone.

The curse of the scallies had struck.

I was soon firmly tucked up in bed although, apparently, my dad was doing a passable impersonation of Fred Astaire. I would not have shared a room with them that night for a very large sum of money, given their state.
The next morning, we met up in the hotel lobby. Stories were compared, mostly involving drink followed by a long walk home. Liverpool is a bit like Glasgow in that you can walk to most places but you wouldn't want to.
So I'm now edging closer to my brother's big day. Surely God or whoever is up there, will allow me my wish to see my brother married.

At times, I have not been there for him. I've also not always been an ideal role model, but I love him dearly and it's comforting to know that, when I leave him, he will have someone who loves him just as much as I do.

Running Handicap:

Jonathan approached the Go Karting, like he did with his Athletics: You don't enter to be second!
Looking at it, logically, Jonathan should not have had a realistic chance to compete and withstand the rough and tumble, and bone- jarring, qualifying rounds. However, his competitive edge, of old, kicked in. He finished top of the qualifiers for the final: driving with a recklessness and nerve, free of fear: that only a dying person can understand. The ultimate irony and sadness, was reserved for the Final, when it was decided that the start would be a "Le Mans" type running start, whereby the finalists run to their cars, jump in and then race off around the circuit.

We instantly felt disappointed for Jonathan, and could see the resignation in his eyes. In former, better days; his fellow finalists would have stood no chance against him in a running start. Instead of running to his Kart, he stoically walked, with dignity, accepting that the spectre of Cancer had again dogged his life. We felt like crying out "Foul", and would happily have punched the Starter's lights out for denying Jonathan the ultimate and deserved "rush" of winning.

Once more, the curse of the "Scallies" had struck.

Henry Wilson

8 July 2001

Winners' Dinner:

IT has been one hell of a week.

Three days later and I'm still recovering. My recovery condition is probably akin to your Sunday morning: throbbing sore head, sick stomach.

Thursday was the major day. I keep a diary, loosely, but the page for Thursday was full. First I was at the Harvest Clinic of Hypnotherapy for some treatments. First up was Indian head massage. Now this does not promise to be any kind of a cure for cancer but it certainly takes you somewhere. Somewhere better, where the pain is not so bad. Next was a session of the Bowen technique. I have to be careful how I describe these alternative therapies as I have a responsibility to report as empirically as possible. If that's not a contradiction. Anyway the Bowen technique, if you believe it, allows the body to reset itself and heal itself via a series of gentle attunements. It is certainly very relaxing and on that level it affects the immune system and hormonal system, so you can see the scope for healing. I find it especially helpful for my sciatica. The standard medical view of Bowen is still sceptical. As I believe in the technique I probably get more from it than a non-believer. That's how holistic medicine works, a bit like religion.

My final appointment was with Angela Trainor who practices Reiki, an ancient Japanese therapy using the vital energy, which flows through all living creatures. It is even possible to treat animals with Reiki, although it is more often used for conditions such as mine. The healer places her hands on the patient's body. It is completely safe and I find it so relaxing that I feel a deep tranquillity. In fact I often fall asleep. All that appears to happen is that the healer's hands change temperature and this is a sign that the treatment is working.

So I was feeling particularly strong, in a psychological sense, after my session, which was just as well because my next appointment was the Scottish Press awards at the Hilton in Glasgow. I was staying over, so that I did not have to drive home. I love staying in hotels. Perhaps if I had the sort of job which necessitated staying in them regularly the novelty would wear off, but for me there can be few pleasures equal to walking around my new room in my underwear, with the bath running, singing along to the radio. I was on the 14th floor, so I could look down at all the cars on the M8 going home. I wondered what the drivers were thinking of, arched over their steering wheels, nose-to-tail in the rush hour jam. The sun was setting so I knew that even if someone looked up, they would not catch a glimpse of a near-naked man.

Despite the fact that I have only been writing this column for two years, I had been short listed in the columnist of the year category, a great achievement and honour when you consider all the other columns that exist in Scotland. We have a great team at the Sunday Herald and there are certain people who have acted as a crutch when the going got tough for me, as I've fought my illness.

I felt very nervous as I rode the lift down to the banqueting hall where the ceremony was to take place, due more to not really knowing anyone than butterflies caused by a chance of winning my category. To be honest, I felt sure I was there to make up the numbers and I was quite happy to do so. I made a tour of the room, but saw no one I knew until I noticed Muriel Gray, perched in a corner, looking as uncomfortable as I felt. I have grown up in a generation where Muriel was a ubiquitous media presence.

She has written books and made films so it was with some trepidation that I approached her to introduce myself. Within minutes I was killing myself laughing at her description of the self-congratulatory bigwigs of the media set. The host for the evening was Jackie Bird and I could not think of a worse crowd to entertain. The public image of the hard drinking, caustic journalist is a bit past it now, but hours spent poring over copy, researching stories and beating deadlines had probably made the assembled hacks a hard bunch to please. Slowly, however, she teased the laughs from the crowd and by the end of her turn the whole hall was laughing.

Then it was time to announce the winners. I do not want to appear biased, but by the time all the trophies were given out, we were struggling for space on our table. It was a great night for the Sunday Herald and I felt proud to be part of it.

As you may have already read elsewhere, I received the runner-up prize and Muriel added the main title to her already burgeoning mantelpiece. I was well chuffed with my award and was really touched by the number of people who took time to come up and congratulate me. I even got a kiss from Jackie Bird — a result in anyone's book.

There was the opportunity to continue drinking and carousing, but I'd had enough. After a quick call to my parents to let them know how I got on — Mum thought I deserved to win, but that's mothers for you — I retired to my room to behave like a real award-winning journalist. I demolished the mini-bar.

Well, the chocolate section anyway.

*Jonathan Wilson was runner up in the Columnist Of The Year category at the Scottish Press Awards.

15 July 2001

Calling the Shots:

MY future is not bright, it's not orange and I don't have a half-day to spare waiting for a call centre automaton to understand what my problem is.

Mobile phones are everywhere; really sad people have two and, if they really want to show the world the depths to which they've sunk, they keep them both switched on in restaurants.

In the space of the last ten years we've seen mobile phones go from the size of a brick to the size of a Lego brick. The support staff's brains have, sadly, shrunk the same way. I own one, I admit it. I'm disabled, it makes sense and in the right situation, they are very helpful: running late, car breakdowns and the like. Being a self-confessed gadget man, I am powerless in the presence of a new model. I have to have it. Sometimes, however, in the heat of my enthusiasm, I overlook the small details.

Around 18 months ago I traded in my old model for a new one. The shop, one of the big mobile phone chains, decided not to cancel my old number. Unbeknown to me, I was paying line rental for two numbers for about six months. (You have better things to do than check your phone bills when you are dying of cancer.) My attempts to sort this out took 18 months and got me nowhere. I wrote to their head office and their customer service department. I might as well have written these letters in crayon, left-handed; for the amount of good they did me.

I realise that since having cancer I have been spoiled because many of the companies I deal with are prepared to go the extra mile to solve my problems. Naturally enough, these tend to be the ones I go back to. I will not, however, be buying another phone from this particular outfit. I am quite happy to write off the £150 pounds so that I do not have to waste any more of my limited time. It's tempting, in my situation, to put a monetary value on my time. Of course this would vary according to the situation. I am off to the Beatson tomorrow and, depending on their prognosis, £150 may be worth a day, or a week. It's a cheering thought. I may be sending a certain mobile phone company an invoice. I am now one week (or £150) away from my brother's wedding, and looking good for making the big day. Once that target passes, I will need to sit down and work out a new aim. Simplistic, I know, but it is the only way I know how to survive. I know I have been lucky so far, in fact I am riding my luck — I could succumb at any time to this horrid disease.

Some days I don't feel lucky at all. Recently I woke up feeling as if I had a broken back. There was no way I could manage up to Glasgow. I couldn't even walk. It took me 35 minutes to get to the toilet. My legs gave way a couple f times and they shook, rattled and rolled like I was 80 years old. I watched the athletics on TV, thinking back to how I used to be as fit as a greyhound. Now I have to drive to the paper shop or garage just for some sweets or a drink because I know the walk would leave me gasping for breath.

I was hoping to feel better for a trip to Arran with my friend Simon. We met working in the Caribbean when we were sharing a cabin that was so small, only one person could get dressed at any one time. In the shower, you could sit on the toilet pan and wash your hair at the same time. That was six years ago and we are still close friends. He visits me twice a year and we go away for a trip. I am proud of my country and like to show it off, hence the trip to Arran.

You would think that working on a ship would have helped me acquire some sort of sea legs. Sadly not and I would like to apologise to my fellow passengers on that fateful Sunday. I thought I had judged the wind correctly to avoid distributing half-digested chicken in oyster sauce among the seafarers on the sun deck. I had not. Instead, they got a surprise taste of the Orient.

Now all I have to do is get better for the wedding.

22 July 2001

Moments to Savour:

ALWAYS the bridesmaid, never the bride – I surely know how that feels.

This weekend I had two consecutive weddings, my friend Roslyn's followed by my brother Christopher's. Roslyn's wedding was on the Friday, down at Seamill, and the weather was glorious. The hotel is a lovely setting and the bride was gorgeous. I felt partly responsible for the big day because I had introduced them on a night out. The groom, Kevin, runs a very successful record label in Glasgow.

It never fails to amaze me that after all the arrangements, the planning, the tears and the fights, every wedding works out perfectly. My brother's was a case in point. He and Susan, the bride, organised the whole event themselves. Their choice of venue, Celtic Park, was designed to underline their shared love of football. That's right my lucky brother has scored himself a wife who will not shout at him for having a few jars after the game. Instead, she will shout at him for not getting the beers in.

To get warmed up, my mum, dad, ex-partner Pauline and I went to Chris's place for a calming glass of champagne. The flat was already full of friends, including the best man. I just could not believe how cool and laid-back Chris was. He was my brother alright, but he was stepping out of the shadows, becoming his own man. I had nothing to offer him except a smile and the feeling that I was losing him in some way. In contrast to Roslyn's beautiful big day, the weather for Chris's wedding was overcast and rainy. The (mis) behaviour of the dressed-up infants, however, more than made up for the weather. Oblivious to the sanctity of the service, they tore around the chapel, shouting and laughing as the priest bravely tried to administer the vows.

Having felt foolishly sentimental at Roslyn and Kevin's wedding, I had a huge lump in my throat when it came to my own brother. I thought of past times we had shared.

One time, when I was about ten, my uncle had left his car at our house. We were having some building work done and there was cement, sand and mortar lying around. At that time there were a lot of burglaries in the area so Chris and I took it upon ourselves to improve the security of my uncle's car. We mixed the ingredients to make concrete then we covered all the locks of the car, followed by the door handles. Job done, we decided to have a concrete fight. By the time my parents saw us, Chris and I could hardly move. For me, that problem was resolved quickly enough. I am sure I can still see the imprint of my father's hand on my backside.

I remember other times when Chris followed my lead, trusting his big brother implicitly. Thankfully, as he grew older, he could decide for himself what was normal behaviour and what was sheer nonsense. Listening to his speech, describing how he met Susan, how the romance turned to love, was special. No matter how many weddings you go to, a man telling a crowd how much he loves a woman is a special thing.

When I first heard that I had cancer, I knew this was one of the things that was being taken away from me. Not wanting to admit to myself that this was the case, I entered into a relationship with a loving, caring, beautiful girl. Pauline was with me at Chris's wedding, even though she has a new friend now. I didn't want to go with anyone else and I also needed the support.

Emotionally, I was all over the place. My mum, being her usual telepathic self, came over to check I was okay. Pauline had left early, so I had the traditional dance with my mum.

It reminded me that at the previous night's wedding, I was dancing with an Irish girl called Helena who works at the BBC. I am a rubbish dancer and stood all over her feet. She was an expert Irish dancer but despite her skill, my lead-footedness meant we were the couple everyone tried to avoid.

I lasted both the nights well, but at Chris's wedding I was happy to sit at the back and watch everyone enjoy themselves. He was leaving for his honeymoon the next day and in the confusion at the end of the night, I didn't get the chance to tell him how proud I was.

With cancer you always look back, back to the good times. Now Chris and Susan, along with Kevin and Roslyn, will have their own stories to make.

And I hope there are plenty of them.

29 July 2001

A Question of Faith:

AFTER my brother's wedding, with my unrelenting descent towards ill health, my emotions have taken me on a roller coaster ride.

Even half-price Prada failed to lift my spirits and I wandered around the shops uninterested. I have lost my usual enthusiasm for yet another shirt or jumper that I don't need.

I had a session booked with Angela at the Harvest Clinic. She is the nearest I get to having a therapist. In America, everybody has a therapist In fact; you are considered weird if you don't have one. Here in Britain we keep our problems bottled up because if you reveal your failings to someone else, it leaves you vulnerable.

I had been feeling particularly burdened with my failing health. Writing articles, going to awards nights, taking trips to Arran. Health wise, I had been kidding myself on. Normally, my strong will pulls my physically bereft body along, but the constant pain, the knowledge that I am going to die, maybe this year, is finally getting me down. I arrived at the clinic with a heavy heart. I was due for a session of Reiki; call it spirituality, hocus pocus or women's intuition, but Angela could tell that what I really needed was a chat. As lapsed Catholics, we both have the guilt complex thing going on.

I am increasingly seeing the Grim Reaper in every little thing I do. At my friends Roslyn and Kevin's wedding, I stood up to go to the bar and all of a sudden I had tunnel vision and a rushing noise in my ears. Surely I could not pass out in front of everyone? I had to plant each foot purposely in front of the other. I must have had a deranged look on my face as the bar staff shied away from my outstretched arm. Even though I was holding a £20 note.

I guess I was looking for Angela to say, 'There there, it will all be better soon', but of course she didn't, because it won't. We discussed the afterlife, whether I thought it really does exist and what form it will take. I was describing my idyllic childhood and how I was a voracious reader: Enid Blyton and the Famous Five and the Secret Seven, followed by Swallows and Amazons. I then progressed to The Hobbit and finally, The Lord of the Rings. I can see it from where I sit typing, dog-eared from constant re-reading. It has being made into a film, a three-parter, but the first part is not out until December. The next two will be out on the following two Decembers.

I will be lucky to see the first part of the trilogy and do you want to know what a saddo I am? I actually asked Angela if she thinks there will be cinemas in heaven? That assumes I will make it into heaven.

I have given the afterlife a lot of thought recently. Is there really a heaven and hell? Is there a long tunnel with a bright light at the end? Does your being take another form once it leaves your body? So many questions and not a long time to find out the answer.

I have done things that I am not proud of, but since finding out that I have cancer, I have tried to right the wrongs. Of course there is no chance of catching them all, but surely the act must count for something. Penance is a strange act, especially when you think back on all the misdeeds in your life.

I am, after all, only 31.

Reincarnation is a comforting thought, coming back to earth as a different person or even an animal. I would like to be reunited with the family and friends I have lost. Sometimes I feel especially close to them, perhaps when going through hard times such as a bad course of chemotherapy. I take heart from my suffering, knowing I am not alone with my sickness, remembering that there have been those I have loved who have died before me, good people, and honest people. Surely their lives have not been for nothing.

What makes it hard to reconcile is that all around there are scum who seem to live without a care or a damn for others. Drug pushers, rapists, child abusers, when do they get theirs? According to my religion, I have to forgive them. This is not easy, especially as my days are numbered and theirs are not.

There has to be a hell, a totting up of sins, a bottom line. There has to be an account of your life and if that means that I have to pay some sort of penance then so be it.

The last year has been so tough. What can God (or Buddha, Allah or whoever) throw at me that could equal the pain that has me sobbing in agony?

5 August 2001

A Helping Hand:

I NEVER thought that I was a "whinger", having lived with cancer symptoms for four years; I have tried to roll with all the punches that have come my way. But sometimes, it's hard to stay positive.

I am now more in tune with my body than I have ever been because having cancer in some parts of my body means that I am always aware of the probability of getting cancer in other areas

I look in the mirror, at my once-proud body, and it was tanned and lean, muscled and strong. Now I have a seven-pack, the extra muscle, pure tumour, growing and aching. It does feel strange, extolling medical health advice when I am such a temple of growths and lumps.

Only today I came across what my mother terms 'a nodule' but which I would call a small lump of tissue. I am so inundated with cancer that another lump does not make that much of a difference. This is not resignation, but facing up to reality. Part of my bathing regime now includes a self-examination. Bath time with the rubber duck, the loofah brush and the probing fingers. With testicular cancer on the increase, I find it important to check the old crown jewels every so often and would urge all males in the 18-50 age group to do the same. I know it's embarrassing, even for lads my age, so I can imagine how older men may feel. But you must. Look at footballer Alan Stubbs, formerly of Celtic. A young, fit man, at the peak of his career, and he succumbed to cancer. Against all odds, he beat the disease, after extreme chemotherapy. Of course the spectre of cancer will always haunt him, but he has returned to his career.

I attended one of Celtic's pre-season friendlies against an English club recently, and along with some friends decided to make a night of it and have some dinner before the game. The catering was perfectly acceptable, but I was disappointed to find that there were only two disabled toilets and I could find no locks on their doors. Needless to say, I did not find this trade-off acceptable. It's vital to have disabled facilities, but you do have to become a public spectacle to use them? You would expect one of Scotland's leading clubs to be setting the standards. I wonder how it is over the river. Are Rangers more accommodating to their disabled supporters?

The Parkhead experience could not have been more different than the one I had recently in Langs hotel. My mum, God love her, noticed that I was feeling depressed this week. Secretly she booked the lot of us into this groovy city centre hotel, convinced from seeing pictures and reading reviews, that it was my kind of place. She and I both respond to the restorative power of a night in a nice hotel. Oh, the decadence of it. It might only be 45 minutes away from the house, but it seems you are transported into another world.

Even though I only had a hold-all, the valet insisted he carried it to the room, which was, actually, a suite. The decor was trendy but cosy enough to encourage you to sit on the comfy chairs and sofas. The furniture was very Seventies, dark brown grained wood, bobbly fabrics and furniture which reminded me of the days when my Mum used to wear headscarves. I could even have a bath and watch TV at the same time because the suite had two sets. It was amazing.

I even got chatting to the manager, who was supervising staff training. The food was outstanding too.

The quality of the whole experience served to show me that I do not get out enough and when I do, I often accept mediocrity because of my condition.

So I will try to get out more, to get in training for the second annual charity weekend that I am hosting at the Cul-de-Sac Southside in September. I don't have an exact format for the weekend as yet but it will involve fun, alcohol, fancy dress costumes and lots of money raised for cancer causes. I am open to offers of ideas, celebrity appearances, promotions or whatever help you can offer.

 Last year's weekend raised more than £3000, but I am sure that, with some of your help, we can easily beat that.

12 August 2001

It's an Alternative Life:

IT was a relief when my parents redecorated the bathroom and took the mirror from the wall.
That way, I don't need to see my face as I pee, a sensation akin to burning hot needles passing through a straw.

I was planning to write about hope this week. About how I hold out against the odds. A reader recently wrote and accused me of providing false hope to cancer sufferers by advocating alternative therapies. Before I make my case for the defence, I would point out that I prefer to call them complementary therapies, as I use them to complement my NHS treatment.

Four years ago I discovered I had cancer and two years ago I was given a magazine column to chronicle my struggle against the disease. It is part of this brief to talk about my treatment, both conventional and otherwise. I have always been treated by the best in the business, so even if those so-called alternative treatments do not work, at least I know that professionals have administered them. Since starting the column I have been astonished by the relentless arrival of mail, snail or email, from readers. Lots of you think the tone of my articles is negative and you suggest all types of cures and concoctions. I have tried some and still take a few on a regular basis. One reader recommended Essiac, a Canadian treatment used by Native Americans. It's a supplement you add to tea and it tastes disgusting but I endure it. Why? Because I am so desperate I would try anything and it is not such a great imposition to include it in my diet.

This can't be said for another recommended regime, called the Gerson treatment. I first heard about this as part of an upbeat message from a reader whose friend had been 'sent home to die', a phrase that always sends the alarm bells ringing. Fortunately, someone had recommended this miraculous diet. It was formulated in the Twenties and involved copious amounts of fruit juices to strengthen the immune system. That sounded OK; I already take vitamins and supplements like Smarties. But, in order to detoxify the liver, you had to administer up to five coffee enemas a day, a service you certainly can't get at Starbucks.

No, an enema is a medical procedure which should only be done by a trained person, and the Gerson treatment is the sort of dangerous procedure that I have no time for. On further investigation, it turned out the poor person who was undergoing this foul-sounding regime was still receiving treatment from the NHS, so they had not been sent home to die after all. There was no way you could categorically say this weird diet was the only factor saving this person. Another phrase that sends shivers up my spine is 'and the doctors just could not believe the turnaround in the condition'. What the person who writes this usually neglects to mention is that the ill person is also getting regular conventional treatment such as surgery, chemotherapy or radiotherapy.

Other strange offers include dodgy clinics in Eastern Bloc countries or Mexico offering unlicensed procedures for hard currency. Unlike conventional medicine, there are few statistics to back up their success. One such statistic, based on the Gerson diet, showed that out of a control group of 20, there were 19 deaths and the last one still had cancer. Of course statistics can be manipulated to show whatever they want. The only option is anecdotal evidence. 'He said, she said, I swear to God ... ' — this is the sort of advice I receive from readers offering help. I do appreciate their kindness, but I am not willing to subject myself to anything that infringes on my already deteriorating quality of life.

My ex-girlfriend's sister's new baby was christened last week. It was her first child, a little girl. I know babies are always cute, but I have never seen such a beautiful baby as little Adrianna. She is absolutely gorgeous. It was a real family day and, as always, I was treated like an adopted son. I was feeling very emotional — weddings, christenings and the like always remind me that these are occasions that I will never be hosting.
Pauline was there with her new boyfriend and she seems very happy. Her happiness is of the utmost importance to me and I do not want to look like a martyr to my illness. Of course it was hard, really hard, to see her with someone else, but I think back to the times towards the end of our relationship and realise how tough it must have been for her.

I was out on Friday night at a friend's engagement party, yet another heart-wrenching event that I won't be having. I don't think I spoke to a single girl. Most of the crowd know me, and my story, so I guess no girl would want to get involved in a protracted chat for fear of getting entangled in a messy "tête-à-tête". I still look good — the photo at the top of the page does not do me justice, honest — and I have always been very self-confident when chatting up girls. So it's not that I have lost my pulling power, it's just that I am not the pull I used to be. I feel a bit like James Stewart in It's a Wonderful Life, except there will not be a ringing bell at the end of this episode.

Just a tolling one.

19 August 2001

A Joint Effort:

IT'S the silly season, so it's time to have the 'should cannabis be legalised?' debate again.

Regular readers might remember my brief flirtation with this weed as a means of pain control and to alleviate my terrible bouts of nausea. It worked on both counts but I was just not happy about ingesting what is basically an untested drug, especially as anything which is smoked is basically carcinogenic. I know there are different ways to take cannabis, but I do not fancy any of them. I prefer my chocolate brownies without any additives.

So I feel as if I know what I'm talking about and I have something to contribute to the argument. One of the regular objections to so-called 'soft drugs' is that they act as a doorway to harder drugs, such as cocaine and heroin. This is nonsense and many people, including Senior Police Officers, Judges and Government Officials have come to agree. All have recently appealed for the decriminalisation of cannabis in Scotland, which they would hardly do if they thought it would make the drug problem worse. The stumbling block is the Scottish Executive, which has vehemently opposed any action, which would lead to the easing of the drugs laws.

I do find it ironic that a relatively minor point of legislation should rouse our MSPs into anger and indignation. When it comes to the major issues, such as the token increase in health spending announced recently, they seem unable to get past the first page of the proposed legislation without arguing over tiny inconsequential matters.
The professionals who want to see cannabis decriminalised see the Executive's decision as narrow-minded and gutless.

At the moment, organisations, which have a legitimate reason for growing cannabis, such as university departments which research cannabis and its properties, are awarded a special licence. This happens in the

Stirling area and some enterprising students have identified the van that the authorities use and followed it to discover the identification of the location of this legal stash. Who said students are lazy? University campuses are traditionally tolerant and laid back but a recent newspaper survey looked at a representative slice of the population. It found that most Scots are against legalisation of cannabis. Only about a third of those questioned wanted the laws relaxed. I think this is because the majority of the public still sees cannabis as a link to harder drugs.

The superficial evidence for this argument is easy to find: all the dealers I know who sell cannabis either have, or have access to, harder drugs. I buy cannabis for a reason and have never been tempted by the little wrap of white/brown powder, although to be honest I am not typical in any way as I am already on some pretty serious medication — and it arrives by prescription.

The most important point to remember from the survey is that only four per cent — that's less than one in 20 of cannabis users — had taken other drugs. Cannabis is a recreational drug used in much the same way as alcohol and cigarettes. I don't need to roll out the figures detailing the dangers of smoking. And if there are fights in car parks after heavy dope-smoking sessions, I have never heard about them. Things are changing, slowly. There is a trial area in Lambeth, North London, where police officers have been ordered to let cannabis users off with a warning. Customs authorities have unofficially used this approach for years. They do not rate dope smugglers as a high priority — it's Class A drug pushers they're after.

The Home Secretary, David Blunkett, recently called for an intelligent approach to the cannabis issue. He has an unlikely ally in Peter Lilley, who shook the Conservative Party's foundations when he recommended that Britain should adopt the Dutch approach to selling cannabis, with licensed outlets selling limited amounts of the drug, which would also carry a medical warning. This, he went on to say, would cut the link between the dealers of hard and soft drugs.

In Amsterdam police are free to pursue big-time dealers and are not bogged down with the paperwork of arresting a few small-time stoners.

You would be surprised how many people smoke cannabis, people of all ages and backgrounds. Whether you like it or not, cannabis will be legalised.

The only question is: will I be around to see it.

In The Nick Of Time:

WHAT were Nick Nairn and I doing in Prestwick Airport? Why have I changed my views on organic vegetables? Where do the fancy dress outfits fit in to the story? Read on.

I met Nick Nairn while writing this column. I had seen him on television of course and always liked his easy-going humour. Yes, he is a top chef, has his own restaurant and all that it entails but I really warmed to him when he had to watch some little highland granny make haggis while he was clearly suffering from a hangover. As the lady poured the day-old sheep's blood into the pot, Nick visibly blanched, which was impressive because he had just returned from a holiday in the Caribbean. The editors cut it off there but you could tell he was one swallow away from a full-on "Chunder".

In real life, we met for lunch at his Glasgow restaurant. I was with my editor and Nick sat at our table in between running to the kitchen to cook other people's lunches. He was down-to-earth, funny and did not patronise me because I have cancer. Instead, he was up-front about the disease and genuinely interested in my progress. Since that day I have met him a few times and I'm glad to say Nick has become a friend. When he phoned out of the blue last week to ask for directions to my house, I was intrigued. He stays in the wilds of Stirlingshire, a good two hours away from Ayr. He said he had a present for me, and rather than him driving through the maze that is Prestwick, I arranged to meet him at the airport. Nobody could miss that.

Mum insisted on coming along to meet the man in person, with me teasing her all the way — 'Oh Nick, you're so talented. I wish I could cook like you' — ringing in her ears.

We share a love of cars, Nick and I, especially impractical ones with no storage space, so when he jumped out of his gorgeous motor with a huge box, I panicked. Previously Nick had donated half his wardrobe to be sold for charity — if this were more, what would he have left to wear? Then I noticed a flourish of greenery. The box was filled with produce. It turns out that at his cookery school's kitchen garden had had a particularly successful season, with plenty to spare for failing columnists who need all the vitamins and minerals they can get. All the vegetables were organic, as were the herbs, and Mum and I were soon imagining roast beef with all the trimmings and delicious veg. The potatoes were absolutely huge and the courgettes ... well formed.

After squeezing this cornucopia of organic produce into my car's very small boot, I felt I owed Nick a coffee at the very least. Now those of you who have visited Prestwick will know it does not boast a Starbucks or branch of Costa but, due to a memorable event back on March 3, 1960, the airport boasts an Elvis Presley lounge. So we sat drinking our cappuccinos out of paper cups and it occurred to me that generous, thoughtful Nick had not done very well out of the transaction.

At the weekend my brother Chris, sister Madeleine and their respective partners came down to the house to enjoy a huge roast beef dinner. Although I previously thought organic produce was only for those of you who stay in Glasgow's West End, and the entire population of Edinburgh, I have changed my mind. The difference in taste is unbelievable. I actually decided to forgo an extra portion of meat to eat extra vegetables.

I can now see where Nick gets his enthusiasm for campaigning to get Scots to eat a better diet. I for one will now try to eat organic whenever it is available.

I have also been running around like a madman trying to organise the charity weekend at the Cul de Sac Southside on September 22-23. Last year we raised almost £4000 but this year we are not having an auction, so will have to make up the shortfall some other way. Some kind readers have already offered prizes for our raffle but I implore those of you who are in a position to offer goodies to get in touch.

Although the main aim of the weekend is to raise money for cancer respite care, the fun element is certainly not being overlooked. Last year we had an Elvis theme night, which sounded great, but my family were the only ones who dressed up. I need to think of a good theme that everyone can get involved in. I know there were cries of cheat, but it was just luck that my friends won the seven-a-side football tournament last year. They will defend valiantly in my name but please feel free to enter your team.

If you think you're hard enough.

Please let me have your ideas and enthusiasm. I'd love to see you there. Come up and say hello. I'm the guy who looks nothing like my photo.

2 September 2001

A Growing Unease:

FAME. What a strange thing it is.

I am not being bigheaded but this column is certainly getting me known. Let me explain.

Earlier this month I was lucky enough to get tickets for Celtic v Kilmarnock at Rugby Park. Deciding to be safe rather than sorry, I phoned to find out about their disabled facilities. The staff were very helpful and promised they had toilets for both home and away fans. Fine, so off we went.

At half-time you get a prize draw, usually hosted by a former player from the club, plus some poor sod dressed as a chipmunk who has the dubious honour of trying to amuse the fans by being the club mascot. Most of the fans respond with suggestions, which I think are physically impossible as they try not to spill the grease and gravy flowing from their half-time pie.

So I was ignoring all this, discussing the game with my dad when Chris, my brother, pointed to the electric scoreboard. As I looked up, a message flashed up. 'Keep on writing Jonathan, congratulations!' I was shocked but chuffed at the same time and thank Kilmarnock for their kind gesture. I'm sure most of the punters were wondering who this Jonathan was. Perhaps some new signing who can write his name as well as kick a ball. As well as their nice message, Kilmarnock kindly gave me permission to park within the ground. All I had to do was get there half an hour before the game and secure my space. Sadly, we were 30 seconds too late. The policeman who denied us access to the ground had a familiar face. The face of the doorman who denies you entry to a nightclub when you are sober and well dressed and with your girlfriend. "Jobsworths" all have the same gormless faces.

As my father, brother and sister-in-law all tried to reason with PC Plod, I felt a strange rush of emotion, a flood of feelings I would never have thought possible, what with me being a nice guy and all. So if you respect me and think I am a special person please skip the next paragraph because what I am about to describe is out of character and despicable. As I sat in the car outside the ground, watching my family trying to persuade the policeman to change his mind, I wished I could have given him my cancer. The only reason I didn't shout this out to him was that he was already being harangued by my family. Imagine the malice, the hatred in my soul, to wish what I have on this poor simple servant of the people.

I still feel bad about it. I feel I have let everybody down. Each week I receive loads of emails and letters of support. How do I repay you? By trying to put a hex on an inept policeman and his blameless family. God forgive me for those thoughts. I've let myself down.

My spleen has started to ache a lot more. I have had a strange relationship with this tumour. All things remaining equal, it's not the one that is going to kill me. About two years ago, it started to protrude from my ribcage and, having always been proud of my body, I was keen to have it removed. Unfortunately, surgery was not an option.

I'll never forget the words of the first surgeon who operated on me. He said he had never seen such a mass of tumour in such a young man. Trust me to be an overachiever.

As the months passed the tumour started to stick out more. I had a blast of chemotherapy and also a dose of radiotherapy. The chemotherapy had a failure rate of 97 per cent, but it was worth a try. The radiotherapy was a different story. Because the tumour was concentrated on one part of my body, the chances were better. The consultant drew a target on my torso, for the radiographer to aim at. This was the first time I had an idea of the size of the beast. It scared the hell out of me. Still, the consultant pronounced it a success, terming my tumours as slow growing. That was a while ago and I feel a bit out of the loop. This is why I advocate pro-active treatment: you have to chase the doctors. Their minds are not always 100 per cent on your case.

With this in mind I have a course of treatments coming up and I am a bit apprehensive. Along with treatment comes tests and results. For the last year I have been living in a cloud (or is that a fog). Now it's time for me to face up to what the cancer has been up to while the medical profession's backs have been turned.

I'm not looking forward to it.

9 September 2001

Pipes Of Peace:

HURRAH. Break out the smoking pipes, start polishing your brass bongs, the government has finally capitulated and National Health Service patients are to be offered cannabis after surgery.

This is the first time that the drug has been evaluated for its pain-relieving properties in a proper medical study.

This initial trial will take place in London and will be regulated by the Medical Research Council. The volunteers will take three types of pill. One third of the patients will be given a form of cannabis, one third will be given a conventional painkiller, say morphine, and the final group will be given a control pill, a dummy, with no side effects.

I am delighted at this news because my main pain relief drug is morphine. Its side effects include addiction, dizzy spells and breathlessness, plus it knocks me for six when mum gives me the injection. I'm sure I'm an addict already.
If my condition were not so serious, my doctor would have downgraded my pain control drug to something like codeine. Unfortunately, no I really mean ironically, this bloody sciatica causes my main pain. To help with this I've started a new treatment at the Harvest Clinic, called Tui-na. As the name suggests it's an oriental kind of massage and the masseur, Fraser, truly does have fingers of steel. The treatment is based on pressure points and as he also works with people who suffer from MS, I knew I was in good hands. After the massage I felt like a new man. The pain returned the next day but that day's relief was well worth it. I am definitely going to follow up this treatment.

Cannabis is an attractive alternative to morphine although Rizlas will not be necessary and will be offered to people suffering from cancer and MS. In fact a hospital in England has already started to use cannabis on patients with these conditions and their experiences will have a great bearing on the government's decision on whether to legalise it or not. Having a proper trial will give them a definitive answer: a standard tablet, with the same amount of the drug given over a controlled period.

Other countries are conducting their own tests, with Switzerland unearthing positive results and some states in America already allowing the drug on prescription. Here in Britain, any evidence is anecdotal. I used it and found it useful. I only stopped because I hate smoking. Smoking the drug carries a high risk of mouth, throat and lung cancer, the same as smoking cigarettes really but without the added nicotine and tar. Patients have been given the choice of taking part in the trial well in advance of their surgery. Let's hope these trials are the first step to proving cannabis useful in treating cancer and MS.

Now, I'm afraid, I'm on the scrounge. With my charity night approaching, I would like to appeal to your better nature in asking for prizes in the raffle. I know everyone is inundated with demands to contribute to charity. When I walk down Buchanan Street, I adopt a criss-cross pattern to avoid the clipboard people. All I can offer is one great weekend of fun, laughs and cheap drink, aimed at raising money for cancer relief. Last year's event was a great success. The only complaints were from those who missed the night and heard from others what a good time everyone had.

Planning the charity weekend gives me something to aim for, because I am close to my next target, my 31st birthday.

I like being 30 though. Most people don't have a clue what they want from life until they hit 30. I felt the same. If I was a normal Joe and not riddled with cancer I would be thinking of going down to London. We constantly talk up Glasgow and Edinburgh but in our hearts we know that staying in Scotland will limit those with infinite ambition.

I really envy those of you younger than me; you have it all in front of you. Suddenly realising that the dream job you have is not so peachy after all is a common complaint I get from readers of my own age.

That's why I believe foreign travel should be a prerequisite for everyone under 25. I have just said goodbye to a friend who is off to work in Greece. He will probably end up "skint" living in some dive, doing some crappy job, but I know he will love every minute of it. God knows I loved my American-Caribbean odyssey and when I came home, I found Glasgow had not changed a bit.

Life is for living. You get one throw of the dice and that is it.

16 September 2001

Losing Patients:

SO, how was your birthday, Jono?

The big three-one, gateway to the mid-life crisis and middle-aged spread?' Well, thanks to our health minister Susan Deacon, I had the worst birthday of my life.

'What, even worse than the birthday spent in a wheelchair with two broken legs?'
Oh yes. Much worse than that. That was bliss compared to this day from hell.

The week before my birthday was particularly tough. Monday was spent at the Beatson Oncology Centre at the Western Infirmary. It's the west of Scotland's Cancer Grand Central Station, but people from all over the country go there because it is supposed to be a centre of excellence. I guess five, maybe ten years ago it probably was, but with the NHS being ravaged, it is a shadow of its former self. The former Head of the Beatson left earlier this year, for a job which was better paid and, more importantly, with better conditions. I can't take out my anger on him, because I would have done the same.

What does make me rage is that they spent over £1million on a cosmetic refit when the whole department is being transferred to Gartnavel. Why? Just so Susan Deacon can be seen cutting a ribbon to a white elephant. Forget the patients' health, just as long as they have a nice new entrance to get wheeled into, with its non-working automatic doors.

So the acting head is now my consultant. I should have been flattered, my doctor being the big cheese now. But wait a minute, doesn't that mean he has less time for me? To be fair, he answered all my questions, then got in a radiotherapist to discuss a future treatment, perhaps the answer to my excruciating back problem. All in all a productive day, compared to previous visits. He wanted to see if there was 'any mischief' in my back region, so the next day I was scheduled for an MRI scan in Ayr. That's when I should

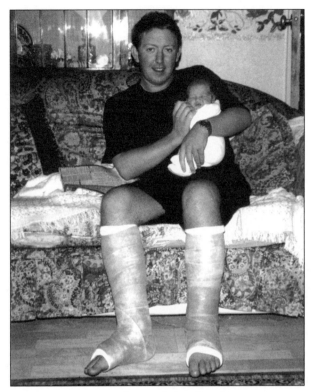

Jonathan with Stookies.

have started to get the heebie-jeebies because when you have two hospitals liaising you are dealing with two giants of administrative nightmarish proportions.

The scan itself was pretty scary. These machines are coffin sized and you are slotted in like prawn rolls into a microwave, with your nose three inches from the top. Definitely not the place for the claustrophobic. There was, however, one comic moment. I love the American writer Brett Easton Ellis, and in the film, American Psycho, at one of the climactic moments, the psycho plays a Phil Collins album. Now in the MRI scanner you have to wear headphones to protect your ears. I put them on and there was Phil Collins. So there I was, laughing hysterically, with the nurses wondering what was wrong with me while I had images of murder and mayhem running through my mind. The next day I had a blissful two-hour massage, which was just the thing to set me up because then it was back into the hands of regular medics at Ayr Hospital to collect my scan, results, to speed things up.

I'm used to my old school friends turning up in professional capacities, so when a former classmate entered the room I wasn't surprised.

In fact, I was happy to catch up and was pleased to note that Brian was pushing the envelope, as far as the medical profession was concerned. I was also happy because the last time we met, Brian had three fingers up my bum. 'So how have you been?' he asked on that memorable occasion 'Been better, to be honest with you,' I replied with my knees at my chin.

Friday I was back for another amazing massage. I had knots upon knots and now my back is a paragon of skeletal magnificence. So I felt ready for the ultra-important appointment on my birthday.

So it came and it was a beautiful day, very hot. Mum and I drove up to the Beatson for my 1.30pm appointment. I was ten minutes early, as always. Two o'clock came and went. I started getting cranky in the heat. People were standing waiting to see their doctor. A nurse came out and wrote on the notice board 'all clinics are running half an our late', which was already a lie as I had been there for 40 minutes. As 2.30pm came and went I was beginning to lose it. Poor Mum watched as her son rocked and fidgeted and berated the NHS. Two hours after my appointment, I was called in. The consultant mumbled hello. I could not speak because it would have been peppered with expletives. Then he started to look through my scans. Surely the most recent ones, the Phil Collins ones, would be at the top. After a good 20 minutes of searching, he admitted what I had started to fear — the scans were not there.

Happy birthday!

I don't blame the nurses, doctors or consultants, although I did wonder if the patient with a bad reaction to his chemo really needed six consultants, all their assistants and 30 nursing staff to look after him. No, the wasted time, the mistakes and delays, fall squarely on the droopy shoulders of Susan Deacon.

We used to have a health service we could be proud of.

No longer!

23 September 2001

Life Goes On?

IN a world gone crazy, where you can watch terrorists fly aeroplanes into skyscrapers full of people live on TV, I have to ask myself a serious question. Is this the sort of world I am struggling to stay in?

Like so many others, I couldn't switch it off. I sat in my house watching the events unfold. As my dad remarked bitterly, they won't be showing Die Hard for a while. Who could have predicted the carnage that was going to unfold?

I immediately thought of my fellow columnist, Aaron, whom I stayed with when I visited the Big Apple. I knew he didn't stay in Manhattan, but as the editor of a stylish GQ-type magazine, he would be flitting around the fast-track world of New York. Where was he? A phone call to the office here made matters worse. My editor, Anna, was there too. She has the same taste in hotels as I have — expensive and probably in Manhattan. Fortunately she checked in at the office; she and Aaron were OK and were reporting on the tragedy. I found it dizzying that an event on the other side of the world could be linked to me. I had spent a good part of the weekend making up some CDs for Aaron. I had been promising to do it for ages, maybe some premonition made me do it that week.

One horrible thought crossed my mind. What if I was one of these sad people who liked to associate themselves with tragedy, whose own pathetic lives are so devoid of anything interesting that they attach themselves to the sorrow of the occasion? I had seen the scenes from the American Embassy in London. They had received so many floral tributes that they had to open up a previously unopened part of the gardens. The last time I had witnessed this sort of mass hysteria on a floral scale, was when Princess Diana died. Wouldn't a prayer or period of quiet reflection be more genuine and sincere? I know that an unfolding tragedy can be compelling — readers regularly tell me that they turn to my page as soon as they get the paper, just to see if I am still alive. That scares me. I suppose they mean it as a compliment, but it feels spooky to me.

As I have already written my last column, you will all find out when I am ready to check out. Writing it has been a bit of a constant struggle. Every week I find a part I don't like, or that I feel that I could improve, so I change it. Now I have an article that is wholly different from the initial one that I wrote. It's a hybrid, a collage of thoughts and ideas that I have had since I have started writing the column. When you think about it, 1000 words is not too much to describe your life and best moments, to remind friends, family and readers just what a special person I was/am.

Meanwhile, I'm getting obsessed about where I would be in life if I did not have cancer. I was reading about young trendy Scots who were taking part in Fashion Week down in London and I knew more than half of them. Without being bigheaded, if that was going to be my chosen career, I would be damned sure I would be near the top of the pile. What is the point of doing a job if you are not going to be the best you can be? I could never be a 9-5 prole, putting in 40 hours a week for 40 years to get a gold Seiko watch and a pittance of a pension to live on in my twilight years. I'm not talking about the red braces, blue shirt with white-collar crowd. The financial sector is full of money, and if you work hard, you can end up with a job, which may not be ideal but would give you the financial freedom to have a life.

But not for me. There are too many people putting in the hours to live for the Friday night after-work crowd, meeting in All Bar One, propping up the bar, trying to look the business, simultaneously hopeful and hopeless, trying to catch the eye of someone of the opposite sex.

The whole social scene has changed since I started to bloom on the Glasgow circuit. I have a younger brother and sister, so it was my job to break down all the social barriers with my parents and stretch the 11pm curfew to 4am at the weekend. The fights were legendary. If only my younger siblings knew what I went through for their benefit. There were not so many bars in Glasgow then, so you could be assured of a warm welcome wherever you went. Nowadays you are lucky if you meet one person you know. Or maybe it's just me being old.

Most people my age are at home with their wives and children, or in London for Fashion Week with their jobs and parties.

What they are not doing is sitting around watching planes fly in to the World Trade Centre, feeling sorry for themselves, because they have cancer.

30 September 2001

Parental Guidance:

AFTER the debacle of my birthday, when I had to wait two hours to see a consultant only to be told that the scans, on which he was going to base my treatment, were not actually in his possession, I was slightly sceptical when the appointment card for my radiotherapy arrived.

Radiotherapy is the only option available for my cancer. Surgery is out of the question as my tumours are touching so many of my organs and there is no form of chemotherapy available that would do me any good.

Actually I am quite happy about this, as the side effects of some of my earlier chemotherapy were quite horrific. Sterility, for example. Not for me the pitter-patter of Jonathan juniors. That was a hard one to bear. I even offered to go on a medical trial, on the off chance that there was a 0.01 per cent probability of it doing me some good, that's how desperate I am. So radiotherapy is the only option I had. I arrived at the clinic early as I always do, stupidly thinking that I would be taken earlier, but to my great surprise, my name was called after only ten minutes. The procedure was split into two parts: the first was to mark the 'targets' on my body with a felt-tip pen. Very technical. I then had to wait until the radiotherapy machine was free. Here we go, I thought, and settled down for a long wait. Imagine my surprise as my name was called after only five minutes.

I was told to strip, no problem there, and lie on a metal bed. The machine itself looks like a big ray gun, similar to the one in Goldfinger, which gave James Bond a fright. The two nurses pushed and shoved my body into the right position and then told me not to move. Then they ran into an adjoining room, as if the machine was in some way harmful. Of course to someone like me, who has radiotherapy once a year, there are no dangerous side-effects (well, maybe a few, but I'll leave that for later) but to the nurses who work day in, day out with the radiotherapy machinery, they cannot afford to take any chances. Still, it was slightly comical, watching them scurry from the room as the machine did its stuff. It reminded me of Homer Simpson at the nuclear power plant, inadvertently causing mayhem.

Now my back pain is not as bad as it was, although I think this is due to the double whammy of Tui-na (oriental massage) and the radiotherapy. I know I always moan about my picture at the top of the page not looking like me but, as I was leaving the clinic, I was recognised by a reader. I guess it is one of the trappings of fame. (That was a joke.) So the radiotherapy was successful. At a price.

My constitution is unpredictable at the best of times but what I am experiencing just now is awful. I am seriously considering moving my portable TV into the toilet; such is the amount of time I spend there every day. My weakened legs mean getting there can be a race against time, especially when I am woken in the middle of the night with the urge. I now know how elderly people must feel, that anxiety. Can I risk that last cup of tea? Will I get to the toilet in time?

Another worry I have is that my parents' health is suffering. How can you measure the effects of living through the gradual loss of your eldest son, someone you have cared for, nurtured, loved? They both take a great interest in my health. My mother, being a nursing sister, takes all the medical stuff in her stride and accompanies me to all the scans, tests and procedures. But I also get support at home.

I often wake her up during the night, looking for relief from pain. She pats my back, as I am being sick and cooks for me, no matter what time it is. Dad is always on hand when Mum is at work. He is turning into quite a professional masseur and nothing is too much trouble.

I have always looked up to my father, but I have to remember that this is not a normal set-up. My parents should be enjoying this period of life, yet they have to look after their eldest son who is dying. Not much of a retirement. They spoil me and when I'm in hospital I sometimes see people who have no family or friends. I remind myself of my fortunate position and try to remember how much more grim it could be.

Facing this slow death without companionship would test my resolve. I do enjoy my own company. but from the position of having friends and family to talk to and fall back on.

Cancer does not just affect one person. It rips through families.

I'm just lucky to have the back up I have.

7 October 2001

Stiff Upper Lip:

LIFE sucks when your lips swell up like Pamela Anderson's.

Sunday saw the second night of my Charity bash, the culmination of months of planning, and I felt sicker than Chris Morris on a diet of bad oysters. There I was with a sore throat, a thermometer- melting temperature and – worst of all- that swollen kisser. Not that this last thing made too much difference. Still, as I have discovered, when you have cancer, a snog is never on the agenda.

One of my closest friends, Rosalyn, says I should be more selfish, but a relationship would be too complicated, and I am loathe to hurt another person. I'm glad that my last girlfriend has got another boyfriend and is enjoying life again. It's not such a bad deal: I still have a good friend, plus a lot of great memories. More and more I find myself reflecting on past relationships, thinking of the good times, but if I'm honest, I look upon my past relationships as lucky escapes. Imagine I had got married when I was younger, had kids, and then discovered I was ill. The writer John Diamond had that to deal with. How do you explain cancer and dying to young child?

Anyway, I had other things on my mind, namely driving to Glasgow for the Charity night. Had I crashed the car, no airbags would have been required. My lips would have done the job. By the time I arrived, I found the bar-"Cul de Sac"- already busy, full of guys recovering from the five-a-side football tournament. Last year, the tournament was won by my friends, securing the snappily titled cup, The Jonathan Wilson Memorial Trophy. One year on, both the cup and I are still around. The prize, once more, was a keg of Miller. Even split between five guys, 88 pints is still a lot of beer, and the competition was fierce. My brother's team was one of the early casualties. Chris has finally discovered that when you reach a certain age, your brain tends to be a second or two ahead of the body. The final was contested between two teams who had my shared allegiance, so either way I was getting a pint from it.

Steep any Scotsman in enough lager and he will begin to believe he is Billy Connolly. Mercifully we were kept in our place by the presence of a gaggle (or should that be giggle?) of real comedians. The Stand Comedy Club provided two of their top laughter jockeys- Bob Doolally and Richard Allen – to keep us entertained. Another Stand Regular, the incomparable Susan Morrison, hosted the auction and raffle. She is to hecklers what Stalin was to democracy, and dispensed withering one-liners with surgical accuracy

Enjoying the entertainment were Jackie Bird and Tam Cowan, who I had somehow persuaded to come along. Jackie was going on holiday the next morning, but- being a staunch supporter of my charity and a real sweetheart- she still turned up. Meeting Tam Cowan was funny. Watching his T.V. series "Taxi For Cowan", I had imagined that he would be a small podgy guy, but he's actually taller than me. Still, he has the physique of a man who admits having eaten five fish suppers in a day! It's amazing, how he finds time to go to the "Chippy", what with the TV series, two newspaper columns and his radio job as a football pundit. And he has the added stress of being a Motherwell supporter.

By the time the auction started, many of the drinkers were" blazing", which was fine by me as I'm sure that alcohol was behind some of the bids.

There were some very interesting prizes, including a day at "Nick Nairn's" cooking school, and a lawyer who offered his services free, if you were buying or selling a house.

A cleaning company said they would clean your house, from top to bottom, plus do your ironing and shopping, and even walk your dog. My Aunt Therese bought this for my mum, who panicked and vowed to have our house spic-and- span for the arrival of the cleaners.

For the more outdoorsy type, there was a day at the "Jackie Stewart" Shooting School at Gleneagles. Susan joked that you could learn to shoot and then buy the signed "Rangers" top. I wonder what foot she kicks with?

With the raffle and auction over, people drifted towards the party in the upstairs bar. Still feeling terrible, I was ready to go home, but was press-ganged into making a speech, no mean feat when you have lips that look like mating zeppelins!

This was our second annual charity do: the first took place one year ago to the day. If at that point you had said to me then that I would still be alive twelve months on, I would have been skeptical. But as I spoke into the microphone and saw all the faces, I promised that I would try my very best to attend the third charity bash.

I know that it is silly to attempt fate, but seeing my family and friends gathered in one place is special, and I'm determined to repeat the experience. Rest assured that I will be there next year, in spirit if not in body.

This isn't just lip service – I mean it!

14 October 2001

Duvet Daze:

IN America, when you skip work and stay in bed for the duration, they call it a duvet day.

For me, this was more than a lazy day under the covers. I used to mock those who classified depression as an illness. Until recently. Now I realise how it creeps up on you slowly.

You miss a meal, you unplug the phone because you can't face talking to anyone, you stay up late so that day becomes night and night becomes day. In the past week I have not been in bed before 3am.

I have all the toys to help me sit up all night: video recorder, DVD player, Sky TV, all played on a wide screen TV. Then there is my Harry Potter collection. Late-night TV is truly trashy, but if you are desperate you can always manage to find something to watch, something to pass another half an hour. My constitution does not help matters and I am often woken up in the middle of the night for the cold trip up to the bathroom. As the house stirs around 8am, with my niece Abbie watching TV, I could break the chain and get up. Sure, I think, I would be tired, but I could nap in the afternoon. I do not, however, get up. Instead I turn over and cover my head with the warm duvet.

Can you blame me for preferring cosy dreamland to horrible reality? I take a cocktail of exotic drugs, which give me vivid dreams. When you consider my real life, losing my health, in pain, sitting around wondering how long I have left, it's hardly surprising I prefer a dream state. There I am fit, healthy and happy, perhaps even married with kids, instead of ill, lonely and maudlin. I would gladly lie in bed all day if it meant I was warm, comfortable and living a life (even though it was just in my mind) without cancer. You may think I am wishing my life away. Whatever happened to brave Jonathan, facing up to his disease, poster boy for the cancer generation, icon to those who suffer from cancer? I get tired, just like anyone else. I used to have a great life, great friends and good times. To an extent I still do, but my days are taking on a familiar pattern and that is not a good thing.

I see my friends getting engaged, getting married, buying flats and I get excited for them. They are embarking on a journey, one that I can never take. So a bit of escapism here and there temporarily lifts my spirits. I get to see and meet people in places and situations that are not possible in real life. Perhaps this is what the afterlife is like. This time last year I was preparing to walk the West Highland Way, 97 miles of pure hell. I loved every minute of it, not just because I raised so much money (and I thank those of you who are also sending cheques this year). It was that I felt so alive, walking in the stunning Scottish scenery, embracing each hill and muddy field. Sure, the weather was terrible, but I will tell you, you never feel as alive as when you are close to death. I would give anything to be fit enough to do the walk again but these days; a walk to the shops is my limit. At least I still have the memories, which I will cherish forever.

It seems I am not the only one who lives in a world of their own. There can't be anyone who was not horrified by the recent acts of terrorism in the United States. The loss of life is hard to understand and tests those of us who have a faith-belief system. In today's information-led society, you are bombarded by the terrible images on the television 24/7, you can't miss the coverage, no matter what channel you watch or so I thought.

Regular readers will be familiar with Gran. She is my only living grandparent and I love her dearly. One of her most endearing qualities is a talent for comedy, although she is not aware of it herself.

With the disaster in New York, European football, including the Celtic game, was called off and put back a week, so of course it wasn't on TV. Now, my grandmother buys a certain Scottish tabloid, mainly for the television listings, so when the time came for the football to come on and it didn't, she was confused. She phoned our house to see if we were getting it. Despite 24-hour TV reporting, blanket coverage in the written Press and radio, she had opened the paper, skipped over the 20 pages or so describing the disaster and made straight for the television page.

Unless a subject comes within her sphere of interest, it might as well not have happened. 'Did you not watch the TV?' we asked. 'Of course.'
'Well, what channel?'

It turns out it was the sci-fi channel. For 12 hours a day, every day, she watches Buck Rogers and Battlestar Gallactica. Perhaps, like me, Gran has her own sort of escapism, shutting out all the bad news to go to a place where she is happy.

Whatever makes life bearable. Go Gran.

21 October 2001

Terminal One:

IT'S fair to say that as I am terminally ill, I am also terminally depressed.

One reader pointed out that the column title means that I have given up already, and that I am already a 'deadman'. I just wish I had the energy to put up an argument, but I don't.

Although I'm on anti-depressants, when I wake up in a cold sweat in the middle of the night, wondering what lies ahead, I am depressed and scared. And who wouldn't be? Some days, it's hard to even raise my head from under the duvet, as I lie in my favourite foetal position, warm and safe. And even when I do venture up from the safe haven of my bed, it's never until at least midday. My next move once I'm up is to retire to the comfort of my reclining chair in my now cocoon-like room. And why not? My mum and dad pop in to see me periodically because they don't like to see me on my own, but company will not cure what I have. I do have visitors whenever I'm up to it though. I'm lucky to have so many good friends who come to see me whenever I need them. And their presence often lifts my spirits.

I have other ways of dealing with the disease that has blighted my life though. I have to admit, I'm a cancer spotter. Ever since I was diagnosed, I do this thing, which has become my obsession — I trawl newspapers, looking for headlines that point to grief, loss or anguish. And it's not the kind of obsession many people could probably identify with. I'm not losing sleep over a girl. I don't bite my nails. And I don't collect rare stamps. I'm just fascinated with reading about cancer in the news and how it affects everyone, celebrities and ordinary folk like me. I like to know how long someone's battle has been, how they fought it; in fact everyone last detail.

I am in the fourth year of my own fight, which is considered a long time when you have the kind of cancer I have. According to the statistics this is the year I should actually pop my clogs, which is perhaps one of the reasons why the depression has kicked in so heavily, and may also explain my increasing obsession with cancer deaths in the press. But at least I don't have a book for clippings. (Well, okay, I do, but it is for clippings mentioning me. I know, forever the narcissist — it'll be the death of me).

I don't limit my obsession to stomach cancer either, oh no. I have been following Sir Jackie Stewart's wife Helen's battle with breast cancer. Despite her having a successful operation at the world-renowned Mayo Clinic in the United States (my first appointment after winning the lottery, thank you very much), the statistics have not been kind to the Stewart clan. Sir Jackie's son, Paul, is also having a long battle with stomach cancer too, (notice a pattern here — I'm sorry but I told you I was completely obsessed). Fortunately Paul is in remission, but as we know, the spectre of cancer will forever have him looking over his shoulder. The statistic of one of us in three falling foul to cancer has been harshly exceeded in their family, and all the money they have, while initially giving them instant access to the best care in the world, will, eventually not amount to much. Cancer pays no heed to dollar signs.

I'm about to digress, but indulge me. At my charity auction, one of the prizes was a day's tuition at the Sir Jackie Stewart School of shooting at Gleneagles, kindly donated by a reader. It is sad to say, but cancer seems to be taking pot shots at the Stewart family.

I just wish them well because even celebrities, rich folk and those who appear in Hello! Magazine, deserve our best wishes. Meanwhile I will go back to scouring the papers, finding justification for my illness, and taking little comfort from it.

Perhaps it's okay to have a duvet day sometimes because perhaps it will keep me from my obsession for another day.

28 October 2001

Hearts And Bones:

IT is almost one year to the day since my friend Karen died.

How odd it is now to think that I had always believed that I would be the one to go first. Karen had cancer too, and we shared painful confidences when we met in the Ayrshire hospice. We both found it comforting to have someone of a similar age to talk to about the poor hand fate had dealt us. Neither of us knew just how sick the other was, and we never discussed how things would end for us. She was incredible, Karen. Even though she was in great pain, she was always cheerful and showed great dignity in the face of cancer.

I do not like visitors to see me when I am in hospital. People expect you to entertain them, but all you've been doing is lying in bed all day. Perhaps you will have gone to the toilet, but that's hardly the stuff of devastatingly witty after-dinner anecdotes. Eventually visitors remember that they are in a hospital looking at a dying person. That's when things get awkward. It's a peculiarly disheartening still life: – Lucozade, Grapes and Silence!!

Karen was different, she made every visiting hour a feel good movie. Her bed was always surrounded by well- wishers, and she kept every single one of them laughing and entertained. I don't know where she got the energy from, but she seemed to have plenty to go round. I'm still grateful to her for giving me strength when I was down.

I remember the last week of Karen's life. I managed to see her just before she passed away, and she was conscious enough to know I was there. I gently chided her for leaving me to face this cancer on my own. Her mother and father must be thinking of her constantly, as must her friends. Her memorial service was packed out, which is no surprise at all. She touched the life of everyone she met, and, even a year on, I think of her and the speed at which she deteriorated from relative health to her eventual death. Selfishly, I wonder if that is how it will be for me. If there is a heaven, Karen will be there, and hopefully looking out for me. The last time I saw her, I made her promise she would.

Now, on to a different subject: blood donation. I am sure that some of you out there are donors. For those of you who haven't yet, ahem, taken the plunge, can I please point you in the direction of my brother Chris, who regularly gives blood despite being approximately half as brave as the cowardly lion from The Wizard Of Oz. There really is no excuse. If Chris can part with a pint, surely we all can. Those of you who have donated blood may consider going a step further. Donors for bone marrow transplants are very much in the minority, I imagine because people are scared by the name. In fact the whole procedure only takes an hour and is pain free. They'll even throw in a cup of tea.

I know from emails and letters that some of you read my column and think something along the lines of, 'Right, here's this guy dying of cancer, but living his life to the full; I'm going to make a difference too.' Now that difference might be a donation to charity or phoning an old friend; the common ground is getting off your sofa and doing something worthwhile. So why not donate some of your bone marrow? It's very worthwhile, it could save a life, and I promise you won't miss it. Through your communications and meeting you at charity events, I hope I have given people a real insight into what it means to suffer and fight cancer. Believe me when I tell you that there are some mornings where it's an absolute fight just to get out of bed, but hopefully by doing so and making my way to the word processor I am helping you become aware of the reality of this illness.

You may read this column every week; I live through it every day. Cancer is a cloud with no perceptible silver lining, but having the privilege of meeting people like Karen takes the edge off the pain.

4 November 2001

Faith, Hope And Party:

"WAYHEY"- It's Saturday and I'm feeling good because I have a party to go to.

My friend Michael had bought a new flat and to celebrate, he decided to hold a flat-warming do. Although my friends go out every weekend, I tend to stay in. I'm not a big drinker, that's one of the side effects of having cancer, but for a special occasion like this, I decided to make an effort especially as Mike is such a good friend, always on the phone asking how I am. As always for a host, he was just a bit nervous before the party. He found himself worried about whether his friends would mix or not. You have friends from school, friends from university and friends from work. Michael is a hotshot lawyer. He works long, long hours reading over boring documents, but then I suppose that is why he can afford such a lovely flat.

Now, I could have crashed at a friend's but I decided to check into a newly refurbished hotel near Michael's flat. It was not too expensive, well run and clean. As I have probably mentioned before, I love staying in hotels. There is something satisfying about walking around in your underpants without having to worry about someone bursting in. The best thing about hotels, for me, is being able to watch TV from the bath. Langs in Glasgow lets you do this but I've decided it's time to check out a few more to get the TV-from-the-bath perspective.

I am no longer tied to the house for my medication because I am quite adept at giving myself an injection of painkilling drugs. To facilitate a relatively pain-free injection, it helps if you have some body fat. This is because you can pinch the skin and the needle enters the body swiftly and unobtrusively. Unfortunately I am down to nine stone — great for showing off my body tone, but not so good for injecting into. Although I can inject, I tend to ask my mother to do it. She just goes ahead and does it telling me to swear out loud if the pain gets too much. It must be hard for her to hurt her son, but the pain I have to suffer from my disease is pretty bad just now so please, God, excuse me for the odd word in vain. And while I'm on the topic of God, when you have a terminal disease you tend to examine your own mortality a lot more.

I read an article recently, "Live Forever", which examined the fountain-of-youth argument about cloning and cell replication. I have no proof of course, but I bet somewhere in a laboratory, scientists have already cloned a human being. Whether it is government-sanctioned or illegally in a private-owned laboratory, you can bet a cloned person exists. They managed to clone a sheep without any difficulties, so why not a person?

If you think about it, once cloning has become acceptable, you could be cured of any ailment by replacing faulty organs with an exact clone and go on and live a healthy life. But then how would we value life? Would it negate religion and our value systems?

I was brought up as a Roman Catholic. It was ingrained in me. I went to a Catholic primary school and to Mass every Sunday with my grandmother before passing the entrance exams to St Aloysius in Glasgow. But by then, I was missing Mass and had begun to doubt my religion. How can you reconcile Darwin's theory of evolution with the story of Adam and Eve? And why was there so much pain and suffering in the world? Why did God allow it? I think it was the Live Aid event, and the pictures of all the starving, suffering children, skin draped over their bones, too tired to flick the flies off their bodies that pushed me over the edge. How could I believe in a God who allowed so much suffering and death?

I stopped going to Mass and in our religious classes, I was always a dissenting voice, always questioning the priest's absolute faith. I passed through my teens and twenties a non-believer, although if anyone asked I would say I was a Christian, because I lived a Christian life.

And then cancer happened. I was hospitalised for more than a month, and every day my Aunt Therese, a faithful Catholic, would pop in. Her faith gave me strength. She also introduced me to her young priest. He was young, handsome and with time to listen to everyone. We had a lot of conversations about God, with me playing the sceptic, but with patience, humour and understanding I gradually came around to the fringes of Catholicism again.

My problem was seeing everything as black or white, whereas life, as I now see it is grey in colour.

Life is what you make of it, and despite being dealt a dodgy hand, I tend to make the best of it.

11 November 2001

Potty About Harry:

I THINK there's a little bit of Harry Potter in all of us.

I found parts of the enchanting tale relating to my own school days; Harry is an outsider when he first goes to Hogwarts School for wizards. I felt like an outsider at Glasgow's St Aloysius College because I had attended a 'normal' primary school and had to sit a separate entrance exam to get in. So I felt different.

Harry has to go to a special shop to get his uniform. I had to do that, plus I had to buy everything from, calenders, diaries, gym kits, which is a totally alien concept when you've gone to a state-run school. Harry is faced with a barrage of new subjects to learn, as I was. If my memory serves me, all the classics teachers that I had were just like Harry's strange professors. Harry excelled at Quidditch, (a fantasy sport played on broomsticks) while I was good at athletics. Neither of us were all that academic, but always very sociable in class.

Just as Hogwarts school has four houses, St Aloysius had four separate classes; Loyola, Gonzaga, Xavier and Ogilvie, all named after Jesuit saints. Competition between the houses was fierce, especially in sporting events. People may level the criticism that this type of education is old fashioned, but I think I got a first-rate education, which helped me cope with what I would have to deal with later on. What I have been surprised at is how quickly the Harry Potter collection of books has become a phenomenon. As the story captured the imaginations of children everywhere, its reputation spread by word of mouth with ferocious speed. From there it was just a short hop to megabucks corporate involvement. But HP is not just about million dollar licensing deals and worldwide domination.

In a small corner of Scotland, Lucy McKenzie runs a small hand-knitted sweater business, which started when she began to sell her mother's knitted clothes to friends. As orders started flooding in, she found herself employing up to 20 people, and business began to boom. In normal stories, this is where the ceiling usually falls in, but fortunately for Lucy, she was blessed with a wave of the HP magic wand. A lucky break in a dentist's office presented her with an opportunity that any manufacturer would bite your hand off for. One of the wardrobe staff from Warner Brothers visited the dentist, picked up a magazine and saw one of Lucy's knitted sweaters. Lucy then got a request for some samples.

Now this is standard procedure in the clothing industry, and it took a couple of days for her to reply. She almost fell off her seat when she realised it was for Harry Potter Productions. Lucy was already a fan of the books, and immediately spun off some sample sweaters, just like the ones in the books with the characters' initials on them. One thing that surprised and delighted Lucy was that Warner Brothers was willing to deal with such a small company. She knitted a pair of fingerless gloves for Maggie Smith's character and a hat for Hermione, one of Harry's best chums (who is actually based on JK Rowling when she was a little girl).

What is most refreshing is that Lucy is not turning her business into a large manufacturing plant for sweaters, what you see is what Warners got, and the prices remain the same. If you want a Harry jumper with an H on the front, it's not going to cost you the price of a Nimbus 2000.

But with a workforce of 20, you are guaranteed exclusivity, plus it also means Lucy's workforce has a steady reliable workload, rather than booms and slumps once the film has done the rounds.

One thing to look out for on your sweater is the odd dropped switch, apparently the film makers did not want the sweaters to look brand new, so if you buy one and it's not perfect, keep a hold of it because it could become a collectors' piece one day.

My generation was the last to read books on a regular basis before the home computers took hold. Lord of the Rings, Catcher In The Rye, the Hobbit, the Box of Delights. All these books transport you to another world, and I will be really interested to compare the film version with the book. There is a certain innocence to reading books because everyone has a different imagination. I am both happy and sad to see that The Lord Of The Rings is being made into a film, but will it be up to my expectations? I doubt it.

This is how I feel about Harry Potter as well, but it looks like I will be waiting a while to see the film because Pottermania is bound to keep the cinemas jam-packed for a while. Whether you like it for not, Harry Potter is here to stay, and although parents may have a few concerns that it is unwholesome to make magic and spells fashionable, at least they know where their kids are, and what they are doing.

Can they say the same when they are surfing dodgy websites?

Here's to the magic of Harry Potter.

18 November 2001

Flight Of Fancy:

IT had the makings of a fabulous trip; temperatures mid-seventies, a beautiful city to explore, lovely food and drink, great company and the chance to see Celtic progress to the next round of the Champions' League. I knew it was too good to be true.

My brother, Chris, his wife Susan and her parents were all going to Porto to watch Celtic play and I had decided to join them on one of those organised trips for fans. My mum was her usual worried self, especially as my bowels have been acting up again. But I had managed to get a supply of special tablets that turn your stomach to concrete, so I could manage the flight.

We checked in and when we made our way to the departure gate, I was impressed with the amount of time the players took to speak to the fans. A new signing, Bobo Balde, spent at least 20 minutes patiently posing for photographs with fans. My brother had his video camera, so he was off bothering every player he saw. Once on the plane, a lot of the fans were imbibing alcohol, and I pitied the air-hostesses as they handed out the airline meals, as they were met with requests for more drink. I had been up at 5.30am, so I slept through most of the flight. But it wasn't until we arrived at Porto airport that things really started to hot up.

The Porto police were obviously unaware that Scottish fans have a good reputation abroad because they had batons drawn at the ready and some ominous looking shields. Fortunately for them, the most vicious thing they had to deal with was the fans' beer breath! We were all shunted on to coaches with our hotel name on the front of them — simple until you take into consideration the level of alcohol consumed and fans getting on wrong buses. I met one of my friends, Mark, who is married to Anne, my last girlfriend's big sister. He said he was going to the Hotel Grande. I cursed his good luck because his hotel sounded better than mine.

The police gave us a high-speed escort into the city, running other cars off the road, so we felt quite important. But this changed as we reached our hotel. It seemed nice enough, but with 150 Celtic fans all arriving at once looking for room keys, chaos reigned. There were only two people behind the reception, and their English was akin to Manuel from Fawlty Towers. I really shouldn't cast aspersions on their language skills because my Portuguese is woeful. Eventually, we all got our rooms sorted and they seemed fine. Then we decided to explore the city because the weather was warm and it seemed to have such a great atmosphere. It's a real cafe society with outdoor cafes on every street, so we had a few drinks to celebrate our arrival (although to be honest, beer never tastes quite so good from a plastic glass.) We toured the city and marvelled at the specialist shops that occupied specific streets; one street specialised in supplies for chapel selling vestments, candles and other religious accoutrements. Turn a corner and we were faced with a whole street full of quite beautiful patisserie shops. I have never seen cakes look this good, and knew I had to sample some before I left.

Now, those of you who have travelled abroad before will know that the visiting support usually occupy part of the city before the game. After a fantastic meal, we decided to find the other fans. It's strange, because if there's a square in a town surrounded by bars, you can bet your bottom dollar that your average footy fan will find it, and after an hour will have taken it over.

When we found the fans, we discovered 'the square' swathed in green and white. It's funny, in Glasgow we have the man on horseback outside Goma who always manages to get a cone on his head, no matter how many times the council removes it. In Porto, there was a statue 30ft high, which somehow had a Celtic Tammy on, and he was tastefully swathed in Celtic flags.

Ah well, you can take the "bhoys" out of Glasgow, – But……..

Anyway, the locals (including the police) watched with detached amusement as the drink flowed. We bailed out early and retired to the hotel bar, where we had a jug of sangria — well it was quicker than ordering coke. We called it a night after that, travel, beer and a good meal all conspiring to add weight to our already heavy eyelids, although I took a couple of valium just to be sure. I had a big day ahead and didn't want a wave of tiredness to waste it. Little did I know what was to come.

Porto, part two: next week.

25 November 2001

Give Us A Real Break:

THE next morning the heavens opened, and the nice sunny weather that had bathed Oporto the day before, had disappeared.

The Porto v Celtic game kicked off at 7.45pm, but in their infinite wisdom, the police wanted us at the ground earlier, so we had to be back at the hotel by 4pm. I was tired, so I crashed out on a sofa in reception. Then my brother asked the hotel manager if there was a room free where I could lie down for an hour. There was, and it was a touching gesture from someone who I have been looking out for all my life, to be looking after me.

The buses came and again we were given a police escort to the ground, or at least as near as we were going to get. We joined the mass of fellow supporters who were in high spirits, and I was pleased to note that the sectarian songs were kept to a minimum. As we neared the ground, we were funnelled by the police into an increasingly narrower queue, and it was only by luck that no one was injured or crushed.

There were roughly 5000 Celtic fans, but there were only two turnstiles open to us. The Portuguese police, once again, displaying mind-numbing ineptitude in their handling of a large crowd. As we entered the ground, my bowels started posting notices of intent. I always carry tissues and wet-ones with me, just in case, but as I entered the old looking toilet block, I could only think of one thing — Trainspotting, you know the scene where Ewan McGregor loses a suppository down the loo and has to retrieve it, excrement and all. This toilet was worse. So I decided not to use it. I returned to my seat and tried to work out how I would amuse myself for the two long hours we had before the game started, and trying not to think of needing the loo.

It was raining again and it was freezing. A combination of chat, jumping up and down to keep warm, and recognition from a group of Sunday Herald readers helped pass the time until the game started. We had high hopes for this game, so when Porto scored in the second minute, the Celtic support was silenced. This set the pattern for the game and by the time the referee blew the whistle for full-time, Porto had won 3-0. We were all frustrated. It was not the dream ending to our trip. Worse was to follow. The police kept us in the ground for an hour after the game to allow the Porto fans to disperse, and while we were waiting, the announcer played classical music over the tannoy, obviously trying to calm the tired, disappointed fans. We were all just dying to get out, get to our coaches and get to the airport.

We made it back to the coach without incident and reached the airport, which was, to be honest, a hellish sight — thousands of Celtic fans all trying to get on planes home. The check-in queue was monstrous, and I knew if we waited in it, we would have missed the flight. I decided to brass it and head for the departure gate without a boarding card. Amazingly we got through customs, I did not even show my passport, or get my luggage checked.

'Just sit anywhere', was the hostess's advice.

I cannot believe in these days of worldwide terrorism that we actually made it on the plane.

Chris and I managed to get seats together, and I asked the airhostess if there was a quiet place that I could use to give myself an injection. She assured me that there was, and that was the last I saw of her.

This was just typical of the shoddy organisation shown by our travel company. We took off two hours late. I was shattered so I took a sleeping tablet, as did my brother who was up at 9am the next day for work. We finally got home by 5.30am.

It is a big 'if' but if Celtic progress in the UEFA Cup, I will organise my own travel arrangements in future. I phoned my friend Mark, who was staying at the opulent sounding Hotel Grande. I was ready to hear about how good his hotel was, but I could hardly contain my laughter as he described a small dingy hotel, stinking of fish with no shower. Which just proves the old adage; there is always someone worse off than yourself.

Football fans in Glasgow on both sides of the river are loyal to the point of blind devotion, but that does not mean they have to accept sub-standard service.

If we all voted with our feet and our wallets then perhaps we would get the service we deserve.

2 December 2001

Funeral Service:

THE Beatson Oncology Centre, supposedly the Scottish centre of excellence for cancer care is dying.

Years of mismanagement, under funding and a general malaise have taken away the goodwill and enthusiasm that the excellent staff once had. Perhaps I am stupid, or maybe I don't understand how government works, but someone has to be responsible. And in my opinion it has to be the person at the top; the person ultimately responsible for crippling staff shortages and misuse of expensive equipment has rightly gone this week.

But as I write and await the announcement of the new Health minister, how many headlines we have to endure? How long will the waiting lists have to get? And how many staff will leave his or her jobs through sheer disillusionment before someone takes some action? The most recent event that compounds this mismanagement is the loss of three top consultants, one of whom was treating me with radiotherapy. I had managed to wangle an appointment with Dr Tim Habeshaw, an expert in radiotherapy, but I still had to wait two hours in the clinic just to see him. When he came into the treatment room, the sweat was pouring off him, his shirt wet through. He was obviously having a bad day, yet throughout the consultation, he was polite and utterly professional.

There was an x-ray missing from my file; not only did he phone the hospital responsible, but he made sure he spoke to the radiologist who had done the scans. He was typical of the Beatson Oncology centre staff, always going that extra mile to help. No wonder he was in such high demand. These are the calibre of healthcare professionals that we should be trying to keep in Glasgow. Now we can't even attract one person to fill the shoes of those who have gone.

So what now? Well unless you actually work in the increasingly horrific conditions, you couldn't imagine how a so-called centre of excellence could lumber from crisis to crisis.

Glasgow is the cancer capital of Europe where statistics show that one in two Glaswegians will face cancer at some point in their life. Yet those who have the power to change what's happening at the Centre seem to be conspicuous by their absence. Almost laughably, an inquiry has been launched — yet another layer of red tape to waste money and add to the frustration of the staff. This inquiry should have been ordered last year when the Royal Infirmary management was crying out for funding and direction.

Now there are a few stopgap emergency measures, which include a programme to improve team building at the Beatson and its relationships with other cancer centres in Scotland and drafting in doctors from other hospitals in the short-term. A clinical support team will be drawn up to advise consultants at the Beatson (but isn't the Beatson a centre of excellence?) and help select a senior manager to support doctors (more than likely a civil servant with no medical experience).

These measures are not going to encourage consultants, doctors or nurses to come back to the Beatson, which is haemorrhaging staff on a daily basis. The Scottish Executive has to make the Beatson a place where people want to work, where excellence is not just a by-word and patients can expect a standard of service that deserves the term 'centre of excellence'.

You know the signs that a new business puts up to advertise its opening — 'under new management'? Well the North Glasgow Trust should have something saying 'under no management'.

A whole community was rubbed up the wrong way when a secure unit was planned for Stobhill without the consultation of the local residents. Then there was the escalation of a bitter dispute with medical secretaries, who organise the consultants' diaries.

The report is out this month, and until then, we must hope that there are no more resignations at the Beatson, as it continues to limp along at reduced capacity, and the measures employed are little more than sticking plasters on a gaping wound.

9 December 2001

A Family Affair:

CALL me a cynic, but there are events that I judge to be invented purely by the card companies to boost their profits.

Take Mother's Day and Father's Day: why bother? Just be nice to them all year round. And then there are anniversaries. Definitely a cause to celebrate, but only for the two people involved, surely? So you can imagine my amazement when I found myself booking my mum and dad into Malmaison for the night. Breaking your own rules is a bad sign, but I thought 35 years of putting up with each other was worthy of a small celebration. The hotel staff found out about the anniversary and made a special deal of them, which was just fantastic.

My brother Chris and I decided to book lunch in a great little Tapas bar in Glasgow. We had a lovely meal, talking over old stories; remembering good times, and then my folks went back to the hotel for a night of spoiling each other. I went home to an empty house. (It was great. The peace and solitude was so relaxing).

While I can enjoy the odd lie-in and relax during the day, my poor brother is working in Edinburgh and has to drive from Glasgow on the M8 every day. He has to be up at 6am and does not arrive home until 7pm. The drive is a nightmare and Chris is unfortunately prone to road rage. He actually bends over the steering wheel as if to wring an extra couple of miles out of the car. I used to be like that before I had cancer, but now there isn't any reason to hurry.
Sometimes, I just look at my brother, a surveyor, and I feel so proud. I wonder where his drive and enthusiasm come from. If I did not have cancer, would I have been a success? What constitutes success? Money, prestige, fulfillment, responsibility?

With cancer, I can't think of anything else that I could be doing. As my disease progresses, and I get more tired every day, I wonder what else I could do. Am I fulfilled? No, not really. I know I could be doing more, and while it is good to be alive, I do have to remind myself of that every so often.

I had to give blood today and went to the Ayrshire Hospice. Walking through, I noticed all the day rooms were full of elderly people, and I felt lucky to have a family to share what time I have left with. I guess that was what the anniversary deal was about. It's not just that I love my parents. But I wanted to say that I realise that what we have is not a typical mum-dad-son dynamic. I know I take a hell of a lot out of both of them, and when able, I want to show them just how much I appreciate them. Talking of appreciation, on Bonfire Night, Chris got some fireworks for Abbie, my niece, while mum made mulled wine, which reminded me of when I was younger. Dad used to make a big deal about getting the fireworks, while Chris and I made a bonfire. In that house, we had an orchard in the back garden, so we got apples, put them in tin foil and heated them until they were hot enough to burn your mouth. Mum used to fuss about the fireworks and we used to marvel at dad lighting them. I hope Abbie has as good a childhood as we had. Children nowadays seem to grow up way too fast and that's something that my parents, as grandparents, take very seriously.

In my role as a spokesman for cancer sufferers, I attended a charity night out, primarily to give a very short speech on cancer, as one of the beneficiaries was the Ayrshire hospice.

I had spoken quite extensively to Michael the organiser about how to raise money, as I had put on a couple of charity nights myself, but to be honest, he embarrassed me with the show he had put on.

I am a terrible public speaker and having David Hayman on right after me only pointed to my inadequacies. Being one of Scotland's most respected actors, his speech on "Spiritaid 2001" was informative and hit the right note. Spiritaid is a worldwide effort to try and iron out the differences between our world and the Third world, but I could not help but think it would take a lot of work and goodwill to make even the smallest of difference.

After the pressure of speechmaking, Pauline, my partner for the night and I decided to try our hand at the table of the card sharp. We tried the game of chance, where there are three pots and you have to guess which one is covering the pea. I guess the trick is to avoid what you think is the right one, and choose one of the other two. Of course, I was a fiver down when I realised this. Still, it was for charity.

The whole night was excellent and I am sure Michael raised lots of cash, although when I saw him last, he was running around, sweat lashing off him. I should have warned him that not everything goes to plan, a bit like life really.

Any future offers on speechmaking, I am afraid I will have to turn down.

I'll just tell them I've got a sore throat.

16 December 2001

Mother Love:

OUT of the blue I received an appointment at the Beatson without having requested one.

It turned out I was due to get radiotherapy from the big ray gun, like the zapper that Goldfinger almost halves James Bond with. The consultant marks out with an indelible marker the area that is going to be zapped, which in my opinion is pretty obvious — guys aspire to a six-pack, while I have a seven-pack. The tumour on my spleen is enormous. That was why I found our hotel in Tenerife great — my room had its own sun deck, I could sit and read or sleep in total privacy without people looking and wondering what the apple-sized protrusion on my torso was.

Anyway, after marking out on my body where the dose of radiation was going, all the staff ran out of the room, and there was an ominous ray gun noise. Then came the bad news, the nurse told me that my stomach may 'react' within an hour as she handed me two cardboard sick bowls. Normally I am a Sunday-style of driver, saving the ozone layer and all that. But if we are making comparisons then my drive home was the equivalent of me standing in the Arctic and spraying super-hold hair spray with both hands. We made it back to Ayr with ten minutes to spare, good news for the car interior, but the way my stomach felt, I could tell that my week and the toilet seat would be interminably linked.

People are nice to me, they know I have cancer, but sometimes they carry out what they think are acts of kindness, but which are, in fact, tests of endurance and character. I have a few people who I am happy to see down at the house, my own private castle, but with a "dicky" stomach from the radiotherapy and an irregular sleeping pattern, I dread those phone calls in which callers say they are 'just popping in to see me' or which encourage me out to some social engagement.

So it was with a heavy heart that I heard that my cousin, Kathleen, a thespian, had a show in Glasgow and was donating proceeds to the charity. There was no way I could not go, so I starved myself for a day beforehand and drove up to the Cottier theatre with mum, stomach knitting buttons. I loved the show. It's called "Check Your Coupon"; it won a prize at the Edinburgh festival and it includes a male stripper who interacts with the mostly female audience. You should go and see it for the charity alone. It runs until Christmas Eve. Of course I would say that, but Kathleen is not my real cousin, although if you went back far enough our families would be related. We grew up in the same street, and shared our childhood dreams and wishes. Kathleen was always an actress, when we played doctors and nurses, Kathleen was always the doctor, I was the nurse, and my brother Chris, the car crash victim in need of urgent surgery. I got to see her briefly after the show, but we did not have time to catch up properly, as my stomach started to call time.

As I waited for my mum to say her goodbyes, some drip of a guy, more than 6ft tall and built like a stick of cane barged past me on the way to the toilet. Unfortunately I think of myself not as the husk of the man I was, but still as the well-built young guy I was, so I pushed the guy back and uttered some expletives. It was only then I realised how weak I was and felt vulnerable. Just them my mum came out and I told her what had happened.
I should have expected it, but as my mum rushed into the gents to lay waste to the creep who pushed me, I took a second to admire her spirit, before rushing into the toilets to haul my mum off of the man.

 In another world he would be lying on the floor holding his nose. It took all my strength as well as the force of my Uncle Farrell to push my mum out of the Gent's toilets as we genuinely feared for the bully's safety.

With cries of: 'That b*****d hit my son who has cancer', the commotion was attracting an audience from the bar, and I was not too happy at everyone knowing my medical condition. I also wanted to make sure my mum still had a modicum of dignity. She was still spitting and cursing as I dragged her out to the car.

'Anyone who hits one of my children will get it from me,' she was saying. I was raging, as I felt physically inept, but also because in my mum's eyes the crime was all the greater because I had cancer. I try never making excuses for myself because of cancer, but at the same time I was proud of her for trying to protect me. I will never know how it feels to be a parent, and if her reaction was an indication of it, then it makes it all the worse — knowing I will never feel that depth of love.

Those of you, who have children, enjoy them and nurture them for all our sakes.

You have the kind of love that does not come and go, which takes precedence over all other emotions.

Verbal Volleys:

Each Sunday, I would turn to Jonathan's article with dreaded anticipation, to find out how he was portraying me. It might be my tights falling down at the Airport, or my verbal abuse of someone who had treated him unfairly.

I am not normally given to using curses, expletives or threatening violence to strangers. However, when you are the mother of a terminally ill child, you become extra protective for their well-being and feelings.

The Ayr traffic warden was a sorry excuse for a human being, let alone a man. He suffers from the "small man " syndrome, puffed up by a uniform and a pad of parking tickets. He showed absolutely no compassion for Jonathan's condition, which was painfully obvious, or even for his disability permit. This was the man who gained notoriety by giving a parking ticket to the driver of a Disability mini-bus, who was disembarking wheelchair-bound passengers at a lunch spot, in pouring rain. His lack of humanity does a disservice to responsible wardens, and his high-handed attitude would have tested the patience of Mother Theresa. I still see him regularly in Ayr, and my hackles still rise at each sight of him, truly he is a sad little man.

The incident at the Cottier Theatre, spoiled what was a truly enjoyable evening for Jonathan and I. Jonathan was always well-mannered, and respectful of people's feelings, but the obnoxious behaviour of the six foot plus moron, left him physically shaken. When I rushed after the cretin, I would have settled for a sincere apology. However, when I confronted him, he was not the least apologetic and told me to p***o**. I was prevented from punching him by a male friend, and it hadn't struck me that I had this confrontation in the Gents Loo.

Needless to say, the cretin beat a hasty retreat from the theatre. I would like to think that he was feeling ashamed or embarrassed, but I doubt he did. I offer no apologies, or feel any sense of shame, for these incidents: any mother in my position would have done the same.

The only difference was that I had a son, who put my actions into weekly print.

Susan Wilson

23 December 2001

Party Animals:

I HAD been worrying about my staff night out for a couple of weeks.

I have very little face-to-face contact with the team at the office as I send my articles in via email. We talk on the phone, but apart from the magazine editor, Jane, and Andrew, the editor of the whole paper, I didn't really know who anyone else looked like.

To make matters worse, I had decided to drive and finding the little bar tucked down Waterloo Street was proving really hard. Normally this would not be a problem, but due to it's location, my car was attracting attention from the local ladies of the night and the police often monitor motorists who drive around there. After five laps of the red light district, I finally stumbled upon Pivo Pivo, which has the smallest sign, and doorway a pub could possibly have.

I walked in to the bar, frantically looking for a familiar face. The trouble is I have a photo in the magazine, so people know who I am, but I do not know those who work behind the scenes, editing and producing it. There was a smattering of magazine staff who were introducing themselves to me and then a guy came up to say hello. It was Mike Tough, the head barman at the Groucho club, who writes the cocktail column in the Mag. It turned out I knew his sister really well, so we were standing both laughing at my terrible photograph in the magazine when another two guys came up to us. I recognised them, just as well as they were both columnists. David Murray is as fit looking as his health column suggests, while Frank Shapiro, who's a life coach, got a kick from me telling him he did not look like he was old enough to have a 17-year-old son.

It only took two minutes to discover that we were all in the same boat. We were all dreading the staff night out, and had planned to leave quietly after a drink or two. Instead we were having a great laugh, doing a bit of male bonding, and before long I found myself dancing to Kylie Minogue with one of the editors. I was beginning to regret bringing the car as I was really enjoying myself; being more gregarious than usual, introducing the boys and myself to all and sundry.

With Glasgow being the cancer capital of Europe, I can see why people are interested in my column, but I was amazed at how so many people were interested in my writing, and were prepared to discuss their own encounters of cancer experience in their individual social circle. After about an hour of this reverie, we headed to Canton Express, my favourite Chinese restaurant in Glasgow. It does not look good from the outside, but you can stand and watch your food being made, plus the place is full of Chinese people, their patronage surely a good sign. And they serve great green tea. Frank, David and I had a great meal, but alas Mike said he wasn't that hungry. Frank bailed out next, but Dave and I went on to Corinthian where the rest of the Sunday Herald staff were still downing cocktails at the piano bar until 3am. As we arrived, the assistant sports editor was singing Your Song by Elton John, and was surprisingly good. That lot really knows how to party. So that was my staff night out, no salacious gossip, no regretted snogs, and no snogs at all in fact (well not on my part anyway), but I made some new friends and that is always a good thing. We made plans to meet up again (Michael, Frank and Dave). Their company was a tonic.

It's great to meet people who do not want to hear about cancer; after all, I am a normal person sometimes.

30 December 2001

Cherish:

LIAM, one of my best friends, is a" blagger"!

He has more bottle than coca-cola and more front than Blackpool. He is quite probably the best salesman I have ever met. Charming and confident, he could well be the Scottish version of Patrick Bateman, the sociopath in Brett Easton-Ellis' American Psycho. He has a major weakness however. He is simply the biggest U2 fan on the planet.

During U2's world tour, he was religiously checking their website every day, because it was a sell-out. And as he had more chance of a meeting with the Pope than getting tickets to see them (yes I know I have met the Pope — but let's get back to Liam), he found out U2's management company number in Dublin, and talked to the band's PA. Using his charm, he managed to blag three tickets with backstage passes to boot. Money no issue here, he had to fork out over 500 dollars, but he reckoned it was worth every penny. He found out that the band would be staying at the Sunset Marquis Hotel on the famous Sunset Strip in West Hollywood. This is a real rock'n' roll hotel where rooms cost upwards of 500 dollars per night. Well, in for a penny, in for a pound, Liam booked himself and his brother into the hotel, hoping to bump into the band. I swear, this guy would move mountains for U2. I was disappointed because if I were not so reliant on the care of my mother, I would have been going with them. Liam knew this and felt guilty about being so happy to be going to see them. That is one of the things I like about him. He has an absolute love for life but never forgets those who are less fortunate.

The night before Liam left for LA, our friend Jack came up from London where he works as a senior manager for a large brewery company. Jack and I have been friends for over ten years, our friendship cemented when we were students and shared a flat together. Jack flew up from London en-route to Frankfurt where his girlfriend is in a stage show. We all decided to go out for dinner to catch up. Jack and I had booked into a hotel before making our way to Liam's city-centre flat for some pre-dinner drinks. We ate out at an expensive restaurant, quaffing champagne by the bottle, before heading for a trendy bar in Glasgow's Bath Street to finish off the evening.

After more champagne (Liam actually hates the stuff, but as Jack was paying, he forgot his aversion to bubbles for a night), and then we all went back to our hotel where the night took another turn.
Jack started arguing with the bar manager who was as oiled as we were, by trying to tell him how to do his job. If you know Jack as well as we do, you'd realise that he is always like this and tend to just switch off. He was also offending the rest of the staff with his 'London' chat and Liam had to apologise. But the bar manager didn't accept this and soon Liam was asked to leave.

It seems like only yesterday we were all doing this and things have not changed a bit. And do you know what? I wouldn't change them for anything. The boys were back and for a brief evening we were all equal again and the cancer was temporarily forgotten. A great, if not eventful evening. I retired to bed and looked forward to Liam's stories of L.A. I met up with Liam on his return and I could see that he had had the time of his life. He managed to meet and chat with the drummer of U2, Larry Mullen, and for the first time in his life admitted he was speechless. Liam's enthusiasm for everything never ceases to impress me and he pointed out an important lesson to me. He said that at the end of the gig, U2 had shown all the names of the people who had died in the attack on the World Trade Centre in New York on September 11.

Looking around the mainly American audience, he noticed that there was not a dry eye in the house.

It was at this point Liam realised that although I have cancer, I will not die suddenly like these people, to leave my family devastated. He has shown to me and other cancer sufferers that we must make good use of what time we do have left and share this with our families. Life is too short — certainly is for some of us. Even at a U2 gig, Liam can see the light at the end of my tunnel.

Enjoy your friends, your family, and your life — and cherish those around you.

I wish you all the very best for 2002.

6 January 2002

New Year, Still Here:

LOOKING back on Christmas, I am happy to say that I was organised very early.

I love giving presents to close family and friends. I think it was last year I remarked to my younger sister that it is a sign of getting old, when you spend as much on your parents as they spend on you. But this time I told everyone not to buy me anything, because as I sit in my room and look around, I see all the material possessions that I have amassed over the years: a shelf full of aftershaves, more clothes than I could ever wear, a huge TV that sits in another corner along with the usual array of electronic extras like videos, a DVD player and a hi-fi. It makes me sad that as I sit here, my life can be measured, by all of these items. Is this how shallow a person I was/ am? I guess it must.

I was contacted recently by a television producer, who wished make a programme about my life, my religion and my beliefs. It will go out on a Sunday, but it is not just about religion. I was asked questions about my life and I made the comment that I feel I am now a better person since I discovered I had cancer. Now that I look at this comment in print, I realise how sad that is. But you see, these days, I really appreciate my family and friends, not just because they are there, but because to me, wealth is measured in how many lives you touch in a positive way. I love my mum and dad, never forgetting they have devoted their life to their children. They live their lives through their children. My mum works until she is fit to drop, while my dad has taken on the role of homemaker, something most men couldn't do.

I think for once I understand the real meaning of Christmas.

Of course I bought presents, but for me the real gift was sitting down on Christmas Day surrounded by my family: my brother and his wife, my sister and her husband, their two kids, my grandmother, my parents and myself. It was quite a day filled with noise and mayhem, yet I wouldn't have had it any other way.

313

Glasgow wisdom dictates that what's for you, won't go by you, and I also believe that good things come to those who wait, so it was nice to hear Susan Deacon on Radio Scotland receiving virtually no calls as she is now an MSP without a portfolio. One caller did ask what medical background she had after being Scottish minister for health for so long. Of course she had none, but then that's OK because she's done nothing for the health of Scotland during her time spent as Scottish health minister.

I really am hoping for big things from Malcolm Chisholm, a good choice according to my mother. He was Scottish local government minister at Westminster, but when the Government wanted to reduce the payments for single parents, he resigned as a matter of principle. I think he would have made an excellent choice as First Minister of Scotland, having no agendas to satisfy. You will not find any sleaze or scandal associated with this chap. I just feel sorry that he has been left with such a monumental task to perform. Whatever he does, he deserves special good wishes for this coming year, as do all of you, my readers.

I was shopping in Ayr today, dressed up like an Eskimo, and five people recognized me from the magazine. The power of the press is an amazing thing—more than I realised.

I also had a great moment last week. I was meeting friends to go to see Lord of the Rings, which, incidentally blows Harry Potter out of the water, and to waste time I was having an amble through Glasgow's latest shopping emporium, Buchanan Galleries. It was there I met one of my boyhood heroes, Billy Stark, ex-Celtic player, now manager of St Johnstone.
And he had recognised me.

He asked me how I was while I just stood like an awestruck fan. This column has opened my eyes to things, has opened others people's eyes to things, and I really do see similarities with Frodo, the main character in Lord of the Rings. He has a burden to carry and as he nears his goal, the weight of the burden gets heavier and heavier. I write my column, ostensibly, about cancer, and sometimes I feel brave enough to write about my life, but my life is getting harder and the column is getting harder to write. It is likely I will die this year. Was my column any good? How can a column about cancer be good?

Well, if I get recognised by people in the street and my writing helps people in a similar situation, then that's what makes it worth it. I hope 2002 is a happy, healthy year for you all.

This time last year I felt so ill I never dreamed I might still be here.

But I am. Happy New Year.

13 January 2002

Taking Stock:

IT'S almost the middle of January, but most of us probably still have a bit of a New Year hangover.

Good or bad, it's a time for reflection. I hope your New Year was everything you wanted it to be. I had a fantastic time. The week between Christmas and New Year is always good for recharging your batteries, but because one of my closest friends, Liam, was celebrating his 30th birthday, we kept on partying. He had a dinner bash at the Arthouse in Glasgow and because I wanted to avoid having to drive home late at night and I wanted to drink, I decided to book in.

Regular readers will know how much I love staying in hotels, so I checked in early, met Liam in the bar and started celebrating in style. I haven't stayed at the Arthouse before so I didn't really know what to expect. It's one of those boutique hotels, which are designed to avoid that horrible bland chain feel, with beautiful individually designed rooms. My room was enormous, had a huge bath and a fabulous velvet bedspread. I met Liam in the bar and ordered champagne. Just to make me feel jealous, he turned up with his beautiful girlfriend, Susie.

We had an amazing dinner and after the main course, I stood up to give a speech. I had planned to say how long we had been friends, how upset Liam had been when I was diagnosed with cancer, and how, when we are on nights out, he always makes sure I am comfortable, and that no one bumps my stomach, which, when it happens, is absolute agony. He is like a big brother to me, and I wanted to put this across to everyone at the table.
Unfortunately I had a lump in my throat, and could barely string two words together, but I think everyone knew what I was trying to say.

One of the guests there, Kenny, took me aside to tell me that he had experienced cancer, and it's always comforting to know that someone has been through something similar to what you have been through.

However, the night was not about me, and as we left for the bar, there were even more of Liam's friends there. To be honest, by this time I was flagging badly. I was sitting at a table with my head nodding and my eyes closing and eventually people started to tell me to go to my bed, which I did. The heart was willing, but my body called time.

Every night out that I have, there is always an element of compromise. I can attend and for a while. I can keep up with the best of them, but then my body reels me in; reminding me about what I am facing.

For some, the New Year is a time of reflection, to look back and take stock of the year. For me there have been no real setbacks. Sure I am constantly in pain, but I am still keeping on. As for looking back, I keep thinking of my initial operation in January 1997. The surgeon then didn't give me a good prognosis, and told my parents as much, giving me maybe three months to live.

It now strikes me that my period of having a terminal disease is longer than some people's time in remission. Being terminally ill for five years is virtually unheard of in cancer care, and is a tribute to the consultants, the doctors, the nurses and staff of our great National Health Service. Also to be commended are the staff of the Ayrshire Hospice, a welcome port of call when things get tough. The Medical Director there, Dr John Bass, is very committed and often visits my house late at night.

There are many such heroes in the medical profession, but unfortunately their monumental deeds are often obscured by the misguided attempts of politicians to revolutionise the health service when what is really needed is a return to the old values and principles that our health service was founded on.

One is cleanliness. I have been in wards that are filthy dirty places. How can you possibly recover from an ailment when the conditions in the wards are likely to give you super bacteria that will not respond to antibiotics? Then there's accountability. Back in the day when my mother was training to be a nurse, each ward had a matron, and her word was law. And what about housekeeping? Never an option, everything was spotless. And last but not least, what about patient care? The ward rounds, hosted by the matron ensured every nurse knew the patient and their specific illness. Now we have agency nurses who work a shift in one hospital, collect an 'over-market value' wage, and then go to work in another hospital. Where is the continuity of caring for patients? It's time we went back to basics and looked after our health service properly.

If you care, write to your local MSP, who will then table a question to the Scottish minister for health.

Remember it is your health service, be proactive, take an interest and make a difference.

The Real Mr. Cool:

It is a rare quality these days that you can have a few genuine friends. Jonathan Wilson was one of my best friends, and like his friendship, he was genuine and rare. A few months back, Jonathan asked me to write an article about him, to let his readers know what he was really like, from someone who knew him the most, apart from his family. I took this as a privilege and an honour. However, such was his resolve, I thought he would last forever and never imagined I would be writing this now. So please bear with me while I tell you about this hero, whom you have all been reading about for the past few years.

I have known Jonathan since 1993 when he was DJ-ing in Glasgow.

We went clubbing together and although we were always "skint", Jonathan used his charming good looks and DJ contacts to "blag" us into nightclubs for free. He somehow managed always to have the best of clothes, was always immaculate and a big hit with the ladies. When I met him, he had just finished working for a shop called the Warehouse, at that time one of Britain's premier designer houses. He certainly helped them promote their wares—Cool as Ice he was, with impeccable taste,

He was diagnosed with cancer 5 years ago, and I remember thinking there must be some mistake. He was too fit for that. For years I refused to believe it. The reason for this was down to him. He still came out, never made a fuss and always made an effort. I have never really appreciated the effort that must have taken till now.

Jonathan always spoke of dying, never in a morbid way, but in a way to help his friends to cope with it. He was kind in that way, although I refused to listen to it. I thought somehow by not speaking about it, it would go away. I was wrong. I remember meeting his girlfriend Pauline, whom Jonathan had met whilst already diagnosed. She was lovely and stood by him all the way. Jonathan told me he had to end the relationship to protect her, as he knew he was going to die. Always considerate in that way, it broke my heart and his. Two young people in love, separated in love by this terrible disease. I cried. However I had the good fortune to meet Pauline's parents at the funeral. They told me that they had kept in close contact, and only days before his death, they were all laughing loud at the toilet scene from the movie "Dumb and

Dumber". Jonathan was crying with laughter, saying he knew how the guy felt! Even in this indignity, he could see the funny side. Absolute class, and funny to the end.

I celebrated my 30th birthday on Boxing Day and held a party in the Arthouse hotel in Glasgow. It was one of those trendy hotels, which Jonathan liked and always wrote about. Of course he was guest of honour, and was looking forward to it. At his request, I met Jonathan before the other guests arrived. He said he wanted to spend "quality time " with me, and wanted to meet my girlfriend Susie. However, I won't lie, when I saw him, I choked. He was so skinny and struggled with his words. He commented how beautiful Susie was, questioned what she was doing with me and said if he was not ill, she would be with him! Ha Ha. I laughed out loud at that one. Noticing I was upset, again made me feel at ease with his wit and humour. During the dinner, Jonathan stood up and gave an impromptu speech. He said he loved me, loved the way I looked after him and thanked my dinner guests for giving him a good nite. It would have brought tears to a glass eye. However, let me turn that around. I loved him, loved the way he looked after me, and want to tell him how much he will be missed by his family and friends. Being one of the last nites I spent with him, it will last forever and I have the memories and photographs to treasure

I was asked to help carry Jonathan's coffin. Not a task I was looking forward to, but did with honour. I was not surprised to see the incredible turnout for the service. The church was full, and most people broke at least one of his wishes— not to cry and be happy. Even by Jonathan's standards, that would have been an impossible task. His brother Chris, and Dr John Bass, Medical Director of the Ayrshire Hospice, gave beautiful and moving speeches whilst fighting their tears. I want to thank them for having done so, and for enlightening the congregation on the lighter side to Jonathan's life.

Through pain, he gave relief to others. Through death he gave life to others. Through incurable cancer, he gave hope to others. For this, we are indebted to you brother.

Right now. Jonathan is in Heaven, quaffing the best vintage champagne: two gorgeous angels at his side, whilst wearing his best "Burberry" outfit. The point here is that we must not worry about Jonathan any more. We must say a prayer for his beautiful family, and for all the families who will suffer a terrible loss

On a final note, I would like to thank, his readers, who helped him to stay alive longer. That in turn, enabled me to be his friend longer. I got strength from him and through his illness, he taught me how to live. For that, I am indebted to you. He lived for his articles and got strength from the support you gave. May you never forget him. He will always remember you.

Goodbye brother, enjoy the rest. You have earned it. X.

Liam C Kidd

20 January 2002

Silent Resolution:

IT was with great sadness that I heard about the death of baby Jennifer, the daughter of Gordon Brown and his wife Sarah. Living with cancer, I witness death more often than other people do, but I hate seeing it, especially where children or babies are concerned. It's so tragic.

My friends went through something similar last year. The couple, while desperately trying for a baby, suffered a series of miscarriages. Fortunately, they had each other, and their love is strong. They also had the support of their families. I felt awkward, I wanted them to know that they were in my thoughts, but how would I approach them? In the end, I sent them a card. I found it hard to understand how life could be so cruel. I have no doubt in my heart that my friends , and Mr. And Mrs. Brown, will make excellent parents one day. They will provide the love and care that wee ones need. I am sure that I speak for all my readers in wishing them peace and hope for the future.

But now, all the Christmas decorations will have been taken down, and your households will be regaining some semblance of normality. You will remember that I wanted to forego any presents because I have everything a 31 –year old cancer sufferer can have. Mum managed to surprise me yet again. Knowing her son's vanity, she found something I did not have- a paraffin spa, guaranteed to give me softer hands and feet. Now, if only I had someone who would notice this, that would be a real Christmas present.
With the New Year past, I suppose that I had better make some resolutions, although at this stage last year, I remember doing the same thing, and not one resolution lasted until the end of January. But then I thought I was going to die last year. And that's how I feel right now.

The book must be a priority, with so many of you e-mailing me and asking about past columns. The real worry that I have is that I find columns hard to write: a project like a book is a huge undertaking, and what would happen if no publishers were interested? Books about cancer have been done before, and by better people than me. Still, I guess a resolution must have the element of challenge. However, I must brush up on my computer skills if I am going to get this book together. In fact, forget brushing up, I started to buy one of those weekly builds-into-a-complete-clever-clogs-guide computer magazines, and I still have to read the first one! My generation was the one that just missed out on the PC revolution. My younger brother is an absolute whiz on the computer, but I struggle to send e-mails.

This year will be different, trust me.

Raising money for charity, now there is a challenge. With a new organization setting up every day, there is less of the pie to go around, so I will need to come up with some new ideas to get the public to part with some money. The West Highland Way walk was great, because as well as raising money for charity, everyone joined together to wish me well. No one was sure that I could manage it, and I was so emotional when I completed it. The charities are really deserving and it was a pleasure to hand the cash over, so any ideas, bearing in mind my deteriorating condition, will be most gratefully received.

I also want to control my "rants". However, before I do stop altogether, a recent report in the newspapers has annoyed me. Apparently Celtic Football Club was up in arms at the toilet facilities at Brockville stadium, where they were due to play a game. The Ladies' toilet facilities are too basic, they claim.

I used to go along to Parkhead stadium, but because none of the locks on the Disabled toilets worked, I had to give up following the team. It is distressing enough to be disabled, without having to bare all at the ground, and it is not the cheap seats, I am talking about either. I wrote to Celtic to complain, but despite receiving a reply promising action, the toilet locks remained inoperable, and I now follow my team via the radio- hardly a worthwhile substitute.

Right now I've said it!

I must also stop ranting about the NHS. Going about waiting times, cleanliness, staff morale is not constructive, and I really want to give the new guy Malcolm Chisholm, every chance to show us how good he can make our Health Service. He has a lot of very competent people working for him right now, but they need leadership. He also desperately needs to recruit staff, the kind of people who care about their jobs and their patients. At the top of the tree, we need to recruit top caliber consultants, but Hey! Listen to me -breaking the resolution again.

The next resolution is a bit tougher; I want to become more in touch with my religion so that I can reconcile my faith with who I am. Sounds a bit New Age, but I believe the only reason that I am alive is that I have faith. I went through a period of denial when I was initially diagnosed. How could there be a God when a regular guy like me gets cancer? While rapists, child abusers and the like seem to get away with it? Then I realized that it's not about them:-It's about me and what I believe in.

It's easy to blame everyone else for your problems, but in the end, you are responsible for your life, and it is about time that I started living my life more in tune with my beliefs.

If I talk the talk, then I must walk the walk.

27 January 2002

Half Measures:

NOBODY listens to you when you have cancer.

Readers of old will be familiar with my parachute jump story — the parachute didn't work and I ended up with broken legs. To make matters worse, at the time I was on chemo so when it came to resetting my bones I was not able to get a general anaesthetic. Instead the doctors gave me that old mix given to women in labour, gas and air. And as I found out, it's absolutely useless and only makes you sick. Thankfully when the doctor tried to set my bones I conveniently wet myself and passed out with the pain.

After an experience like that, I warned all my friends to steer well clear of diving out of aeroplanes. That's why when my ex-girlfriend Pauline phoned up with exciting news of her parachute jump for the Deadman Walking charity, we both burst out laughing. I reminded her that you can do other safer daredevil acts to raise money, and of the time when I dyed the "stookies" on my legs green, to match my "Celtic-Tartan" kilt at a friend's wedding.

However, it was not as bad as it seemed, because Pauline is doing a tandem jump — that is, she is strapped on to an expert — not a solo effort like my disaster. Hopefully, when Pauline takes the massive plunge on Easter Sunday, she will have a perfect landing with no rolling down hills in agony.

Okay, that was the jaunty start to the column — now it's all downhill.
When people ask how I am doing I say, 'good days and bad days', and today is a bad day. I didn't get out of bed until 2pm and that was only because my brother, his wife and my grandmother came down to visit. But I don't mind telling you, it took all my effort to do so. People just do not understand what real fatigue is. It is when you have to shout to your dad so he can accompany (more or less carry) you to the toilet. It is when you can only type one-handed and each sentence takes a huge effort because your arms are so heavy.

I would be lying if I said all days are this bad. I do have normal periods. For instance when my friend Michael suggested I go to Portpatrick for a trip last week. There were fourteen of us descending on the small village, which has a very picturesque harbour. The BBC uses the setting for their programme Two Thousand Acres of Sky, and when you look at the place, you can understand why locals are so proud of it. Fishing boats moored at the quay, lobster pots on the harbourside, and fishing nets on the jetty. We had booked lunch at the one premier restaurant in the place, but the other car with the rest of our gang had been held up; one of the boys had forgotten his hair gel or something. As a result we were sitting in the restaurant with the waitress standing tapping her feet impatiently as the kitchen was about to close. Michael had to resort to desperate measures — he had to read the menu over his mobile phone to the other car. He must have felt a bit of a turkey, shouting 'corn-fed chicken' into his phone.

Since there were so many of us, we were split into two guesthouses, and I was lucky to be in the same one as our visit last year when we received a warm welcome. Portpatrick only has three pubs, so when news spread that 14 thirsty Glaswegians were in town, the publicans were rubbing their hands with glee.

It is not a paper umbrella type of town, but I spied the basic ingredients of a tasty cocktail that is just right to get the party going. The barmaid must have been cursing as I ordered fourteen tequilas, fourteen vodkas, fourteen cans of Red Bull and to top it all off, you fill the remainder with champagne. Four times I ordered this drink, the only reason I stopped, was that we had drunk the bar dry of bubbly.

In Portpatrick you can walk almost anywhere in five minutes. I had treated myself to a new pair of Chelsea boots, the type with wooden soles and top-notch leather. The only problem is, it will take about six months to break them in. Well, that's my excuse as to why it took me 45 minutes to go 200 metres after leaving the boozer. I'm sure you have all walked the zig-zag path of the drunkard at some point in your life, crashing into cars, falling over hedges and the like. I managed to find my guesthouse eventually, and fell into bed.

The next day I decided I was going to stay off the sauce. It wasn't a hard resolution to keep. I sipped a pint and immediately threw it back up. I was back in bed for 6pm.

My body is telling me my binge drinking days are over. Yet another facet of my life has been closed off by cancer. I can still enjoy the trips with the boys, the camaraderie and laughs, but with me having liver cancer, it isn't a good idea to have it taxed to the limit with full-on drinking weekends.

And if your friends are really your friends, then they will understand.

About A Boy:

Jonathan Wilson: 1970-2002

THE last time I saw Jonathan Wilson I was Christmas-party drunk and leaving an upmarket Glasgow watering hole at two in the morning. He was coming in.

This kind of sums Jono up perfectly. Only he, suffering from liver cancer, could have come waltzing into the party just as those who considered themselves pretty hardcore were leaving.

We'd spent the evening at the Sunday Herald Christmas bash at another bar, where I was amazed to find him robust, cheerful, "cheeky" and with a very noticeable twinkle in his eye. He was on fine form. I remember thinking how incredibly skinny he was, but as usual dressed in hip and up-to-the-moment gear with his trademark aftershave following him around like a good smell.

Jonathan was very much the party boy. To the fury of his mother Susan, he gave up a year at Harvard Law School to instead become a DJ. He spun on cruise ships in the Caribbean, at the Ministry of Sound in London and practically every club in Glasgow. When I first met him two and half years ago, he was still DJ-ing at a bar near this office.

I have a secret habit of watching people on Sunday mornings reading their papers over brunch. Inevitably, if someone was reading this magazine, they would turn to this page first. It never ceased to amaze me the pull that Jonathan had. Whenever I told people what I did, the first thing they always asked me was how Jonathan was. Research showed he was our most popular columnist. He knew some of those who tuned in were — in his words — 'coffin watchers', but he also acknowledged that he touched people, especially those with cancer or who had suffered a loss through cancer.

There is always a danger of succumbing to cliché and hyperbole when talking about someone who has died. Jonathan wasn't an angel, or a saint. Jonathan wasn't even, by his own admission, a writer. What he was, was real and ordinary, but with extraordinary courage in the face of his fear and his pain. He wanted to touch people in his situation and to try to bring them comfort, and sometimes he wanted to shake up people's complacency about cancer. Often he provoked ire, leaving me under fire from a fuming reader or unfortunate target of his column. From personal hates to politicians, he wanted to shake things up a little. But most of all, in the midst of dying, he wanted to live.

Jonathan had tremendous will to live; he rallied on several occasions when everyone thought he was definitely on his way out. He organised charity nights and dressed up as Elvis, he tried to reply to every email and letter he received, and he walked the West Highland Way in seven days to raise £16,000 for his favourite charities, the Ayrshire Hospice and Macmillan Cancer Care.

He would go to concerts, parties, dinners and weddings and doubtless puke or lose control of his bowels or need to administer serious injections, all of which he described in this column in his typical sanguine manner and without pulling his punches.

One thing I know Jonathan would want me to mention is the deep and grateful love he had for his parents Susan and Henry, his brother Christopher and his sister Madeleine. He understood the distress his illness caused his family and he also knew how much they tried to conceal it for his sake. He knew he was simultaneously a burden and blessing and he loved them all for keeping strong and for caring for him at his lowest and most ill. And although they have all been living with Jonathan's cancer for five long years, I know they are hollow with their loss. Knowing it was coming, in the end, didn't make it any easier to bear.

On Wednesday, five years to the day since he was diagnosed with stomach cancer, Jonathan Wilson slipped away peacefully, surrounded by the family who loved and cared unstintingly for him.
By the time you read this I will have attended Jonathan's funeral and the big party (yes he wanted a party with music and dancing and no tears) afterwards. He put a lot of thought into the planning of his farewell do; our Jono loved to party and he loved his friends.
This Tuesday marks this paper's third birthday. There's another big bash — one that Jonathan had promised to make, but won't. But we will still raise our glasses and spin a few tunes for the party boy. Just like he would have wanted

JANE WRIGHT

His Father's Son:

As a family, we were overwhelmed by the hundreds of Mass cards, letters and E-mails of condolence from people who had been touched by Jono.

While we offer thanks to all, we would respectfully ask for no one to feel pity or sorrow for our loss. When Jono was born, we named him Jonathan- which means "A Gift From God"- little did we realize how accurate that name would be. Jono was not a saint-he was just a boy and a young man who regarded the world as his oyster from which he picked the richest pearls.

As parents we were truly blessed for 31 years, and despite the final five years of our lives being filled with pain, worry, and degrees of indignity for Jono, they were exceptionally happy; filled with love, and a great deal of laughter. As a family we have always had a wicked sense of humour, and this probably sustained us through many harrowing times. Each of us grieved individually and privately for those five years, but at all times our strength was gleaned from Jono. We were always close as a family, but a special bond grew up through him.

It is far more tragic for parents to lose a child from a sudden death; it leaves them with many unsaid things and feelings of regret. Our family has no regrets in that respect. During his final days, we all spent precious time with him to share our private thoughts and memories. Each of us received a big cuddle- Jono was a man unafraid of showing great love. They say the measure of a man, is in the number and quality of the friends he keeps, and Jono had many. At his funeral mass, we tried to involve as many as possible.
Six friends carried him into the chapel, six carried him out, and a few more laid him to rest.

Jono was an incredibly organised young man. He had previously told us that he did not want a "tacky" send off; namely the traditional "Sit Down Steak-Pie Dinner. Rather, he wanted a party with "Champers": his favourite music, and a celebration of his life- rather than a mourning of his death. Anyone who appeared to be morose was to be ejected onto the street. We promised to abide by his wishes, and he chose his favourite venue: the "Cul de Sac" where he had previously dee-jayed and the site of his various charity nights.

Upon his death, we discovered three notebooks; One containing details to settle his affairst: the Second for Chris and Madeleine, and the Third for his mum and dad. Although Jono conveyed the air of the ultimate "Mr.Cool" he was very self-deprecating. His main worry was that not many people would attend his funeral and final bash- how wrong he was. In our notebook, were pages of names and phone numbers of friends, he wanted contacted on his demise.

He had informed many of his close friends that he did not want them to attend him in his final days, but rather remember him from happier times. At the bottom of the two pages was a P.S. which said: "When you phone, please ask my friends, if they know anyone who would like to come to my bash, tell them it will be great-I'll Be There!"

We all shared the phone calls last Wednesday morning and found ourselves apologising to, and consoling each recipient for conveying the bad news. Well, needless to say Jono's bash was a riot. It was heartening to have so many young people approach Susan to express their gratitude and to say that his party was typically Jono.

We have so many close friends who have supported us -: there are too many to mention. The main ones have featured in Jono's columns, but we must give thanks to a special few.

Dr.John Bass is the head of The Ayrshire Hospice, who first encountered Jono five years ago. His introduction to our family was receiving a kick on the leg from my granddaughter, Abbie. On his next few visits, he must have thought our home akin to "One Flew Over The Cuckoo's Nest". But gradually we rounded off this reserved Englishman, who quickly became, not only Jono's personal physician, but also a close family friend. Along with Christopher at the funeral, he gave a heart-felt eulogy full of personal feelings but full of humour-how else could you speak of Jono?

Dr. Bass regarded Jono as a total enigma; defying all medical diagnosis, and he has learned from him. Jono relied on him and as a family, we gained a special friend.
Jono also had a special affinity with Colin: a friend, nurse and care worker at the Hospice, who called faithfully every Wednesday, and no matter how ill Jono was, he perked up in Colin's presence and was able to confide in him.

Willie, who accompanied Jono to the Ritz, arranged the music at Jono's funeral to perfection.
Father Mackle, whose parish is in Maryhill, Glasgow, and first met Jono when he was diagnosed with cancer at the Victoria Infirmary, and has remained in constant contact. He made the mass personal and full of feeling. When he spoke of Jono, he spoke of someone he knew.
Finally his Gran: who had a great input into his formative years, and with whom he always had a special relationship. She sat through his bash and appreciated it like the party that Jono had requested, even though her heart was breaking. She always did what Jono wanted and on the day, did him proud.

Our lives will never be the same.

Susan will never be able to shop in Buchanan Street again, without re-living the memories of the pleasurable days she spent with Jono, who as you will be aware, loved shopping.
Chris, his younger brother, idolised Jono: for Jono broke down all the barriers and made his passing into

adulthood that bit easier. He emulated and pursued Jono in his earlier years: —at Athletics: St.Aloysius College, and University.

Madeleine: well Mad is simply Jono's image. She adored him. It's difficult to contemplate life without him.

Abbie, who was born two days after Jono's disastrous parachute jump, grew up, only knowing Jono as being sick. She brought great comfort to him, and is reconciled with the fact that Jono is no longer sick. Me, his father: whenever I smell an expensive after-shave—and God knows he had the full set—I turn around expecting to see him, and I have no doubts I will.

As for Paulie, Jono's ex-girlfriend, she has the biggest cross to bear; they had a special love destined to be unfulfilled. Alex her dad, grieved as much as I did.

As for you, his readers: -Remember Jono's philosophy on life: —It is precious:-It should not be wasted: Make the most of it and get living! Such was Jono's legacy, and we are truly blessed.

So do not cry for us –for Jonathan will never be gone.

Henry Wilson

Finality Of It All:

Jonathan often referred to, in his columns and in conversation with his family, that he had already pre-written his final article: he also alluded that he was constantly updating same, as his perceptions of people and events changed by his experiences. Since his death, however I have been unable to trace this treasured and much anticipated article through his computer files. I genuinely believe that this article does exist. And that he entrusted it to someone for safekeeping. Unfortunately, that person has not come forward, and we as a family, and The Sunday Herald, have been inundated with questions of its whereabouts from his regular readers.

In absence of this final column, and in view of the fact that Jonathan told his story, "warts and all", I feel obliged to maintain Jonathan's intentions and integrity, to write of his final week. The amount of prominent personalities, who have written or e-mailed their condolences and have professed to being "Coffin Watchers", has been quite staggering. There is nothing unhealthy in having an interest in someone dying, especially when you have faithfully followed that person's decline, weekly in his column. Jonathan would have wanted his death chronicled, as a means of assuaging people's fears and superstitions of death.

It falls to me, as his mother and nurse, to articulate on his final days.
My long-held belief, that death is just an extension of life, does not negate or nullify my heart-felt sadness at the loss of Jonathan, but as he previously wrote-"All of us are dying from the moment we are born."
Everyone is curious and fearful of what it must feel like to die: it is a subject no one knows about. Death does not have a precise time-scale; no doctor can predict the exact moment when it will occur. Eventually, all of us will experience death, but no one has returned from beyond the grave to enlighten us.

Is death simply a long sleep as Jonathan considered? Is it a bright light? Do you see your dearly departed relatives waiting for you with open arms? No one knows. What is important, however, is that the death of a loved one should be made a comfortable, loving and peaceful occasion. Personal weeping and sorrow only causes the dying person distress, and should be set aside until after his, or her, demise. This may seem clinical and cold, but we had five years to prepare for Jonathan's death, and with advice from Dr.Bass, a man unfortunately well experienced in death, we resolved not to tax Jonathan's strength with dozens of well- intentioned friends and relatives. Rather, with his agreement, we restricted contact to his immediate family and selected friends. My main aim was to minimize his pain and distress: If I had failed him in that respect, I would never have forgiven myself.

The week before his death, Jonathan had been invited, by The Sunday Herald Fitness Guru, David Murray to accompany him to The Edinburgh Sheraton, to indulge himself in their luxurious Spa treatments. Regular readers will know of Jonathan's love of hotels. He had recently returned from his "lad's" weekend at Portpatrick and was completely enervated, but he was totally seduced by this offer of splendid pampering and agreed to participate. Since he was so listless, his father offered to drive him to Edinburgh, but Jonathan declined, preferring to be independent. Dressed in his latest designer "gear", he set off in his MG sports, with his medication in tow. He had an enjoyable evening, in David's company, but next morning was too tired to participate in his long awaited pampering spa treatment. He rested for a while and then set off for home.

When he arrived home, he was dreadfully ill looking, and immediately shuffled, stiffly, to the toilet. I went into his study, switched on his fire, and prepared an injection. When he came to me, he sat down and put his head on my shoulder and simply said:" Mum, I'm completely done!" As he was recounting the "tid bits" of his stay, Dr. Jilly Taylor, our ex GP, arrived to visit, and was shocked to see his appearance. Formerly, she had been one who had encouraged Jonathan to go for whatever he wanted, but she now cautioned him, as a friend, that he had to be realistic of what his body could now achieve. He was unable to eat, but was able to take fluids. His vomiting and diaorrhea continued as usual, but it was business as usual throughout the weekend-He watched TV, was rather sleepy, but pain-free. Christopher and his wife came to visit and Jonathan enjoyed the "Craich". On Sunday evening, he started vomiting faecal fluid, but his bowels were not obstructing.

Before his journey to Edinburgh, he had taken large doses of Codeine Phosphate to stop his diaorrhea, and I thought that his small bowel had gone into spasm, this also caused him to be sleepy and he was totally listless. I tried to coax him to wear an incontinence pad, so that he could sleep in confidence, but he refused: We struggled to get him to the toilet, several times throughout the night, due to his condition. He eventually slept, but upon awakening vomited copiously. I contacted Dr. Bass at the Ayrshire Hospice and he attended immediately, and confirmed that Jonathan's bowels were still active. Dr. Bass suggested inserting a Naso Gastric tube to give Jonathan IV fluids, but Jonathan did not want a tube passed, so I gave him ice- lollies and sips of water. Apart from his vomiting, there were no further problems. I then lay beside Jonathan, we watched TV and his dad kept the crushed ice and sick bowls coming. We watched an episode of the Sopranos, in which two of the main characters became lost in a wood, in deep snow, while trying to eliminate a rival "hood". Jonathan and I were hysterical with laughter and looked forward to the concluding episode, which was to be screened the following week.

The next day, Jonathan wanted to go downstairs, to sit in his study, so my husband and I carried him in a "Fireman's Lift". He continued vomiting but was not distressed and was well enough to have some soup. This small snack is not one of the usual treatments, but it was normality, and that was important- I knew he was becoming weaker.
He insisted on walking upstairs to the toilet, and my husband and I followed behind. When he reached the landing on the stairs, he suddenly collapsed, and we both lunged to support him. I was holding him from

the back and it was obvious that he had suffered a respiratory arrest, and had stopped breathing. I automatically resuscitated him, and he came round, completely unaware of what had happened. I told him, that under no circumstances, would he be allowed to go to the toilet on his own. He then insisted on going back downstairs to his study. I now decided to phone my other two children: I had previously prepared my daughter for this event, but I was unsure how Christopher would react. I phoned and told him to clear his workload and inform his employers that he would be absent, until necessary.

During the next two days, Jonathan sent for people whom he wished to see, among those was Father Mackle, his long-time friend and Confessor. The previous day, Dr.Bass had attended Jonathan, and had told him that his death was imminent, and also stated that, despite his experience, he never thought that this day would actually come- such was Jonathan's spirit. Jonathan asked Dr.Bass what death would be like and he told him that he would feel very tired, and would simply drift into a deep sleep from which he would not awaken. The next day, he asked Fr. Mackle, if he truly believed in an "after-life". Father Mackle confirmed that he did believe that there was. Jonathan replied: "That will do for me!"

Dr.Bass returned later that evening, and attended Jonathan until 1.30 am. I sat beside Jonathan in his bed, with his father at his other side; he was in no discomfort and was totally pain free and entirely lucid.

As we talked, Jonathan suddenly said: "The saddest thing about dying, is the finality of it all". He did not explain what he meant, but I think that he had accepted that it had finally come to this. He possibly thought, that death was exaggerated to be some major event, but in the end, a dying person is on his own, and was really no big deal.
When I thought that it was time, I awoke my son and daughter, and they joined us at his bedside. Jonathan was conscious and in no distress to the end. He died with me holding him to my shoulder, with his dad, brother and sister, all holding him. I held him to my shoulder, as I could not face watching him dying. Just as he died, a tear flowed from his left eye, was this mechanical/ physical? Was it sadness? We will never know.
There was no lightening of his face; he just stopped breathing.

He was correct in what he said- "The saddest thing about dying, is the finality of it all."
He never did get to watch the final episode of the Sopranos, and I did not have the heart to watch it either.

Jonathan died 5 years and 4 days after his initial diagnosis, and tragic prognosis of only three months. This "longevity" was due, almost entirely, to Jonathan's determination, positive attitude and will to live.

The day on which he died was the thirtieth anniversary of his paternal grandfather's death.

Susan Wilson

Columnist Of The Year:

We learned in April 2002 that Jonathan had been nominated, and then short-listed for The Columnist Of The Year award.

The Sunday Herald invited Henry and I to the ceremony on 22nd May at the Holiday Inn, the evening being compered by Dougie Donnelly, and the awards being presented by Jack McConnell, First Minister of Scotland. We were made feel extremely welcome by the Sunday Herald Staff during the evening, but I was in the early throes of pneumonia, and everyone in the function suite seemed to be chain smokers, which did not help my condition.

After the short-list of candidates was announced for Columnist Of The Year, "Chariots of Fire" rang out and Jonathan's picture flashed onto the large TV screen on the podium. Henry and I were absolutely beside ourselves with delight, and I went forward to accept the award on Jonathan's behalf. It was a bitter-sweet moment for both of us—full of pride in Jonathan winning, but heavily tinged with sadness that he was not there himself, to receive the ultimate accolade for his writing. For last year's award ceremony, at which he was runner-up, he had bought a new dinner-suit, which he had only been able to wear on that one occasion. Henry decided that it was only fitting that he should wear it on this evening, so in a way Jonathan was there.

After the awards ceremony, Jack McConnell came to our table and congratulated us on Jonathan's award, and admitted that he had been one of Jonathan's regular "Coffin Watchers" every Sunday. He was very natural and unassuming, and I felt that Scotland's welfare was in good hands, with him at the helm.

The night continued, and we were overwhelmed by the numerous writers, and editors of Scotland's newspapers, who all professed their admiration for Jonathan's writing. We left the function suite to the late revelers, and clutching the award, returned to the Malmaison hotel. Henry was showing all the symptoms of a promising hangover for the next morning. Sure enough, I was obliged to go down to breakfast alone, but when I discovered that it was a breakfast buffet, all the happy memories of similar breakfasts in Tenerife with Jonathan, came rushing back, and I burst into a flood of tears. The ranks of business suited gentlemen diners just stared at me in amazement. When it came to it, I just couldn't face breakfast and returned sobbing to my room.

After accompanying and nursing Jonathan, it's the unexpected memories that spring at me and bring the loss of him sharply to the forefront of my mind.

His award takes pride of place in his study, where he did all his writing, so it is only fitting that it should reside there.

Susan Wilson